Vocabulary Workshop
Fifth Course

- **Words in Context**
- **Analogies**
- **Synonyms**
- **Prefixes, Suffixes, Roots**

HOLT, RINEHART AND WINSTON

A Harcourt Classroom Education Company

Austin • New York • Orlando • Atlanta • San Francisco • Boston • Dallas • Toronto • London

EDITORIAL

Director
Mescal Evler

Manager of Editorial Operations
Bill Wahlgren

Executive Editor
Emily G. Shenk

Project Editor
Cheryl L. Christian

Writing and Editing: Janis D. Russell

Editorial Assistant: Kim Soriano

Copyediting: Michael Neibergall, *Copyediting Manager;* Mary Malone, *Senior Copyeditor;* Joel Bourgeois, Elizabeth Dickson, Gabrielle Field, Julie A. Hill, Jane Kominek, Millicent Ondras, Theresa Reding, Dennis Scharnberg, Kathleen Scheiner, Laurie Schlesinger, *Copyeditors*

Project Administration: Marie Price, *Managing Editor;* Lori De La Garza, *Editorial Operations Coordinator;* Thomas Browne, Heather Cheyne, Diane Hardin, Mark Holland, Marcus Johnson, Jill O'Neal, Joyce Rector, Janet Riley, Kelly Tankersley, *Project Administration;* Gail Coupland, Ruth Hooker, Margaret Sanchez, *Word Processing*

Editorial Permissions: Janet Harrington, *Permissions Editor*

ART, DESIGN AND PHOTO

Graphic Services
Kristen Darby, *Manager*

Image Acquisitions: Joe London, *Director;* Tim Taylor, *Photo Research Supervisor;* Rick Benavides, *Assistant Photo Researcher;* Elaine Tate, *Supervisor;* Erin Cone, *Art Buyer*

Cover Design
Sunday Patterson

PRODUCTION

Belinda Barbosa Lopez, *Senior Production Coordinator;* Simira Davis, *Supervisor;* Nancy Hargis, *Media Production Supervisor;* Joan Lindsay, *Production Coordinator;* Beth Prevelige, *Prepress Manager*

ELECTRONIC PUBLISHING

Carol Martin, *Senior Electronic Publishing Manager;* Robert Franklin, *Electronic Publishing Manager;* Indira Konanur, *Project Coordinator;* JoAnn Brown, Richard Chavez, Jim Gaile, Heather Jernt, Lana Kaupp, Christopher Lucas, Robin McKinney, Nanda Patel, *EP staff;* Emilie Keturakis, Katelijne Lefevere, Sally Williams, *Quality Control Coordinators*

MANUFACTURING

Shirley Cantrell, *Supervisor of Inventory and Manufacturing*

Printed in the United States of America

ISBN 0-03-056214-7

16 17 18 19 054 09 08 07 06

Consultant

Norbert Elliot, the general editor of *Vocabulary Workshop,* has a Ph.D. in English from The University of Tennessee. He is a professor of English at New Jersey Institute of Technology. A former site director for the National Writing Project, he has directed summer language arts institutes for kindergarten through twelfth-grade teachers in the public schools. A specialist in test development and evaluation of writing, Norbert Elliot has written books and articles on writing assessment, communication, and critical thinking. Dr. Elliot is the father of five children and is married to Lorna Jean Elliot, under whose care, he says, "everything thrives."

CONTENTS

American Literature and Culture

MAKING NEW WORDS YOUR OWN 1

SKILLS AND STRATEGIES
- Context Clues
- Word Structure
- Sound Clues
- Dictionary Definition
- Sentence Completion

CONTEXT: The Literature

CONTEXT: The People

CONTEXT: The Land

CONNECTING NEW WORDS AND PATTERNS 123

SKILLS AND STRATEGIES
- Understanding Analogies
- Types of Analogies
- Solving Analogies

READING NEW WORDS IN CONTEXT **141**

> **SKILLS AND STRATEGIES**
> • Reading Longer Passages
> • Finding Synonyms
> • Reading Strategically

CONTEXT: The Literature

CONTEXT: The People

CONTEXT: The Land

VOCABULARY WORDS **233**

The following tables list some common roots, prefixes, and suffixes. Use these tables to help you determine the meaning of a word by examining its structure.

GREEK ROOTS		
BASE	**MEANING**	**EXAMPLES**
anthropo	human being	**anthropo**logy, **anthropo**id, phil**anthro**pic
aster, astro	star	**astro**nomy, **astro**nomical, **aster**isk
baro	pressure	**baro**meter, **baro**metric
biblio, bibli	book	**biblio**grapher, **biblio**mania, **bibli**cal
bio	life	**bio**logy, **bio**chemistry, **bio**degradable
chrom	color	**chrom**atic, **chrom**aticity
chrono	time	**chrono**logy, **chrono**meter, **chrono**scope
cosmo	world, order, universe	**cosmo**logy, **cosmo**naut, **cosmo**politan
crac, crat	rule, govern	aristo**cracy**, aristo**cratic**, demo**crat**
dem	people	**dem**ocracy, **dem**agogue, epi**dem**ic
derm	skin	**derm**atitis, **derm**atology
ethno	nation	**ethn**ic, **ethno**centrism
eu	good, well	**eu**phoria, **eu**phony, **eu**phemism
gam	marriage	mono**gam**y, poly**gam**y, bi**gam**y
geo	earth	**geo**logy, **geo**centric, **geo**dynamics
gno, kno	to know	**kno**wledge, **gno**stic, a**gno**stic
graph, gram	to write, draw, record	auto**graph**, tele**gram**, para**graph**
gymno, gymn	athletic	**gymn**astics, **gymn**asium
hydro	water	**hydro**gen, **hydro**dynamics, **hydro**plane
hypno	sleep	**hypno**sis, **hypno**tic, **hypno**tize
hypo	under, below	**hypo**dermic, **hypo**tension, **hypo**thermia
lith	stone	mono**lith**, mega**lith**
logue, logo	idea, word, speech, reason	dia**logue**, mono**logue**, epi**logue**, **logo**ical
meter, metr	measure	dia**meter**, **metr**ic, milli**meter**
micro	small	**micro**scope, **micro**organism
mim	to copy, imitate	**mim**ic, **mim**e, **mim**eograph
miso	hatred of	**miso**neism, **miso**logy

GREEK ROOTS (continued)

BASE	MEANING	EXAMPLES
mono	one	**mono**logue, **mono**gamy, **mono**graph
mor	fool	**mor**on, **mor**onic
morph	form	pseudo**morph**, meso**morph**, meta**morph**osis
neur, nerv	nerve	**neur**ology, **nerv**ous, **neur**itis
nym, onym, onom	name	acro**nym**, hom**onym**, **onom**atopoeia
opt	eye	**opt**ic, **opt**ical, **opt**ician
ortho	straight	**ortho**dontics, **ortho**pedics
pan	all	**pan**genesis, **pan**gram, **pan**theism
path	feeling	a**path**y, sym**path**y, **path**etic
peri	around	**peri**meter, **peri**scope, **peri**phery
petr	rock	**petr**ify, **petr**oleum, **petr**oglyph
phe	speak, spoken about	eu**phe**mistic, pro**phe**t
phil, philo	love	**philo**dendron, **philo**logy, **phil**harmonic
phob	fear	**phob**ia, claustro**phob**ia, acro**phob**ia
phon	sound, voice	**phon**etics, **phon**ics, tele**phon**e
photo	light	**photo**graphy, **photo**flash, **photo**genic
pneu	breath	**pneu**monia, **pneu**matic
polis, polit	citizen, city, state	metro**polis**, **polit**ician, **polit**ical
poly	many	**poly**chromatic, **poly**ester
pseudo	false	**pseudo**nym, **pseudo**salt, **pseudo**morph
psych	mind, soul, spirit	**psych**ic, **psych**ology, **psych**oanalysis
pyr	fire	**pyr**omania, **pyr**otechnic
scope	to see	kaleido**scope**, tele**scope**, micro**scope**
soph	wise	philo**soph**er, **soph**isticated
syn, sym	together	**sym**phony, **syn**thesize
techn	art, skill	**techn**ical, **techn**ology, **techn**ique
tele	at a distance	**tele**scope, **tele**phone, **tele**commute
the, them, thet	to place, put	epi**thet**, anti**thes**is, **the**me
thea, theatr	to see, view	**thea**ter, **theatr**ical, ampi**thea**ter
theo	God	**theo**logy, **theo**cracy, **theo**centric
therm	heat	**therm**ometer, **therm**onuclear, **therm**al
topo	place	**topo**graphy, **topo**logy

LATIN ROOTS

BASE	MEANING	EXAMPLES
act	to do, drive	**act**ion, **act**or, re**act**, trans**act**, en**act**
alt	high	**alt**itude, **alt**imeter, **alt**iplano
anima, anim	life, mind	**anima**l, **anim**ated
ann, enn	year	**ann**ual, per**enn**ial, bic**ent**ennial
aqua	water	**aqua**rium, **aqua**marine, **aqua**naut
arm	army, weapon	**arm**ory, **arm**ament
arbitr, arbiter	to judge, consider	**arbitr**ator, **arbitr**ary, **arbiter**
art	craft, skill	**art**ist, **art**sy, **art**isan
aud	to hear	**aud**ience, **aud**itorium, **aud**ible
bell	war	**bell**igerent, **bell**icose
cede	to go; to yield	inter**cede**, super**cede**, con**cede**
cele	honor	**cele**brate, **cele**brities
cent	one hundred	per**cent**, bicent**ent**nial, **cent**ennial
cept, capt, cip, cap, ceive, ceipt	to take hold, grasp	inter**cept**, re**ceive**, re**ceipt**, **capt**ure
cert	to be sure, to trust	**cert**ain, ascer**t**ain, **cert**ifiable
cess, ced	to go; to yield	**cess**ation, con**cess**ion, ac**ced**e, pro**cess**ion
cid, cis	to cut off, be brief; to kill	con**cis**e, homi**cid**e, geno**cid**e
circ, circum	around	**circum**ference, **circ**le, **circ**ular
clin	to lean, lie, bend	de**clin**e, in**clin**e, re**clin**e
cog	to think, consider	**cog**nition, **cog**nitive, re**cog**nize
comput	to compute	**comput**er, **comput**ation
cor, cord, card	heart	**card**iovascular, **cor**onary
corp	body	**corp**se, **corp**ulence, **corp**orate
cred	to believe, trust	**cred**ibility, in**cred**ible, **cred**it, **cred**ential
crit, cris	to separate; to discern, judge	**crit**icism, **crit**ique, **cris**is
culp	fault, blame	**culp**rit, **culp**able
curs, curr, corr	to run	**curr**ent, oc**curr**ence, **curs**or, **corr**al
custom	one's own	**custom**ized, **custom**er, ac**custom**
dent	tooth	**dent**ist, **dent**al, **dent**ifrice
dic, dict	to say, to speak; to assert	**dic**tion, **dict**ionary, **dict**ate
duct, duc	to lead; to draw	aque**duct**, ab**duct**, con**duct**, re**duc**e
dur	hard, lasting	**dur**ation, **dur**able, en**dur**e

BASE	MEANING	EXAMPLES
ego	I	**ego**tistical, **ego**centric, **ego**ism
equ	equal, fair	**equ**ality, **equ**ation, **equ**ator
fac, fic, fect, fact	to make, do	**fac**simile, **fac**ility, de**fect**, ef**fic**ient
fer	to carry, bear, bring	of**fer**, trans**fer**, aqui**fer**
fid	trust, faith	**fid**elity, in**fid**el, in**fid**elity
fin	end, limit	**fin**ish, **fin**ite, in**fin**ite, **fin**al
flu	to flow	**flu**id, **flu**x, **flu**ctuate
form	shape, form	**form**al, **form**ative, in**form**
fort	strong	**fort**ress, **fort**ify, **fort**ification
frig	cool	**frig**id, re**frig**erate, **frig**orific
fum	smoke; scent	**fum**ing, **fum**igate, per**fum**e
gen	race, family, kind	**gen**ealogy, **gen**eral, **gen**eration
grad, gress	step, degree, rank	**grad**e, **grad**ual, re**gress**
grat	pleasing, thankful	con**grat**ulate, **grat**itude, **grat**ify
grav, griev	heavy	**grav**itate, **grav**ity, **griev**e
hab	to have, hold; to dwell	**hab**it, **hab**itat, in**hab**it
hom	man, human	**hom**age, **hom**icide
hosp	guest	**hosp**ital, **hosp**itality
host	enemy, stranger	**host**ile, **host**ility, **host**
init	to begin, enter upon	**init**ial, **init**iate, **init**iation
jur, jus, judic	law, right, judgment	**jur**ist, **jus**tify, **judic**ial
juven	young	**juven**ile, **juven**ility, re**juven**ate
labor	work	**labor**atory, **labor**er, **labor**ious
lat	lateral, side; wide	**lat**itude, **lat**itudinal
laud	praise	**laud**, **laud**able, **laud**atory
leg	law	**leg**al, **leg**islator, **leg**itimate
lev	to make light, to lift	e**lev**ator, **lev**er, **lev**itate
liber	free	**liber**al, **liber**ate, **liber**tarian
lingu, langu	tongue	**langu**age, sub**lingu**al
loc	place	**loc**al, **loc**alize, re**loc**ate, dis**loc**ate
locu, loqu, locut	word, speak	e**locu**tion, e**loqu**ent, **loqu**acious
luc, lumin	light	il**lumin**ate, **luc**ent, **luc**id

LATIN ROOTS *(continued)*

BASE	MEANING	EXAMPLES
manu	hand	**manu**al, **manu**facture
mar	sea	**mar**inate, **mar**ine, **mar**itime
med, medi	middle	**med**iate, **med**ieval, **med**iocre
medic	physician, to heal	**medic**al, **medic**ine, **medic**inal
memor	mindful	**memor**ial, **memor**y
mon	to remind, advise, warn	ad**mon**ish, **mon**itor, pre**mon**ition
ment	mind	**ment**al, **ment**ally, **ment**ality
migr	to move, travel	im**migr**ant, **migr**ation, **migr**atory
mit, mis	to send	re**mis**sion, **mis**sive, trans**mit**
mort	death	**mort**al, **mort**ality, **mort**ify
mov, mob, mot	to move	**mob**, **mob**ile, re**mov**e, **mot**ion
mut	change, exchange	**mut**ant, **mut**ate, trans**mut**ate
necess	unavoidable	**necess**ary, **necess**itate, **necess**ity
noc, nox	harm	in**noc**ent, in**noc**uous, **noc**ent, ob**nox**ious
noc, nox	night	equi**nox**, **noc**turnal, **noc**turne
nomen, nomin	name	**nomin**al, **nomin**ate, **nomen**clature
null, nihil, nil	nothing, void	**nihil**ism, **nil**, **null**ify
ord, ordin	to put in order	**ord**er, **ordin**al, **ordin**ary
par, pair	to arrange, get ready, set	**par**ade, **pre**pare, re**pair**
part, pars	portion, part	**part**ial , **part**icle, **part**ner
ped	foot	**ped**estal, **ped**estrian, **ped**al
pend, pond, pens	to weigh, pay; to consider	**pens**ion, **pens**ive, **pond**er
pli, plic	to fold	**pli**able, **plic**ate, re**plic**ate
plur, plus	more	**plur**al, **plur**alistic, sur**plus**
port	to carry	im**port**, ex**port**, **port**able
pos	to place, put	**pos**ition, **pos**itive
pot	powerful	im**pot**ent, **pot**ent, **pot**ential
prim, prin	first	**prim**ary, **prim**e, **prim**itive, **prin**cipal
priv	separate	de**priv**e, **priv**ate, **priv**ilege
prov, prob	to prove, test	**prob**ate, **prob**ation, **prov**e
reg, rig, rect	to rule; right, straight	**reg**al, **reg**ent, **reg**ion, **rect**ify
rupt	to break, burst	dis**rupt**, e**rupt**ion, **rupt**ure

LATIN ROOTS *(continued)*

BASE	MEANING	EXAMPLES
sacr, secr, sanct	sacred	desecrate, **sacr**ifice, **sacr**ilege, **sanct**ify
sat, satis	enough	insatiable, **satis**fy, **sat**iate
sci	to know	conscience, **sci**ence, **sci**entist
scrib, script	to write	inscribe, subscription, script
sed, sid, sess	to sit; to settle	**sed**ate, **sed**iment, subside, **sess**ion
sent, sens	to feel	**sens**e, **sent**imental, **sent**inel
sequ, secut	to follow; sequence	consequence, **sequ**el, consecutive
simil, simul, sembl	like, similar	**sembl**ance, **simul**ate, **simil**e
sol, soli	alone, lonely	**sol**iloquy, **sol**o, **soli**tary
somn	sleep	**somn**ambulate, **somn**olent, **somn**iloquy
son	sound	**son**ic, **son**iferous, **son**net
spec, spect, spic	to see, look at, behold	in**spect**, re**spect**, **spect**acle, **spec**ies
spond, spons	to pledge, promise	**spons**or, **spons**orship, re**spond**
tac, tic	silent	**tac**it, **tac**iturn
temp	time	**temp**orary, **temp**er
ten, tain, tent	to hold	con**tain**, **ten**ant, re**tent**ion
tend, tens	to stretch, strive	**tend**on, **tens**ion, dis**tend**
termin	boundary, limit	**termin**al, **termin**ate, de**termin**e
test	to witness, affirm	at**test**, con**test**, **test**ify
tract	to pull, draw	at**tract**, re**tract**, **tract**ion
trib	to allot, give	at**trib**ute, **trib**ute
vac	empty	e**vac**uate, **vac**uous, **vac**uum
ven, vent	to come	ad**vent**, con**ven**e, re**ven**ue
ver	truth	**ver**acity, **ver**ify, **ver**itable
vers, vert	to turn	ad**vers**e, con**vers**ion, in**vert**
vest	garment	**vest**, **vest**ment
vestig	to track	in**vestig**ate, **vestig**e
via	way, road	**via**, **via**duct
vir	manliness; worth	**vir**ile, **vir**ility, **vir**tue
vis, vid	to see, look	re**vis**ion, **vid**eo, **vis**ible
viv, vit	life	**vit**al, **viv**acious, **viv**id
voc, vok	voice, call	in**voc**ation, re**vok**e, **voc**al

PREFIXES

PREFIX	MEANING	EXAMPLES
ab–	from; away from	**ab**normal, **ab**duct, **ab**sent, **ab**hor
ad–	to; motion toward; addition to	**ad**apt, **ad**dict, **ad**here, **ad**mit
aero–	air	**aero**bic, **aero**biology, **aero**space
amphi–	both; around	**amphi**bian, **amphi**theater
an–	not	**an**archy, **an**esthesia, **an**onymous
ante–	before	**ante**bellum, **ante**cede, **ante**date
anti–	against; opposite; reverse	**anti**aircraft, **anti**freeze, **anti**biotics
ap–	to; nearness to	**ap**proximate, **ap**point
auto–	self	**auto**matic, **auto**graph, **auto**biography
bene–	good	**bene**diction, **bene**factor, **bene**volent
bi–	two	**bi**facial, **bi**focal, **bi**ennial
circum–	around	**circum**navigate, **circum**ference
co–, con–	together	**co**author, **co**operate, **con**front, **con**found
contra–	against	**contra**dict, **contra**distinguish, **contra**ry
de–	opposite of; away from; undo	**de**activate, **de**form, **de**grade, **de**plete, **de**scend
dis–	opposite	**dis**agree, **dis**arm, **dis**continue, **dis**honest
ex–	out; beyond; away from; former	**ex**cel, **ex**clude, **ex**hale, **ex**ile
extra–	outside; beyond; besides	**extra**ordinary, **extra**curricular
for–	not	**for**bid, **for**get, **for**go
fore–	before	**fore**cast, **fore**word, **fore**stall, **fore**thought
hyper–	more than normal; too much	**hyper**active, **hyper**critical, **hyper**tension
il–	not	**il**legal, **il**legible, **il**literate, **il**logical
im–	into	**im**mediate, **im**merse, **im**migrate, **im**port
im–	not	**im**balance, **im**mature, **im**mobilize
in–	not; go into	**in**accurate, **in**active, **in**decisive, **in**habit
inter–	among; between	**inter**action, **inter**cede, **inter**change
intra–	within	**intra**mural, **intra**state, **intra**venous
ir–	not	**ir**redeemable, **ir**regular, **ir**responsible
mal–	wrong; bad	**mal**adjusted, **mal**function, **mal**ice
mis–	wrong; bad; no; not	**mis**fire, **mis**behave, **mis**conduct
non–	not; opposite of	**non**committal, **non**conductor, **non**partisan
ob–	against	**ob**stacle, **ob**stinate, **ob**struct, **ob**ject

PREFIXES (continued)		
PREFIX	**MEANING**	**EXAMPLES**
per–	through	**per**colate, **per**ceive
post–	after	**post**glacial, **post**graduate, **post**erior
pre–	before	**pre**amble, **pre**arrange, **pre**caution
pro–	before; for; in support of	**pro**gnosis, **pro**gram, **pro**logue, **pro**phet
pro–	forward	**pro**ceed, **pro**duce, **pro**ficient, **pro**gress
re–	back; again	**re**call, **re**cede, **re**flect, **re**pay
retro–	backward	**retro**active, **retro**spect, **retro**cede
se–	apart	**se**cure, **se**cede, **se**cession
self–	of the self	**self**-taught, **self**-worth, **self**-respect, **self**ish
semi–	half; partly	**semi**circle, **semi**formal, **semi**trailer
sub–	under; beneath	**sub**contract, **sub**ject, **sub**marine, **sub**merge
super–	over	**super**abound, **super**abundant, **super**human
sur–	over; above	**sur**charge, **sur**face, **sur**mount, **sur**pass
trans–	across; over	**trans**atlantic, **trans**cend, **trans**cribe, **trans**fer
ultra–	extremely	**ultra**liberal, **ultra**modern, **ultra**sonic
un–	not; lack of; opposite	**un**able, **un**comfortable, **un**certain, **un**happy

SUFFIXES

SUFFIX	MEANING	EXAMPLES
–able, –ible	able to be; capable of being	intelligible, probable, inevitable
–ade	action or process	blockade, escapade, parade
–age	action or process	marriage, pilgrimage, voyage
–al, –ial	of; like; relating to; suitable for	potential, musical, national
–ance	act; process; quality; state of being	tolerance, alliance, acceptance
–ant	one who	assistant, immigrant, merchant
–ary	of; like; relating to	customary, honorary, obituary
–ate	characteristic of; to become	officiate, consecrate, activate
–cle, –icle	small	corpuscle, cubicle, particle
–cy	fact or state of being	diplomacy, privacy, relevancy
–dom	state or quality of	boredom, freedom, martyrdom
–ence	act or state of being	occurrence, conference
–ent	doing; having; showing	fraudulent, dependent, negligent
–er	one who; that which	boxer, rancher, employer
–ery	place for; act, practice of	surgery, robbery
–esque	like	picturesque, statuesque
–ess	female	goddess, heiress, princess
–ful	full of	careful, fearful, joyful, thoughtful
–ic	relating to; characteristic of	comic, historic, poetic, public
–ify	to make; to cause to be	modify, glorify, beautify, pacify
–ion	act, condition, or result of	calculation, action, confederation
–ish	of or belonging to; characterized by	tallish, amateurish, selfish
–ism	act, practice, or result of; example	barbarism, heroism, altruism
–ity	condition; state of being	integrity, sincerity, calamity, purity
–ive	of; relating to; belonging to; tending to	inquisitive, active, creative
–ize	make; cause to be; subject to	jeopardize, standardize, computerize
–less	without	ageless, careless, thoughtless, tireless
–let	small	islet, leaflet, owlet, rivulet, starlet
–like	like; characteristic of	childlike, waiflike
–logy	study or theory of	biology, ecology, geology
–ly	every	daily, weekly, monthly, yearly

SUFFIXES *(continued)*		
SUFFIX	**MEANING**	**EXAMPLES**
–ly	like; characteristic of	father**ly**, queen**ly**, dead**ly**
–ly	in (a specified manner; to a specified extent)	officia**lly**, sincere**ly**, kind**ly**
–ment	action or process	develop**ment**, govern**ment**
–ment	state or quality of	amuse**ment**, amaze**ment**, predica**ment**
–ment	product or thing	frag**ment**, instru**ment**, orna**ment**
–ness	state or quality of being	kind**ness**, abrupt**ness**, happi**ness**
–or	one who	act**or**, audit**or**, doct**or**, don**or**
–ous	having; full of; characterized by	riot**ous**, courag**eous**, advantag**eous**
–ship	state or quality of being	censor**ship**, owner**ship**, governor**ship**
–some	like; tending to be	meddle**some**, bother**some**, noi**some**
–tude	state or quality of being	soli**tude**, multi**tude**, apti**tude**
–y	characterized by	thrift**y**, jealous**y**, frequenc**y**, stick**y**

KINDS OF CONTEXT CLUES

CONTEXT

The words, phrases, or sentences around an unfamiliar word often provide clues to the word's meaning. In some cases, *signal words* can act as clues.

Restatement Clues

Words or phrases such as *in other words* or *that is* can signal the restatement of a word.

EXAMPLE   The veterinarian treated every animal owner in an *affable* manner; **in other words**, she was gentle and friendly with them.

From the context, readers can tell that *affable* means "gentle and friendly." The phrase *in other words* signals that the words *gentle* and *friendly* restate the meaning of the word.

Restatement Signal Words		
in other words	that is	these

Example Clues

Words or phrases such as *such as, for example,* or *likewise* can indicate to readers that an unfamiliar word is being restated in more familiar terms.

EXAMPLE   Many types of *fauna*, **for example** the javelina, the coyote, and the peregrine falcon, live in Big Bend National Park.

From the context, readers can tell that *fauna* are the animals of a particular region. The words *for example* signal that the animals listed are examples of the word *fauna*.

Example Signal Words		
for example	such as	in that
likewise	especially	

Contrast Clues

Words or phrases such as *but, by contrast,* or *although* indicate that an unfamiliar word contrasts with another word in the passage.

EXAMPLE   Maria was *enthralled* by the new movie, **but** her friend found it dull and uninteresting.

From the context, readers can tell that *enthralled* means "fascinated." The word *but* signals that *enthralled* contrasts with the words *dull* and *uninteresting*.

Contrast Signal Words		
but	not	on the other hand
however	still	some . . . but others
although	despite	in contrast

Cause and Effect Clues

Words or phrases such as *lead to, cause,* and *because* show how one word may be a cause or effect related to an unfamiliar word.

EXAMPLE **Because** he wanted to marry a divorcée, Edward VIII chose to *abdicate* the British throne in 1936.

From the context, readers can tell that *abdicate* means "to formally give up power." The word *because* signals that abdicating is an effect of Edward VIII's wanting to marry a divorcée.

Cause and Effect Signal Words		
leads to	effect	reasons
cause	as a result	since
because	consequently	why

Definition/Explanation Clues

A sentence may actually define or explain an unfamiliar word.

EXAMPLE The title of F. Scott Fitzgerald's novel *Tender Is the Night* contains an *allusion,* or **reference**, to a poem by John Keats.

From the context, readers can tell that *allusion* means "reference." The appositive phrase "or reference" signals the meaning of the word.

How We Make New Words Our Own

Use the **Context Structure Sound Dictionary (CSSD)** strategy to improve your vocabulary, to make new words your own. Use one or more of the strategies to determine the meanings of each word you do not know. The exercises that follow will show you how to go about making new words your own.

HOW TO DO EXERCISE 1 *Wordbusting*

In these exercises, you will read the Vocabulary Word in a sentence. You will figure out the word's meaning by looking at its **context,** its **structure,** and its **sound**. Then you will look up the word in a **dictionary** and write its meaning *as it is used in the sentence*.

Here is an example of the Wordbusting strategy, using the word *transcribe.*

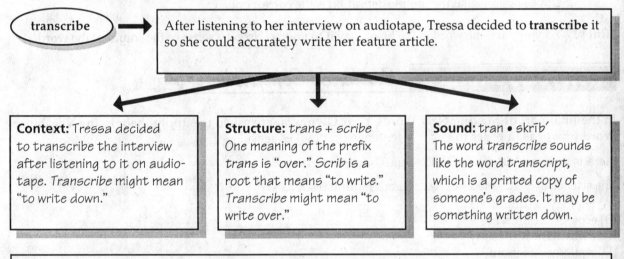

transcribe → After listening to her interview on audiotape, Tressa decided to **transcribe** it so she could accurately write her feature article.

Context: *Tressa decided to transcribe the interview after listening to it on audiotape. Transcribe might mean "to write down."*

Structure: *trans + scribe* One meaning of the prefix *trans* is "over." *Scrib* is a root that means "to write." *Transcribe might mean "to write over."*

Sound: *tran • skrīb'* The word *transcribe* sounds like the word *transcript,* which is a printed copy of someone's grades. It may be something written down.

Dictionary: *"to write or type out a copy of, as from a speech or notes"*

Hint #1 Context: Look for clues to the meaning of the word in the sentence. For example, *after* signals cause and effect and helps reveal the meaning of *transcribe*.

Hint #2 Structure: Examine the word parts for roots, prefixes, and suffixes that you know. Consult the word-part tables on pages ix–xviii for meanings of parts you do not know.

Hint #3 Sound: Say the word aloud and listen for any word parts you know.

Hint #4 Dictionary: If you cannot determine a word's meaning from applying context, structure, and sound strategies, look up the unfamiliar word in a dictionary. Read all the definitions, and choose one that best fits the given sentence.

Again, you will see the new word used in a sentence. This time, however, you're actually given a set of definitions, and you must match the new word with its meaning.

Here's an example of a context-clue exercise:

COLUMN A	COLUMN B
___G___ word: _____ecology_____ **n.** the relationship between living things and their environments; the science of such relationships	(G) Aldo Leopold (1866–1948) learned to think like a mountain so that he could understand and preserve the **ecology** of nature. Nature's rights, he felt, must be respected.

Hint #1 Read Column B first, and look for clues to the meaning of the word. You might imagine that thinking like a mountain would give you strong opinions about how nature should be treated. For example, as part of the earth, you would make sure that the rights of the earth were respected.

Hint #2 You should scan Column A for a likely definition of the word. In this case, the idea of relationships suggests that the sample definition is the correct one.

Hint #3 As you write the word in the blank, say it to yourself to get a sense of the sound of the word.

HOW TO DO EXERCISE 3 *Sentence Completion* ☞

In the final part of **Making New Words Your Own,** you are asked to supply the missing Vocabulary Word or words in order to create a sentence that makes sense.

Here is an example of a sentence-completion exercise:

The science of _____ allows us to _____ our natural resources.
(A) zoology . . . diminish
(B) ecology . . . preserve
(C) cultivation . . . destroy
(D) zoology . . . ignore
(E) ecology . . . exhaust

Hint #1 Think about the logic of the sentence. You are looking for a type of science that deals with natural resources. You can assume that the ultimate aim of any science is some kind of improvement.

Hint #2 Substitute the words in choices (A) through (E) in the sentence to see which pair of words completes the logic of the sentence.
   • The pairs containing the word *zoology* can probably be ruled out, since *zoology* deals with animals in particular, not all natural resources.
   • Cultivation has something to do with natural resources, but it is unlikely that the aim of any science is to destroy.
   • Similarly, you can rule out answer E because the aim of ecology is not to exhaust but to preserve our natural resources. This conclusion leads to the correct answer, B.

As you complete these three types of exercises, you will develop the ability to make an educated guess about the meaning of a word by thinking about its context.

MAKING NEW WORDS YOUR OWN

Lesson 1 | CONTEXT: The Literature

Frederick Douglass and Martin Luther King, Jr.

Frederick Douglass and Dr. Martin Luther King, Jr., stand out as two American masters of rhetoric, or persuasion. Both men used their remarkable speeches to protest unfair treatment of African Americans. Their efforts greatly furthered the cause of civil rights in the United States. Born more than a century apart, Douglass and King shared a vision of freedom and equality for African Americans.

In the following exercises, you will have the opportunity to expand your vocabulary by reading about Frederick Douglass and Dr. Martin Luther King, Jr. These ten Vocabulary Words will be used.

accentuate	comprehensive	intricacy	provocative	usurp
ambiguous	felicitous	introspective	rhetorical	vernacular

EXERCISE 1 | Wordbusting ☞

Directions. Follow these instructions for this word and the nine words on the next page.
- Figure out the word's meaning by looking at its **context,** its **structure,** and its **sound.** Fill in at least one of the three **CSS** boxes. Alternate which boxes you complete.
- Then, look up the word in a dictionary, read all of its meanings, and write the meaning of the word as it is used in the sentence.
- Follow this same process for each of the Vocabulary Words on the next page. You will need to draw your own map for each word. Use a separate sheet of paper.

1.

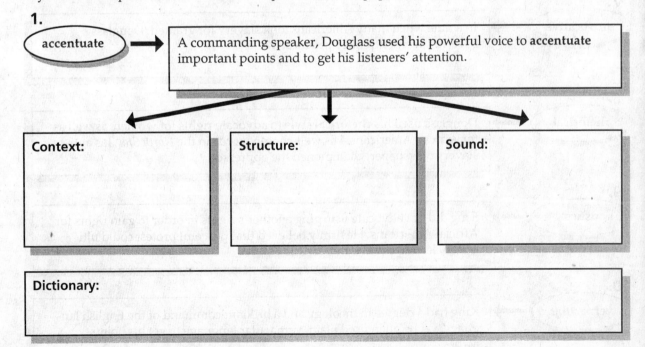

accentuate → A commanding speaker, Douglass used his powerful voice to **accentuate** important points and to get his listeners' attention.

Context:

Structure:

Sound:

Dictionary:

Name _____ Date _____ Class _____

2.

Neither Douglass nor King were **ambiguous** in their demands; they both made it perfectly clear that nothing less than equal rights for African Americans was acceptable.

3.

King demanded a **comprehensive,** nationwide commitment to civil rights for African Americans.

4.

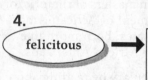

Douglass's **felicitous** manner of speaking made his ideas seem agreeable as well. He persuaded many people to support the cause of the abolitionists.

5.

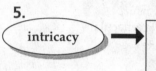

King knew that segregation was not a simple issue. Yet his clear sense of justice helped him cut through the **intricacy** of the problem.

6.

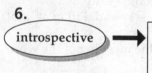

Both King and Douglass were **introspective** people who thoughtfully examined their own beliefs.

7.

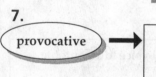

In a time when many Americans took slavery for granted, Douglass's speeches were extremely **provocative**.

8.

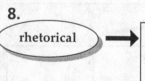

Douglass used his **rhetorical** style to advocate rights for women, as well as for African Americans. His well-chosen words in the *North Star*, his anti-slavery newspaper, championed the oppressed.

9.

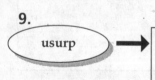

King did not advocate **usurping** another's rights in order to gain rights for African Americans. He firmly believed that peaceful protest could ultimately lead to equal rights for all.

10.

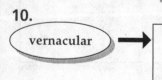

King had a degree in theology and a brilliant command of the English language, yet he often used plain, **vernacular** language to get his points across.

EXERCISE 2 Context Clues ☞

Directions. Scan the definitions in Column A. Then think about how the boldface words are used in the sentences in Column B. To complete the exercise, match each definition in Column A with the correct Vocabulary Word from Column B. Write the letter of your choice on the line provided; then write the Vocabulary Word on the line preceding the definition.

COLUMN A

_____ **11.** word: _____:
n. the native language or dialect of a country or region; everyday or informal language; *adj.* using everyday language

_____ **12.** word: _____:
adj. the effective use of words (particularly in prose composition) designed to be impressive; showy and oratorical

_____ **13.** word: _____:
adj. stimulating; pushing or tending toward action, thought, or strong feeling

_____ **14.** word: _____:
v. to emphasize; to heighten the effect of; to pronounce or mark with an accent

_____ **15.** word: _____:
n. condition or state of being complex, involved, or detailed; elaborateness

_____ **16.** word: _____:
adj. given to examination of one's own thoughts and feelings; contemplative

_____ **17.** word: _____:
adj. well chosen for the occasion; appropriate; apt; having an agreeable or delightful manner of writing or speaking

_____ **18.** word: _____:
v. to take (power, rights, position, etc.) by force, wrongfully, or without rights

_____ **19.** word: _____:
adj. of wide scope; inclusive; thorough

_____ **20.** word: _____:
adj. having more than one possible meaning; uncertain; vague or unclear

COLUMN B

(A) It's 1841, and you're attending an antislavery convention in Massachusetts. You have just been impressed by Frederick Douglass's **felicitous** and timely speech on the subject of slavery.

(B) Douglass's clear, powerful language served to **accentuate** his descriptions of the horrors of slavery.

(C) Douglass's **provocative** speech roused the crowd to anger against slaveholders.

(D) His listeners became convinced that he was not just being **rhetorical**, but instead he was both eloquent and truthful in stating how, since its beginning, the institution of slavery has violated human rights.

(E) While listening, you wondered how such a sensitive, **introspective** person could speak out so strongly and effectively.

(F) Everyone in the room was moved by Douglass's belief in the dignity of all human beings. He felt that African Americans were not taking anything from others by working toward their own freedom. It was not a question of **usurping** rights; these privileges belonged to all.

(G) The **intricacy** of his argument is even more impressive when you consider that Douglass had no formal education.

(H) You believe that Douglass should give many more speeches. Why not launch a **comprehensive** lecture campaign to reach audiences throughout the North?

(I) Douglass has **ambiguous** feelings about the idea, but he is clearly willing to give the plan a try.

(J) Douglass's formal, dignified language, which seems more eloquent than the common **vernacular,** makes him an especially effective speaker.

EXERCISE 3   *Sentence Completion* ✍

Directions. For each of the following items, circle the letter of the choice that best completes the meaning of the sentence or sentences.

21. Douglass urged Abraham Lincoln to free the slaves in the South. In 1863 Lincoln's Emancipation Proclamation declared the _____ end to slavery throughout the United States.
(A) vernacular
(B) felicitous
(C) ambiguous
(D) comprehensive
(E) provocative

22. Lincoln's delivery of the Emancipation Proclamation was a _____ event. As Douglass had predicted, it helped the war effort.
(A) ambiguous
(B) felicitous
(C) provocative
(D) comprehensive
(E) intricate

23. The Emancipation Proclamation was not _____; it clearly proclaimed freedom for all slaves.
(A) comprehensive
(B) ambiguous
(C) provocative
(D) rhetorical
(E) introspective

24. When Douglass was a slave, his thoughtful nature was considered _____ by the overseers; _____ often angered the overseers.
(A) rhetorical . . . intricacy
(B) ambiguous . . . vernacular
(C) accentuated . . . felicity
(D) vernacular . . . introspection
(E) provocative . . . introspection

25. Douglass's white playmates taught him to read, and he was drawn to a book of impressive, _____ speeches that condemned slavery and injustice.
(A) provocative
(B) vernacular
(C) felicitous
(D) ambiguous
(E) rhetorical

26. In his speeches, King often _____ injustices to African Americans to make people pay attention and call for _____ legislation that would end segregation.
(A) comprehended . . . vernacular
(B) provoked . . . felicitous
(C) accentuated . . . comprehensive
(D) provoked . . . intricate
(E) accentuated . . . provocative

27. In his "I Have a Dream" speech, King skillfully used repetition to _____ key words and ideas.
(A) provoke
(B) comprehend
(C) make ambiguous
(D) accentuate
(E) contemplate

28. As a public speaker, King used bold images and simple but effective language; he did not use _____ phrasing.
(A) provocative
(B) accentuated
(C) intricate
(D) vernacular
(E) insightful

29. King sometimes expressed himself with _____ language. For example, he used an everyday phrase when he said that African Americans had come to cash a check for their freedom.
(A) rhetorical
(B) introspective
(C) felicitous
(D) provocative
(E) vernacular

30. Tragically, King's _____ speeches earned him fierce enemies. Many felt that King attempted to _____ freedoms that were not the rights of the African American.
(A) introspective . . . felicitous
(B) provocative . . . usurp
(C) provocative . . . intricate
(D) ambiguous . . . vernacular
(E) ambiguous . . . provocative

MAKING NEW WORDS YOUR OWN

Lesson 2 | CONTEXT: The Literature

Davy Crockett and Daniel Boone

America's literary tradition owes a debt of gratitude to its oral tradition. Some of the most exciting tales are about our pioneers. True, some of the tales told about men like Davy Crockett (1786–1836) and Daniel Boone (1734–1820) may contain more fiction than fact, but there is no denying that these people had remarkable qualities: self-sufficiency, adaptability, hardiness, and courage. These traits became an important part of the ideal of the heroic individual used in American literature.

In the following exercises, you will have the opportunity to expand your vocabulary by reading about Davy Crockett and Daniel Boone. Below are ten Vocabulary Words that will be used in these exercises.

allegory	despicable	ferocity	misanthrope	protagonist
conjecture	dissolute	incongruous	prologue	terse

EXERCISE 1 *Wordbusting*

Directions. Follow these instructions for this word and the nine words on the next page.
- Figure out the word's meaning by looking at its **context,** its **structure,** and its **sound.** Fill in at least one of the three **CSS** boxes. Alternate which boxes you complete.
- Then, look up the word in a dictionary, read all of its meanings, and write the meaning of the word as it is used in the sentence.
- Follow this same process for each of the Vocabulary Words on the next page. You will need to draw your own map for each word. Use a separate sheet of paper.

1.

allegory → People still tell the story of how Davy Crockett used his rifle as a club after running out of ammunition at the Battle of the Alamo. If this tale were an **allegory,** Crockett would represent the heroic attitude of someone willing to fight to the last for freedom.

Context:

Structure:

Sound:

Dictionary:

Name _____ Date _____ Class _____

2.

protagonist →

Crockett was one of the **protagonists** at the Alamo. As William Travis's second-in-command, he was a principal player in the battle.

3.

incongruous →

To many observers, Davy Crockett's presence in the U. S. House of Representatives seemed **incongruous**. His backwoods clothes and colorful speech did not conform to what people expected of a representative.

4.

terse →

Davy Crockett was not a naturally **terse** speaker. His speeches were full of rambling anecdotes, digressions, and jokes.

5.

prologue →

Boone's first attempt to colonize Kentucky in 1773 was the **prologue** to the successful colonization of the region in the years that followed.

6.

ferocity →

Settlers and American Indian groups fought with great **ferocity** in conflicts such as the battle for Boone's fort, Boonesborough. Neither side asked for nor showed mercy.

7.

conjecture →

The biographers of Boone and Crockett are forced to make **conjectures** when hard evidence about what these men actually did is lacking.

8.

despicable →

Daniel Boone had only scorn for the lawyers and politicians who declared his titles to land in Kentucky invalid. He regarded them and their underhanded practices as **despicable**.

9.

misanthrope →

Some of the pioneers were probably **misanthropes** who preferred the loneliness of the backwoods to the company of people.

10.

dissolute →

It was tempting for people living on the frontier to fall into **dissolute** ways of living because many of the ethical constraints that people in urban society accept were absent on the frontier.

EXERCISE 2 Context Clues 👉

Directions. Scan the definitions in Column A. Then think about how the boldface words are used in the sentences in Column B. To complete the exercise, match each definition in Column A with the correct Vocabulary Word from column B. Write the letter of your choice on the line provided; then write the Vocabulary Word on the line preceding the definition.

COLUMN A	COLUMN B
_____ 11. word: _____: *n.* introductory lines of a play; the preface to a literary work; an introductory or preceding event	(A) The pioneers could not afford to be **dissolute**. Their survival often depended upon great self-discipline.
_____ 12. word: _____: *n.* an opinion without proof; guesswork; *v.* to speculate; to guess	(B) Boone is the **protagonist** of John Filson's *Discovery, Settlement and Present State of Kentucke*, a work that contains the supposedly autobiographical "Adventures of Colonel Daniel Boone."
_____ 13. word: _____: *adj.* brief and to the point (in writing or speaking); concise	(C) When doubts were expressed about his "autobiography," Boone's response was **terse**; he simply said, "Every word is true," and left it at that.
_____ 14. word: _____: *n.* an individual who dislikes or distrusts other human beings	(D) The Shawnee people viewed as **despicable** the actions of the white settlers who took their land. Yet they respected Boone and adopted him after his capture.
_____ 15. word: _____: *n.* a symbolic story in which people, settings, or actions represent ideas or moral qualities	(E) The story of how Boone helped bring about the defeat of the people who had adopted him could be read as an **allegory** symbolizing the history of relations between the white settlers and the Native Americans.
_____ 16. word: _____: *adj.* lacking moral restraint; very wicked; immoral; undisciplined	(F) There is something **incongruous** about a man like Boone keeping a tavern. His life had been action-packed, and the life of a tavern-keeper is uneventful by comparison.
_____ 17. word: _____: *n.* the main character in a story or play; a person who plays a leading or active part in something	(G) Although he loved to hunt alone, Davy Crockett was certainly no **misanthrope**. His reputation and his wit made him popular among the voters, and he enjoyed entertaining them.
_____ 18. word: _____: *adj.* contemptible; deserving of scorn; vile	(H) We can only **conjecture** what William Travis said to Crockett on the eve of the battle at the Alamo. No witnesses survived.
_____ 19. word: _____: *adj.* not suitable or appropriate; not consistent; not conforming to a pattern	(I) The **ferocity** of the attack on the Alamo is indicated by the fact that every single one of those defending it was killed.
_____ 20. word: _____: *n.* the quality or state of being fierce, savage, or relentless	(J) Crockett and his comrades were massacred at the Alamo; but that battle was only the **prologue** to the decisive battle six weeks later at San Jacinto, which the Texans won.

EXERCISE 3 Sentence Completion 👉

Directions. For each of the following items, circle the letter of the choice that best completes the meaning of the sentence or sentences.

21. One popular image of the western pioneer is that of a suspicious, unfriendly _____ who says little beyond the occasional, curt, _____ remark to those he meets.

(A) protagonist . . . ferocious
(B) misanthrope . . . terse
(C) prologue . . . incongruous
(D) allegory . . . dissolute
(E) conjecture . . . despicable

22. Boone left his wife alone for months while he explored the woods. Some women would have found his behavior _____, but Boone's wife didn't condemn him.

(A) terse
(B) incongruous
(C) allegorical
(D) despicable
(E) ferocious

23. Some find it _____, or inconsistent, that Boone fought against the Shawnee after having been adopted by them.

(A) incongruous
(B) ferocious
(C) dissolute
(D) terse
(E) allegorical

24. Although it cannot be proved, there have been _____ that the main character in James Fenimore Cooper's *The Last of the Mohicans* is based on Boone. There are similarities between Boone and the novel's _____.

(A) prologues . . . protagonist
(B) incongruities . . . misanthrope
(C) allegories . . . incongruity
(D) conjectures . . . protagonist
(E) conjectures . . . ferocity

25. Davy Crockett may have had his faults, but he was not _____. In his own way he was a very moral individual.

(A) terse
(B) ferocious
(C) incongruous
(D) misanthropic
(E) dissolute

26. People often smiled at the _____ of Crockett's coonskin cap in places where formal dress was the expected attire.

(A) incongruity
(B) allegory
(C) protagonist
(D) terseness
(E) ferocity

27. Crockett was not known for being _____ when he spoke. The _____ to one of his stories was likely to be as long and as rambling as the story itself.

(A) dissolute . . . misanthrope
(B) ferocious . . . ferocity
(C) terse . . . prologue
(D) incongruous . . . allegory
(E) despicable . . . protagonist

28. The various theories about why Crockett called his rifle "Old Betsy" are mere _____. No one knows for sure.

(A) protagonists
(B) prologues
(C) allegories
(D) misanthropes
(E) conjectures

29. Some historians say that Davy Crockett surrendered at the Alamo and was executed. Others strongly defend his honor and denounce that claim with great _____ as a _____ lie.

(A) terseness . . . allegorical
(B) ferocity . . . despicable
(C) allegory . . . misanthropic
(D) conjecture . . . terse
(E) incongruity . . . dissolute

30. The story of _____, distrustful settler living alone in the woods could be seen as _____ tale symbolizing our relationship with nature.

(A) an incongruous . . . a misanthropic
(B) a misanthropic . . . an allegorical
(C) a terse . . . a despicable
(D) a conjectural . . . a dissolute
(E) a dissolute . . . a terse

Name _____ Date _____ Class _____

MAKING NEW WORDS YOUR OWN

Lesson 3 | **CONTEXT:** The Literature

Isaac Bashevis Singer

Isaac Bashevis Singer (1904–1991) delved into the past to create his memorable and moving stories of Jewish life. His works capture the flavor of life in the *shtetls*, or Jewish small towns, of eastern Europe, which were destroyed by Hitler in the 1930s.

Singer wrote in Yiddish, a language derived from Middle High German and spoken by eastern European Jews. His works were later translated into English.

In the following exercises, you will have the opportunity to expand your vocabulary by reading about Isaac Bashevis Singer and his work. These ten Vocabulary Words will be used.

| epithet | evoke | infer | lucid | scrutinize |
| evasive | foreshadow | laudable | perpetuate | symposium |

EXERCISE 1 *Wordbusting* ✍

Directions. Follow these instructions for this word and the nine words on the next page.
- Figure out the word's meaning by looking at its **context,** its **structure,** and its **sound.** Fill in at least one of the three **CSS** boxes. Alternate which boxes you complete.
- Then, look up the word in a dictionary, read all of its meanings, and write the meaning of the word as it is used in the sentence.
- Follow this same process for each of the Vocabulary Words on the next page. You will need to draw your own map for each word. Use a separate sheet of paper.

1.

(epithet) → Because Singer's writing is so original, critics have had a difficult time finding an **epithet** that can briefly describe his work.

| Context: | Structure: | Sound: |

| Dictionary: |

2.

evasive →
Singer was never **evasive** about his goals as a writer; he made it plain that his aim was mainly to entertain his readers with a good story.

3.

evoke →
In his stories, Singer masterfully **evokes** the sights and sounds of the Polish neighborhoods that he knew as a child. The reader often feels as if he or she visited the story's setting.

4.

perpetuate →
Singer wrote in Yiddish to help **perpetuate** that language; he felt it was important to keep it alive.

5.

foreshadow →
Sadly, the decline in Singer's Yiddish readership may **foreshadow** the eventual disappearance of the language.

6.

infer →
Singer doesn't directly state his philosophy in his stories, but readers may **infer** from his fiction a deep religious faith.

7.

laudable →
Not all of Singer's characters are **laudable**—in fact, some of them are mean and corrupt.

8.

lucid →
Singer wrote **lucid** accounts of the forces that shape people's lives. Reading his stories, we may come to a clearer understanding of love and hate, good and evil, hope and despair.

9.

scrutinize →
Singer was careful not to force his personal interpretations on his readers. Instead, he left it up to us to **scrutinize** his characters' motives.

10.

symposium →
Singer's work is always a likely topic for discussion at a **symposium** on Yiddish literature.

EXERCISE 2 *Context Clues* ☞

Directions. Scan the definitions in Column A. Then think about how the boldface words are used in the sentences in Column B. To complete the exercise, match each definition in Column A with the correct Vocabulary Word from Column B. Write the letter of your choice on the line provided; then write the Vocabulary Word on the line preceding the definition.

<table>
<tr><th>COLUMN A</th><th>COLUMN B</th></tr>
<tr>
<td>

_____ **11.** word: _____:

n. a meeting for discussing a particular subject; a collection of writings on a subject

</td>
<td>

(A) Have you ever known someone who was a fatalist? That **epithet** aptly describes the main character in Singer's story "The Fatalist."

</td>
</tr>
<tr>
<td>

_____ **12.** word: _____:

v. to indicate or suggest beforehand; to give a warning of

</td>
<td>

(B) Fatalism is the belief that everything is determined by fate or destiny. Thus, you can **infer** from the story's title that Singer's character doesn't believe in chance.

</td>
</tr>
<tr>
<td>

_____ **13.** word: _____:

v. to examine closely or critically

</td>
<td>

(C) Benjamin, the fatalist, discusses his beliefs at a **symposium** held by a group of young scholars.

</td>
</tr>
<tr>
<td>

_____ **14.** word: _____:

adj. avoiding by cleverness; not straightforward; misleading

</td>
<td>

(D) Benjamin's philosophy is so **lucid** that it begins to make sense to some of the villagers.

</td>
</tr>
<tr>
<td>

_____ **15.** word: _____:

v. to conclude on the basis of reasoning or observation

</td>
<td>

(E) Benjamin's comments about fate **foreshadow** the clever plot twists in the story. Even so, the events are sure to surprise you.

</td>
</tr>
<tr>
<td>

_____ **16.** word: _____:

adj. easily understood; clear; rational and sane

</td>
<td>

(F) The fatalist's beliefs **evoke** scorn in Heyele, the young woman he wants to marry. She doesn't hide her feelings, but he proposes to her anyway.

</td>
</tr>
<tr>
<td>

_____ **17.** word: _____:

v. to make perpetual, ongoing or constant; to cause to be remembered

</td>
<td>

(G) Benjamin proposes an extraordinary bet to test whether their marriage is fated. After **scrutinizing** his offer carefully, looking for any possible tricks, Heyele accepts the wager.

</td>
</tr>
<tr>
<td>

_____ **18.** word: _____:

v. to call forth; to bring out; to elicit; to produce (a reaction)

</td>
<td>

(H) The bet is this: Benjamin will lie in front of an oncoming train, and if it doesn't hit him, Heyele has to marry him. The villagers find his courage **laudable,** but they can't believe he'd do something so foolish.

</td>
</tr>
<tr>
<td>

_____ **19.** word: _____:

n. a word or phrase that describes or characterizes a person or thing; a descriptive name

</td>
<td>

(I) By going forth with this foolish bet, Benjamin certainly **perpetuates** his fatalistic outlook.

</td>
</tr>
<tr>
<td>

_____ **20.** word: _____:

adj. praiseworthy; commendable

</td>
<td>

(J) Does Benjamin win the bet? I don't mean to be **evasive,** but you will have to read the story to find out!

</td>
</tr>
</table>

EXERCISE 3 *Sentence Completion* ☞

Directions. For each of the following items, circle the letter of the choice that best completes the meaning of the sentence or sentences.

21. What an honor! You've been asked to speak at a national _____ on the work of Isaac Bashevis Singer.
    - (A) epithet
    - (B) foreshadowing
    - (C) symposium
    - (D) scrutiny
    - (E) evasion

22. Singer felt that the purpose of literature was to tell stories, and he used his writing to _____ the long-standing tradition of storytelling.
    - (A) perpetuate
    - (B) infer
    - (C) scrutinize
    - (D) evoke
    - (E) foreshadow

23. After carefully _____ a few of Singer's stories, you can probably _____ the general themes in Singer's work.
    - (A) foreshadowing . . . scrutinize
    - (B) scrutinizing . . . infer
    - (C) evoking . . . laud
    - (D) evading . . . infer
    - (E) lauding . . . evade

24. You decide to talk about how Singer _____ his readers' emotional responses through his retelling of personal memories.
    - (A) foreshadows
    - (B) evokes
    - (C) infers
    - (D) scrutinizes
    - (E) exacts

25. In preparation for your talk, you _____ the story "The Washwoman," paying careful attention to all the characters and details that _____ the outcome of the story.
    - (A) evade . . . evoke
    - (B) foreshadow . . . scrutinize
    - (C) evoke . . . infer
    - (D) scrutinize . . . foreshadow
    - (E) infer . . . evade

26. The story tells about one of the people Singer's family had contact with. Singer just calls her "the washwoman," an appropriate _____ since her work was her whole life.
    - (A) evasion
    - (B) symposium
    - (C) lucidity
    - (D) inference
    - (E) epithet

27. The washwoman's work is so _____ that it _____ praise even from Singer's demanding mother.
    - (A) laudable . . . infers
    - (B) laudable . . . evokes
    - (C) lucid . . . foreshadows
    - (D) evasive . . . evokes
    - (E) foreshadowed . . . scrutinizes

28. In a(n) _____, straightforward narrative, Singer describes how the woman walked hours to pick up and drop off the laundry.
    - (A) evasive
    - (B) laudable
    - (C) foreshadowed
    - (D) evocative
    - (E) lucid

29. His description early in the story of the old woman's frailty _____ the day when she is too sick to bring the wash.
    - (A) foreshadows
    - (B) scrutinizes
    - (C) evokes
    - (D) infers
    - (E) perpetuates

30. When the woman struggles from her sickbed for the last time to bring her customers their laundry, Singer is not _____ about the impression she made on him. He says clearly that he cannot imagine such a person being turned away from paradise.
    - (A) scrutinizing
    - (B) lucid
    - (C) laudable
    - (D) evasive
    - (E) evocative

MAKING NEW WORDS YOUR OWN

Lesson 4 | CONTEXT: The Literature

The Comic Talent of James Thurber

James Thurber (1894–1961) is considered one of America's greatest humorists. Through the form of the comic short story, Thurber expressed his insightful and quirky vision of twentieth-century life. Thurber first received national recognition as a writer, cartoonist, and editor for *The New Yorker*, a magazine he helped establish. In the late 1920s, he began writing the humorous collections of stories that would earn him a devoted audience both in the United States and abroad.

In the following exercises, you will have the opportunity to expand your vocabulary by reading about James Thurber and his work. Below are ten Vocabulary Words that will be used in these exercises.

| affluent | brevity | embellish | nostalgic | reiterate |
| banter | connotation | imbibe | novice | stipend |

EXERCISE 1 Wordbusting

Directions. Follow these instructions for this word and the nine words on the next page.
- Figure out the word's meaning by looking at its **context,** its **structure,** and its **sound.** Fill in at least one of the three **CSS** boxes. Alternate which boxes you complete.
- Then, look up the word in a dictionary, read all of its meanings, and write the meaning of the word as it is used in the sentence.
- Follow this same process for each of the Vocabulary Words on the next page. You will need to draw your own map for each word. Use a separate sheet of paper.

1.

(affluent) → Though *The New Yorker* was once regarded as a magazine for the elite, Thurber's humor appealed to people from all walks of life—not just an **affluent,** sophisticated audience.

| Context: | Structure: | Sound: |

| Dictionary: |

2.

banter → Underneath Thurber's **banter** was a fundamental anger and sadness. He has been compared to Mark Twain in his use of mockery to show frustration at a world that humanity finds difficult to understand.

3.

novice → Having worked as a reporter for the *Columbus Dispatch*, Thurber was no **novice** when he began writing for *The New Yorker*.

4.

brevity → Thurber, who wrote very short prose pieces, believed that **brevity** was essential to an effective style.

5.

connotation → Like any skilled writer, he would choose words carefully for their **connotations** as well as for their literal meanings.

6.

embellish → Thurber often told about real-life people and events, though he may have been guilty of adding an **embellishment** or two for effect.

7.

imbibe → Comedy lovers **imbibe** his hilarious tales as they might drink down a delightful refreshment.

8.

nostalgic → Bewildered by the modern world, Thurber's characters often display a **nostalgic** longing for a simpler way of life.

9.

stipend → Many writers must struggle to earn a living, but Thurber lived comfortably on the **stipend** he received from *The New Yorker* and on the royalties from his books.

10.

reiterate → Today, admiring critics **reiterate** the words of praise that critics in Thurber's own time applied to his work.

EXERCISE 2 · *Context Clues* ✍

Directions. Scan the definitions in Column A. Then think about how the boldface words are used in the sentences in Column B. To complete the exercise, match each definition in Column A with the correct Vocabulary Word from Column B. Write the letter of your choice on the line provided; then write the Vocabulary Word on the line preceding the definition.

COLUMN A	COLUMN B

COLUMN A

_____ **11.** word: _____:
n. an inexperienced person; a beginner

_____ **12.** word: _____:
n. teasing or mocking in a good-natured, playful manner; *v.* to engage in such playfulness

_____ **13.** word: _____:
n. the suggested, or implied, meaning of a word, not its strict literal meaning; an idea or feeling associated with a word

_____ **14.** word: _____:
adj. having a longing for things past

_____ **15.** word: _____:
n. fixed or regular pay; a salary or allowance

_____ **16.** word: _____:
adj. wealthy; abundant; plentiful

_____ **17.** word: _____:
v. to restate; to repeat

_____ **18.** word: _____:
v. to decorate or adorn; to improve a story by adding details, even false ones

_____ **19.** word: _____:
n. briefness of duration; shortness; the quality of being concise or to the point

_____ **20.** word: _____:
v. to drink; to drink in or absorb; to take in with the mind and keep (as in ideas or principles)

COLUMN B

(A) At age seven, Thurber had an accident that left him blind in one eye. **Nostalgic** for the sports he could no longer play, he satisfied his need for adventure by dreaming up stories.

(B) As an adult writer, Thurber often **reiterated** the theme of a sensitive daydreamer at odds with the dull realities of everyday life. We see this theme again and again in his stories.

(C) His rich imagination helped him **embellish** his experiences by adding details to create artful, humorous fiction.

(D) In Thurber's famous story "The Secret Life of Walter Mitty," the main character is an expert at fanciful thoughts but a **novice** at practical tasks.

(E) Driving past a hospital, Mitty imagines he is a brilliant doctor who saves the life of a millionaire. But just as he's about to operate on his **affluent** patient, a parking lot attendant yells at him for driving in the wrong lane.

(F) The humor lies partly in the forced **brevity** of Mitty's fantasies, which always end abruptly when reality intrudes.

(G) Deprived of excitement in his real life, Mitty secretly **imbibes** melodrama, like a sponge soaking up water.

(H) His practical wife doesn't **banter** with him. In fact, she bullies him, dominating her quiet husband.

(I) "The Secret Life of Walter Mitty" was published long ago, but to this day the name Walter Mitty has the **connotation** of a hopeless dreamer.

(J) Thurber stories show an easy familiarity with the clichés of popular movies. Perhaps the young Thurber, like many children, spent the few coins that made up his weekly **stipend** on Saturday matinees.

EXERCISE 3 Sentence Completion ✍

Directions. For each of the following items, circle the letter of the choice that best completes the meaning of the sentence or sentences.

21. Thurber not only used _____ in his writings; he also drew humorous sketches.
(A) embellishment
(B) nostalgia
(C) connotation
(D) banter
(E) brevity

22. Through his comically confused characters, Thurber speaks to anyone who has felt like a _____ at handling the complexities of modern life.
(A) banter
(B) connotation
(C) stipend
(D) imbiber
(E) novice

23. Thurber's stories appeal to a wide range of people—young and old, _____ and poor, literary and nonliterary.
(A) nostalgic
(B) novice
(C) banter
(D) affluent
(E) embellished

24. His _____ accounts of growing up in a small city are comical, though they are perhaps _____ for comic effect.
(A) nostalgic . . . embellished
(B) affluent . . . imbibed
(C) affluent . . . reiterated
(D) embellished . . . nostalgic
(E) novice . . . nostalgic

25. At first, the _____ of Thurber's prose pieces made critics reluctant to examine his work in depth. They didn't believe that short, comic sketches deserved the same critical attention a novel would receive.
(A) connotation
(B) affluence
(C) brevity
(D) embellishment
(E) stipend

26. Thurber frequently _____ his debt to the novelist Henry James. The humorist repeatedly named James as a strong influence, especially in Thurber's early days as a _____ writer.
(A) imbibed . . . connotation
(B) reiterated . . . stipend
(C) embellished . . . stipend
(D) embellished . . . novice
(E) reiterated . . . novice

27. In the 1940s, Thurber began to focus more intensely on the sounds and meanings of words. Not a single _____ of a word escaped his notice.
(A) brevity
(B) connotation
(C) affluence
(D) nostalgia
(E) novice

28. Thurber _____ and enriched his later writings with playful, witty puns on the various _____ of words.
(A) reiterated . . . brevities
(B) embellished . . . stipends
(C) embellished . . . connotations
(D) reiterated . . . banter
(E) connoted . . . brevities

29. Thurber did not let his visual impairment defeat him. He was able to earn a regular _____ for his editorial work and maintain a reasonable, if not _____ lifestyle.
(A) stipend . . . affluent
(B) connotation . . . nostalgic
(C) novice . . . nostalgic
(D) brevity . . . embellished
(E) embellishment . . . novice

30. On a chilly night, you might like to curl up by the fireside and _____ a cup of hot chocolate while reading one of Thurber's books.
(A) reiterate
(B) embellish
(C) connote
(D) imbibe
(E) congregate

MAKING NEW WORDS YOUR OWN

Lesson 5 | CONTEXT: The Literature
American Indian Folklore

If you've ever heard or read folk tales, you know that some of the most interesting stories are anonymous. The beauty of folk tales and myths is that they belong to everyone, and each culture has its own stories that have been passed down through the ages by word of mouth. American Indian myths and folk tales can't really be grouped as a whole because each American Indian group has its own stories. Yet each can be enjoyed both for itself and within the context of a rich oral tradition.

In the following exercises, you will have the opportunity to expand your vocabulary by reading about American Indian folklore. Below are ten Vocabulary Words that will be used in these exercises.

anagram	coherent	goad	noncommittal	quixotic
assertion	fulminate	inexplicable	proboscis	surmise

EXERCISE 1 | *Wordbusting* ☞

Directions. Follow these instructions for this word and the nine words on the next page.
- Figure out the word's meaning by looking at its **context,** its **structure,** and its **sound.** Fill in at least one of the three **CSS** boxes. Alternate which boxes you complete.
- Then, look up the word in a dictionary, read all of its meanings, and write the meaning of the word as it is used in the sentence.
- Follow this same process for each of the Vocabulary Words on the next page. You will need to draw your own map for each word. Use a separate sheet of paper.

1.

(anagram) → Just as you make an **anagram** by mixing up the letters of one word to make another word, people often mix elements of old folk tales to make a new story.

Context:	Structure:	Sound:

Dictionary:

2.

(**assertion**) ➤ The **assertion** that American Indian tradition doesn't include dramatic works is simply untrue. Anyone who makes this claim hasn't seen the drama of the Hopi ogres.

3.

(**coherent**) ➤ The dramatic ritual "The Visitation of the Ogres" may not seem **coherent** to the non-Hopi viewer, yet all the parts of this children's play are logically connected.

4.

(**fulminate**) ➤ The ogres are greedy, lazy monsters who sleep through the planting and harvesting time and then **fulminate** because they have nothing to eat. They curse and shout angrily because they see that the hard-working Hopi have plenty of food for the winter.

5.

(**goad**) ➤ The ogres love to eat Hopi children, so they try to **goad,** or urge, Hopi parents into giving up youngsters who have misbehaved.

6.

(**inexplicable**) ➤ This frightening story may seem **inexplicable** to observers who don't understand Hopi ways.

7.

(**noncommittal**) ➤ People dressed as ogres enter the village and pretend to be **noncommittal**. Although they're really set on eating children, the ogres claim they will be satisfied if the children grind enough corn or catch enough game for them to eat.

8.

(**proboscis**) ➤ The ogre costume often includes a hideous mask with a long **proboscis** in the place of a human nose.

9.

(**quixotic**) ➤ The parents, who are part of the drama, make a **quixotic,** tremendously noble effort to "save" their children.

10.

(**surmise**) ➤ You might **surmise** that "The Visitation of the Ogres" has little purpose other than to frighten misbehaving children into minding their parents. But this guess touches on only one level of the ritual's meaning.

EXERCISE 2 — Context Clues ✍

Directions. Scan the definitions in Column A. Then think about how the boldface words are used in the sentences in Column B. To complete the exercise, match each definition in Column A with the correct Vocabulary Word from Column B. Write the letter of your choice on the line provided; then write the Vocabulary Word on the line preceding the definition.

COLUMN A

_____ **11.** word: _____:
n. a word or phrase formed from another word or phrase by changing the order of the letters

_____ **12.** word: _____:
n. a prod for driving cattle; anything that drives or urges; an irritating stimulus; *v.* to prod into action; to urge on

_____ **13.** word: _____:
adj. not committing to any one position or course of action; not revealing one's purpose or position

_____ **14.** word: _____:
n. the act of declaring something; a claim or declaration stated positively

_____ **15.** word: _____:
adj. impractically idealistic; marked by a romantic notion of noble or chivalric ideas and deeds

_____ **16.** word: _____:
adj. logically connected; consistent; clearly expressed

_____ **17.** word: _____:
v. to talk or argue violently and loudly; to denounce; to explode suddenly

_____ **18.** word: _____:
n. the long snout of an animal; a nose, especially a prominent one; a tubular organ

_____ **19.** word: _____:
adj. impossible to explain or understand

_____ **20.** word: _____:
v. to guess or suppose; *n.* a guess based on little evidence

COLUMN B

(A) Some observers have made the **assertion** that the Hopi ogres represent qualities that are unacceptable in Hopi society. This claim is based on the fact that the ogres are lazy, greedy, and gluttonous.

(B) In light of this, it might seem **inexplicable** that the ogres warn children to behave. If the ogres are bad, why would they want children to be good?

(C) Yet the ogres' actions are **coherent,** or consistent, within the framework of the drama.

(D) Based on a glimpse of the play, you might **surmise** that the ogres also represent lack of compassion.

(E) The angry ogres **fulminate** about the children's bad behavior, while the adults talk kindly about the children's good qualities.

(F) The **quixotic** efforts of the parents convince the children that they are loved and respected.

(G) The Hopi may be mysterious about some aspects of the drama, but they aren't **noncommittal** about one purpose: comic relief.

(H) As an ogre stomps around, snorting through his big **proboscis,** the adults and the children shriek with laughter.

(I) The ogres never actually harm anyone, but they are an effective **goad** to urge the naughty children to behave themselves.

(J) This Hopi ritual is a coded form of communication that is subtle and difficult to read, somewhat like a riddle or the mixed-up letters of an **anagram**.

EXERCISE 3 Sentence Completion ✍

Directions. For each of the following items, circle the letter of the choice that best completes the meaning of the sentence or sentences.

21. A Tsimshian story about the Bear People might seem _____ if you don't know that folk-tale animals can change forms. If you know this, the story becomes _____.
  - (A) noncommittal . . . quixotic
  - (B) inexplicable . . . coherent
  - (C) assertive . . . inexplicable
  - (D) quixotic . . . goaded
  - (E) coherent . . . inexplicable

22. You have to accept some fantastical statements in folk tales. For example, you must accept the _____ of a talking bear.
  - (A) fulmination
  - (B) coherence
  - (C) assertion
  - (D) surmise
  - (E) proboscis

23. In the tale "The Girl Who Married a Bear," the girl, Peesunt, is far from _____ in her opinion of bears; she says flat out that they are ugly, horrid creatures.
  - (A) assertive
  - (B) goaded
  - (C) inexplicable
  - (D) noncommittal
  - (E) coherent

24. Walking in the forest with her friends, Peesunt falls behind. The sounds of their voices _____ her onward, but she becomes afraid until a young man finds her and _____ that she is lost.
  - (A) goad . . . fulminates
  - (B) surmise . . . goads
  - (C) fulminates . . . surmises
  - (D) assert . . . fulminates
  - (E) goad . . . surmises

25. After her violent _____ about the Bear People, perhaps Peesunt should _____ from the evidence of his big bearskin cloak that the man is not as he seems.
  - (A) goading . . . assert
  - (B) fulmination . . . surmise
  - (C) assertion . . . goad
  - (D) surmise . . . fulminate
  - (E) fulmination . . . goad

26. However, the stranger doesn't look like a bear; he doesn't have claws or a bearlike _____, or snout.
  - (A) surmise
  - (B) goad
  - (C) proboscis
  - (D) anagram
  - (E) coherence

27. The Bear People capture Peesunt, and although she is _____, or indifferent, about staying with them, they give her no choice.
  - (A) quixotic
  - (B) inexplicable
  - (C) noncommittal
  - (D) coherent
  - (E) assertive

28. No amount of _____ on Peesunt's part will convince the Bear People to release her. Reluctantly, Peesunt marries the stranger, the Bear Man.
  - (A) anagram
  - (B) fulmination
  - (C) proboscis
  - (D) surmise
  - (E) coherence

29. When Peesunt's brothers find her, the Bear Man shows his _____ nature by letting them kill him. He was so noble that he couldn't let his wife remain unhappy.
  - (A) fulminating
  - (B) coherent
  - (C) inexplicable
  - (D) noncommittal
  - (E) quixotic

30. Back home, Peesunt misses the Bear People; she trades her human skin back for bear skin. This puzzles her family as much as any riddle, code, or _____.
  - (A) anagram
  - (B) fulminattion
  - (C) proboscis
  - (D) coherence
  - (E) surmise

MAKING NEW WORDS YOUR OWN

Lesson 6 | CONTEXT: The Literature

Our Mothers' Gardens: Alice Walker

Born to sharecroppers in Georgia, African American writer Alice Walker (b. 1944) takes great pride in her origins. In the essay "In Search of Our Mothers' Gardens," Walker explores her heritage. She begins with the question: How did the overworked black women of earlier generations give expression to their creativity? Walker finds an answer in the beautiful gardens her mother cultivated. Thus the "gardens" of the essay's title represent the powerful creative spirit that African American women may claim as their legacy.

In the following exercises, you will have the opportunity to expand your vocabulary by reading about the work of Alice Walker. Below are ten Vocabulary Words that will be used in these exercises.

anecdote	epilogue	fidelity	hypochondriac	staunch
climactic	extemporaneous	forte	prodigy	stigma

EXERCISE 1 — Wordbusting 👈

Directions. Follow these instructions for this word and the nine words on the next page.
- Figure out the word's meaning by looking at its **context,** its **structure,** and its **sound.** Fill in at least one of the three **CSS** boxes. Alternate which boxes you complete.
- Then, look up the word in a dictionary, read all of its meanings, and write the meaning of the word as it is used in the sentence.
- Follow this same process for each of the Vocabulary Words on the next page. You will need to draw your own map for each word. Use a separate sheet of paper.

1.

anecdote → Walker illustrates the creativity of African American women with a brief story; she tells an **anecdote** about her mother's fame as a gardener.

Context:	Structure:	Sound:

Dictionary:

2.

extemporaneous → Walker's description of her mother's gardens may seem **extemporaneous** at first, but it is actually a deliberate, carefully developed image.

3.

fidelity → Walker's mother's gardens show her **fidelity** to her artistic gifts—gifts that she could have easily abandoned.

4.

climactic → In her essay, Walker builds up to the **climactic** moment when she realized her mother was an artist.

5.

epilogue → Like an actor giving an **epilogue** at the end of a play, Walker concludes her essay with a poem about the women of her mother's generation.

6.

prodigy → Earlier in her career, Walker revealed herself to be a **prodigy** with remarkable gifts. She had completed college, worked in the voter registration and welfare rights movements, and published her first volume of poetry by the time she was twenty-four.

7.

forte → It is difficult to say whether Walker's **forte** is prose or poetry; she is a master of both mediums.

8.

hypochondriac → There is a difference between a **hypochondriac** who enjoys complaining about illness and a suffering person who truly seeks a cure. Likewise, there is a difference between a writer who merely complains about social problems and one who actively seek solutions to them.

9.

staunch → Walker is a **staunch** supporter of women, and African American women in particular. Her writings reveal a loyalty to these women and their heritage.

10.

stigma → In fact, Walker encourages African Americans to view their heritage not as a **stigma** but as a source of pride and inspiration.

EXERCISE 2 *Context Clues*

Directions. Scan the definitions in Column A. Then think about how the boldface words are used in the sentences in Column B. To complete the exercise, match each definition in Column A with the correct Vocabulary Word from Column B. Write the letter of your choice on the line provided; then write the Vocabulary Word on the line preceding the definition.

COLUMN A

_____ **11.** word: _____:
adj. of the highest point; of the most intense part of a story or event

_____ **12.** word: _____:
n. loyalty, faithfulness; accuracy; accuracy of the reproduction of a sound or picture

_____ **13.** word: _____:
n. a brief, entertaining account of an interesting incident

_____ **14.** word: _____:
adj. loyal, steadfast; strong or solid; watertight; *v.* to check the flow of (blood, etc.)

_____ **15.** word: _____:
n. a person with extraordinary talents, especially a highly gifted child; an act or thing that causes amazement; a marvel

_____ **16.** word: _____:
n. something that someone does very well; a strong point

_____ **17.** word: _____:
n. a short concluding section at the end of a literary work; speech at the end of a play

_____ **18.** word: _____:
n. a mark of shame; a stain; in botany, the portion of a flower's pistil on which pollen is deposited for germination

_____ **19.** word: _____:
n. a person suffering from abnormal anxiety about his or her health; one who imagines he or she is sick or has symptoms of a disease

_____ **20.** word: _____:
adj. done, said, or performed with little or no preparation; unrehearsed; offhand

COLUMN B

(A) Walker points out that the poet Phillis Wheatley (1753?–1784), an eighteenth-century slave, was taught to reject her African heritage as if it were a terrible **stigma**.

(B) Wheatley was so frail that she often needed a servant to look after her. Far from being a **hypochondriac,** she suffered from genuine illnesses that may have been worsened by her inner conflicts.

(C) Walker mourns the fate of women who might have been artistic **prodigies** if only they had been free to express their creativity.

(D) A nineteenth-century African American woman whose **forte** was poetry or sculpture had little hope of developing her talents.

(E) Indeed, artists who can't practice their art are deprived and might be compared to a leaky vessel; neither of them is **staunch**.

(F) Those thwarted artists often expressed their creativity in any way they could; for example, if a woman was a gifted storyteller, she may have told **anecdotes** to entertain and instruct her children.

(G) As Walker points out, the lives of those women are not closed books. The artistic achievements of their children and grandchildren serve as inspiring **epilogues** to the women's stories.

(H) Perhaps, Walker imagines, Phillis Wheatley's mother shared her daughter's **fidelity** to the ideal of art.

(I) Walker values the bond of sympathy between women. In her novel *The Color Purple*, one of the **climactic** moments, or turning points, occurs when the narrator finds a bundle of letters from her long-lost sister, Nettie.

(J) Nettie's letters are a form of art. In her correspondences, she makes meaning out of events that others might only refer to in an **extemporaneous** remark.

Name _____ Date _____ Class _____

EXERCISE 3   Sentence Completion ☞

Directions. For each of the following items, circle the letter of the choice that best completes the meaning of the sentence or sentences.

21. Have you ever known someone whose _____ was telling stories? Perhaps this person could tell an entertaining _____ better than anyone else.
    (A) prodigy . . . stigma
    (B) epilogue . . . forte
    (C) forte . . . anecdote
    (D) stigma . . . anecdote
    (E) forte . . . hypochondriac

22. Did he or she know how to build suspense before revealing the _____ event of a story?
    (A) extemporaneous
    (B) staunch
    (C) climactic
    (D) prodigious
    (E) anecdotal

23. Some people do have a special gift for storytelling. Still, you don't have to be a _____ to write fiction; everyone has interesting stories to tell.
    (A) extemporaneous
    (B) forte
    (C) hypochondriac
    (D) stigma
    (E) prodigy

24. In "In Search of Our Mothers' Gardens," Alice Walker recalls how her mother told stories _____, with little fuss or preparation, during the course of an ordinary day.
    (A) climactically
    (B) laboriously
    (C) grudgingly
    (D) extemporaneously
    (E) hypochondriacally

25. Like Walker, you probably heard many stories when you were growing up. Your memory of these stories may be surprisingly good, like an old cassette tape that still has high _____. Your ability to recall these stories could be considered your _____.
    (A) stigma . . . prodigy
    (B) fidelity . . . epilogue
    (C) prodigy . . . fidelity
    (D) fidelity . . . forte
    (E) stigma . . . climax

26. You may want to write down some of these _____ so that other people can enjoy them.
    (A) epilogues
    (B) anecdotes
    (C) stigmas
    (D) fidelities
    (E) fortes

27. You might add _____ to your story. In this ending, you might explain where, when, and from whom you heard the story.
    (A) an epilogue
    (B) an anecdote
    (C) a forte
    (D) a stigma
    (E) staunchness

28. Everyone likes to hear tales about eccentric relatives. For example, was your great-aunt a _____ who thought she had rare, tropical diseases? Or did your great-grandfather boast that, when he was young, the doctors almost couldn't _____ the blood from the cut on his leg?
    (A) forte . . . stigma
    (B) prodigy . . . climax
    (C) prodigy . . . staunch
    (D) hypochondriac . . . staunch
    (E) stigma . . . hypochondria

29. Like the _____ of flowers dusted with pollen, we all collect the seeds of stories.
    (A) stigmas
    (B) prodigies
    (C) fidelities
    (D) epilogues
    (E) anecdotes

30. In Walker's story "Everyday Use," quilts made from old rags become valuable treasures, almost a collection of _____. The _____ events of a woman's life become a priceless record for the next generation.
    (A) fidelity . . . extemporaneous
    (B) staunchness . . . climactic
    (C) anecdotes . . . extemporaneous
    (D) prodigies . . . climactic
    (E) anecdotes . . . fidelity

26   LESSON 6

MAKING NEW WORDS YOUR OWN

Lesson 7 | CONTEXT: The Literature
Gary Soto

At one time or another, someone has probably advised you to write about what you know. Personal experiences are often the best launching-off points for stories and poems. The experiences that Gary Soto (b. 1952) writes about include childhood misadventures, from schoolyard brawls to factory work and farm labor. The touching honesty of Soto's writing strikes a chord with his readers, however different their experiences have been.

In the following exercises, you will have the opportunity to expand your vocabulary by reading about the work of Mexican American poet Gary Soto. These ten Vocabulary Words will be used.

bumptious	consonant	repartee	sanction	subservient
cite	gibe	rudiment	satiate	vivacious

EXERCISE 1 — Wordbusting ✍

Directions. Follow these instructions for this word and the nine words on the next page.
- Figure out the word's meaning by looking at its **context**, its **structure**, and its **sound**. Fill in at least one of the three **CSS** boxes. Alternate which boxes you complete.
- Then, look up the word in a dictionary, read all of its meanings, and write the meaning of the word as it is used in the sentence.
- Follow this same process for each of the Vocabulary Words on the next page. You will need to draw your own map for each word. Use a separate sheet of paper.

1.

(bumptious) → What were you like as a child? Were you shy and unassuming, or were you noisy and **bumptious**?

Context:	Structure:	Sound:

Dictionary:

2.

cite →

In the story "Being Mean," Gary Soto **cites** several humorous incidents as examples of his childhood meanness.

3.

consonant →

However, Soto's description of himself as mean may not be **consonant** with readers' impressions. After finishing the story, readers may conclude that Soto was just an ordinary, mischievous child.

4.

gibe →

Soto describes being the victim of someone else's meanness, too. One time, a boy shouted a cruel **gibe** at Soto and his friends, and the taunting remark led to a fight.

5.

repartee →

Soto was clearly too offended to give a witty reply. Instead of yelling a **repartee,** he fought the boy and was badly hurt.

6.

rudiment →

Soto suggests that all of his friends had some basic meanness in them; he seems to think that being mean is a **rudiment** of childhood.

7.

sanction →

The narrator neither **sanctions** nor disapproves of his own childhood behavior. He simply describes the experiences as they happened.

8.

satiate →

Soto's stories are sure to **satiate** your appetite for vivid description.

9.

subservient →

In other words, Soto hasn't made his story **subservient** to his judgments as an adult. Instead, the story itself is in charge.

10.

vivacious →

After finishing the story, you might conclude that Soto and his spirited, troublemaking friends were more **vivacious** and mischievous than mean.

EXERCISE 2 *Context Clues* ✍

Directions. Scan the definitions in Column A. Then think about how the boldface words are used in the sentences in Column B. To complete the exercise, match each definition in Column A with the correct Vocabulary Word from Column B. Write the letter of your choice on the line provided; then write the Vocabulary Word on the line preceding the definition.

COLUMN A

_____ **11.** word: _____:
adj. submissive; obedient; useful or of service, especially as a subordinate

_____ **12.** word: _____:
n. a fundamental principle, rule, or step (usually used in the plural); an early or undeveloped form or stage or something

_____ **13.** word: _____:
v. to make mocking remarks; to jeer; to scoff at; *n.* a derisive remark; a taunt

_____ **14.** word: _____:
adj. conceited and arrogant; crudely and unpleasantly forward

_____ **15.** word: _____:
n. a quick, witty reply or retort; skill in making clever, witty replies

_____ **16.** word: _____:
adj. in agreement, accord, harmony; *n.* any letter of the alphabet that is not a vowel

_____ **17.** word: _____:
v. to satisfy an appetite fully; to provide with more than enough; to glut

_____ **18.** word: _____:
n. authorized permission or approval; a step taken by a country to force another country to obey international law; *v.* to confirm, approve, or permit officially

_____ **19.** word: _____:
adj. animated; lively; spirited; sprightly

_____ **20.** word: _____:
v. to quote; to mention by way of example or proof; to commend for bravery in an official report; to summon before a court

COLUMN B

(A) Migrant farm laborers have difficult lives. Often, they must be **subservient** to unjust employers because they fear they will lose their jobs if they do not obey.

(B) Such unfair treatment does not have the **sanction** of the government. Laws exist to protect the rights of migrant workers.

(C) Even the most **vivacious** person might be tired, sullen, and dispirited after a day of mind-numbing toil in the fields.

(D) In "Field Poem," Soto and his brother dream of eating restaurant food after a day in the fields. But they can't afford to **satiate** their longing for this simple pleasure.

(E) The **consonant** rhythms of nature underlie many of Soto's poems. For example, in "Stars" the moon is like a shepherd leading a willing flock of stars toward daybreak.

(F) Soto has **cited,** or mentioned, the Latin American writer Gabriel García Márquez as a strong influence on his work.

(G) He also credits the poet Philip Levine with teaching him the **rudiments,** or basics, of analyzing poetry.

(H) Soto is not **bumptious** about his success, but he will modestly acknowledge that he has a talent for poetry.

(I) Having suffered the **gibes** of prejudiced people himself, Soto feels a special bond with other Mexican Americans.

(J) His critically acclaimed writings may be considered a **repartee,** or witty response, to those who judged him unfairly.

EXERCISE 3   *Sentence Completion* 👈

Directions. For each of the following items, circle the letter of the choice that best completes the meaning of the sentence or sentences.

21. Your teacher has just _____ the topic you chose for your English essay—Gary Soto's story "The Jacket." Now that you have official approval, you're ready to get to work.

    (A) cited
    (B) gibed
    (C) sanctioned
    (D) satiated
    (E) serviced

22. You're free to express your own ideas about the story. But don't forget to _____ specific examples to support your points!

    (A) satiate
    (B) sanction
    (C) gibe
    (D) cite
    (E) concede

23. In "The Jacket," Soto describes a time when he was far from _____. He felt depressed and shy because of his ugly green jacket.

    (A) subservient
    (B) consonant
    (C) sanctioned
    (D) satiated
    (E) vivacious

24. Do you know people who are _____ to the tyranny of fashion, or who act _____ just because they have all the "right" clothes?

    (A) consonant . . . vivacious
    (B) subservient . . . bumptious
    (C) gibe . . . uppity
    (D) bumptious . . . satiate
    (E) subservient . . . rudimentary

25. Soto's mother couldn't afford to _____ his desire for expensive, fashionable clothes. Instead of the black leather jacket he wanted, he got a green vinyl one.

    (A) exceed
    (B) satiate
    (C) gibe
    (D) cite
    (E) recite

26. Soto thought that his classmates were _____ him behind his back because he had a guacamole-colored jacket. He was too embarrassed to give a clever _____.

    (A) praising . . . retort
    (B) sanctioning . . . consonant
    (C) citing . . . answer
    (D) gibing . . . repartee
    (E) reciting . . . rudiment

27. However, Soto's suspicions may not have been _____ with what people were really saying. He never actually heard anyone _____ him about his jacket.

    (A) truthful . . . consonant
    (B) consonant . . . gibe
    (C) sanction . . . rudiment
    (D) vivacious . . . sanction
    (E) bumptious . . . repartee

28. Many people worry about how they look. Sensitivity about one's appearance seems to be a _____ of human behavior.

    (A) repartee
    (B) rudiment
    (C) citation
    (D) consonance
    (E) sanction

29. For three years Soto imagined the _____ his classmates might be making about his jacket. He couldn't have felt worse if he had been _____ by a court of law and accused of a crime.

    (A) gibes . . . cited
    (B) repartee . . . tried
    (C) rudiment . . . sanctioned
    (D) gibes . . . bumptious
    (E) vivacity . . . satiated

30. "The Jacket" is a satisfying story. Its characters are drawn in a way that is _____ with the _____ of good storytelling.

    (A) vivacious . . . events
    (B) subservient . . . sanctions
    (C) satiated . . . consonants
    (D) consonant . . . rudiments
    (E) bumptious . . . repartee

30   LESSON 7

MAKING NEW WORDS YOUR OWN

Lesson 8   **CONTEXT: The Literature**

Citizen Kane *and the American Dream*

What is "the American dream"? Traditionally, it is the idea that anyone may strive toward greatness. In the early 1900s, William Randolph Hearst (1863–1951) built the largest newspaper chain in the country and became one of the most influential people of his time. But Hearst's critics say he practiced unethical journalism in his pursuit of wealth and power.

In 1941, director and actor Orson Welles (1915–1985) made film history with *Citizen Kane,* a controversial film loosely based on Hearst's life. Welles's film raised important questions about wealth and success.

In the following exercises, you will have the opportunity to expand your vocabulary by reading about *Citizen Kane.* Below are ten Vocabulary Words that will be used in these exercises.

comely	erroneous	hypercritical	miscreant	pretentious
decadence	flaunt	irascible	ostentatious	stereotype

EXERCISE 1   *Wordbusting* ✍

Directions. Follow these instructions for this word and the nine words on the next page.

- Figure out the word's meaning by looking at its **context,** its **structure,** and its **sound.** Fill in at least one of the three **CSS** boxes. Alternate which boxes you complete.
- Then, look up the word in a dictionary, read all of its meanings, and write the meaning of the word as it is used in the sentence.
- Follow this same process for each of the Vocabulary Words on the next page. You will need to draw your own map for each word. Use a separate sheet of paper.

1.

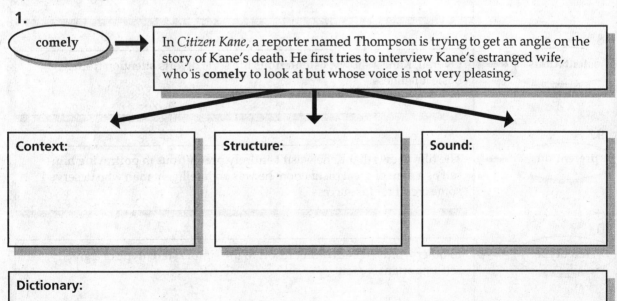

comely → In *Citizen Kane,* a reporter named Thompson is trying to get an angle on the story of Kane's death. He first tries to interview Kane's estranged wife, who is **comely** to look at but whose voice is not very pleasing.

Context:	Structure:	Sound:

Dictionary:

2.

(decadence) ➔ We get hints of Kane's **decadence** through the eyes of people who knew him. One example of his moral decay is his reckless spending on luxuries he doesn't even enjoy.

3.

(erroneous) ➔ Thompson believes that the word *rosebud,* which Kane uttered at his death, may provide a clue to Kane's character. Is Thompson's belief **erroneous,** or is *rosebud* really the key?

4.

(flaunt) ➔ Kane **flaunted** his wealth, but despite his show of material success, he was basically unhappy.

5.

(hypercritical) ➔ Kane tended to be **hypercritical;** he was harsh in his judgments of others and always pushed them to do things his way.

6.

(irascible) ➔ Through flashbacks, we also see that Kane was **irascible**—that his quick temper drove off people he cared for.

7.

(miscreant) ➔ Yet despite these negative qualities, Kane isn't portrayed as a **miscreant.** We see him as a complex man with good qualities as well.

8.

(ostentatious) ➔ Overall, Kane's showy, **ostentatious** life style diverts attention from his basic loneliness.

9.

(pretentious) ➔ The film shows that Kane wasn't entirely **pretentious** in portraying himself as a man of great distinction; he was an intelligent man who deserved some credit for his success.

10.

(stereotype) ➔ In other words, Welles didn't resort to the simple **stereotype** of a greedy, self-important tycoon.

EXERCISE 2   *Context Clues* 👉

Directions. Scan the definitions in Column A. Then think about how the boldface words are used in the sentences in Column B. To complete the exercise, match each definition in Column A with the correct Vocabulary Word from Column B. Write the letter of your choice on the line provided; then write the Vocabulary Word on the line preceding the definition.

COLUMN A	COLUMN B

COLUMN A

_____ **11.** word: _____:
adj. having a pleasant appearance; attractive; suitable

_____ **12.** word: _____:
n. a villain; an evildoer; *adj.* criminal; evil

_____ **13.** word: _____:
v. to show off; to display oneself proudly or conspicuously

_____ **14.** word: _____:
adj. false; mistaken; incorrect

_____ **15.** word: _____:
n. a process, condition, or period of decline or decay; deterioration; moral decay

_____ **16.** word: _____:
n. a generalized, oversimplified view or opinion that members of a group rigidly apply to a thing, an idea, or another group

_____ **17.** word: _____:
adj. claiming an undeserved distinction; affectedly grand

_____ **18.** word: _____:
adj. too showy; done in an overly elaborate way to attract attention

_____ **19.** word: _____:
adj. too severe in judgment

_____ **20.** word: _____:
adj. easily angered; given to outburst of temper; irritable

COLUMN B

(A) Even **hypercritical** film reviewers have called *Citizen Kane* one of the greatest movies ever made.

(B) *Citizen Kane* was a groundbreaking film in the 1940s; it defied the **stereotypes** of what a Hollywood movie should be.

(C) Suspicions that Kane's character was based on Hearst were not **erroneous**. Welles admitted that he and the script writer had Hearst in mind.

(D) Hearst, who had a reputation for being **irascible,** was probably outraged when he heard about the film.

(E) Before the film's release, Welles softened some of the negative characterizations of Kane. The film company didn't want to risk a lawsuit by implying that Hearst was a **miscreant**.

(F) Unlike the grand openings of blockbuster films today, the opening run of *Citizen Kane* was not **ostentatious**. Some major theaters wouldn't even show the film.

(G) Yet many well-known people, dressed in **comely,** elegant attire, attended the New York premiere.

(H) Fear of Hearst may have prompted one theater chain to shelve *Citizen Kane*. Although the film didn't directly suggest that Hearst himself led a life of **decadence,** the implication offended him.

(I) *Citizen Kane* received nine Academy Award nominations, but after the ceremony Welles had only one award to **flaunt** among his colleagues.

(J) Some people thought that Welles was **pretentious** in claiming so much credit for the script. The scriptwriter, Herman Mankiewicz, clearly deserved recognition as well.

EXERCISE 3 *Sentence Completion*

Directions. For each of the following items, circle the letter of the choice that best completes the meaning of the sentence or sentences.

21. *Citizen Kane* has strong visual appeal. Some of the most attractive and _____ images result from Welles's use of lighting and camera angle.
    - (A) stereotypical
    - (B) erroneous
    - (C) comely
    - (D) irascible
    - (E) hypercritical

22. Kane's luxurious home is probably meant to suggest the Hearst estate, which consisted of four mansions. Many people called Hearst's display of wealth _____.
    - (A) irascible
    - (B) stereotypical
    - (C) hypercritical
    - (D) erroneous
    - (E) ostentatious

23. Welles appeals to viewers' _____ notions of mystery stories. The gloomy setting and music lead us to expect a mysterious tale.
    - (A) miscreant
    - (B) stereotypical
    - (C) pretentious
    - (D) ostentatious
    - (E) irascible

24. Lighting is extremely important in films. If a character is a _____, he probably won't be shown in soft, golden light that gives him a _____ appearance.
    - (A) stereotype . . . pretentious
    - (B) miscreant . . . irascible
    - (C) decadence . . . comely
    - (D) stereotype . . . irascible
    - (E) miscreant . . . comely

25. The wrong lighting can give the viewer a misleading, or _____, impression of a character. How might a filmmaker use lighting to show a character's gradual decline from a virtuous life into _____?
    - (A) erroneous . . . decadence
    - (B) irascible . . . ostentation
    - (C) ostentatious . . . stereotype
    - (D) comely . . . decadence
    - (E) decadent . . . pretension

26. At the end of the film, Welles gives us a last glimpse of Kane's _____ storeroom full of showy, useless treasures. The _____ collection reminds us that Kane was obsessed with material things.
    - (A) comely . . . erroneous
    - (B) ostentatious . . . pretentious
    - (C) ostentatious . . . irascible
    - (D) decadent . . . erroneous
    - (E) stereotypical . . . flaunted

27. Kane's efforts at accumulating wealth seem ironic, since at the end of the film he is no longer alive to _____ his riches.
    - (A) pretend
    - (B) criticize
    - (C) flaunt
    - (D) deteriorate
    - (E) stereotype

28. It may be too harsh to say that Welles was a _____ director who judged his own work too severely. But like any serious director, he had high standards and grew _____ when people didn't meet them.
    - (A) decadent . . . irascible
    - (B) hypercritical . . . decadent
    - (C) pretentious . . . erroneous
    - (D) hypercritical . . . irascible
    - (E) irascible . . . ostentatious

29. Welles may have been _____ in claiming most of the credit for *Citizen Kane*, but the film's success is still a tribute to his genius.
    - (A) stereotypical
    - (B) comely
    - (C) hypercritical
    - (D) irascible
    - (E) pretentious

30. If the _____ Hearst had vented his temper by preventing the release of the movie nationwide, film buffs might have judged him as a _____ with a bad attitude.
    - (A) comely . . . miscreant
    - (B) ostentatious . . . pretention
    - (C) irascible . . . miscreant
    - (D) decadent . . . stereotype
    - (E) hypercritical . . . stereotype

Name _____ Date _____ Class _____

MAKING NEW WORDS YOUR OWN

Lesson 9 | **CONTEXT:** The Literature

Maxine Hong Kingston's Woman Warrior

Most American families originally came from someplace else. One way that different groups preserve their heritage is by handing down the myths and folk tales of their original cultures.

Award-winning author Maxine Hong Kingston (b. 1940) brings a unique cultural perspective to her writing. A second-generation Chinese American, she has won national acclaim for her blending of Chinese folklore, history, and language with autobiographical narrative.

In the following exercises, you will be given opportunities to expand your vocabulary by reading about Maxine Hong Kingston. These ten Vocabulary Words will be used.

abridge	finality	impromptu	lucrative	supercilious
emendation	garrulous	invoke	shrew	verbose

EXERCISE 1 *Wordbusting*

Directions. Follow these instructions for this word and the nine words on the next page.
- Figure out the word's meaning by looking at its **context,** its **structure,** and its **sound.** Fill in at least one of the three **CSS** boxes. Alternate which boxes you complete.
- Then, look up the word in a dictionary, read all of its meanings, and write the meaning of the word as it is used in the sentence.
- Follow this same process for each of the Vocabulary Words on the next page. You will need to draw your own map for each word. Use a separate sheet of paper.

1.

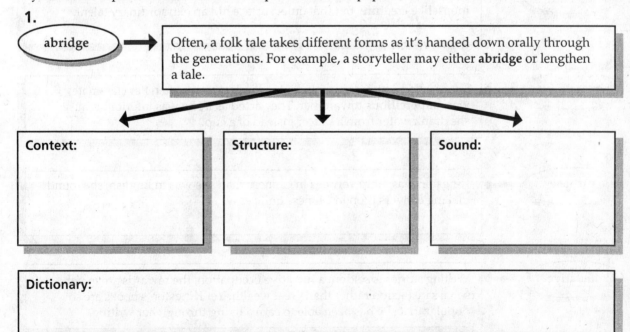

abridge → Often, a folk tale takes different forms as it's handed down orally through the generations. For example, a storyteller may either **abridge** or lengthen a tale.

Context:

Structure:

Sound:

Dictionary:

2.

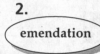

emendation → These **emendations** may become permanent if the storyteller puts the new version in writing.

3.

finality → However, **finality** is not usually a quality of folk tales. Instead of being conclusive, a new version may lead to other changes and improvements.

4.

garrulous → Maxine Hong Kingston was not **garrulous** when she started school; she didn't talk much because she knew very little English.

5.

impromptu → Speaking English required thought and preparation, so for a long time she couldn't join in **impromptu** conversations.

6.

invoke → She couldn't **invoke** her parents' help because they spoke no English. Eventually, though, she learned English through her own efforts.

7.

shrew → As a child, Kingston may have seemed to others like a meek little **shrew,** or mouselike creature, but that quiet surface hid an extraordinary talent.

8.

supercilious → She recalled a humorous incident in kindergarten when her classmates were **supercilious** toward her. They acted as if she was inferior because she drank water from a saucer instead of a cup.

9.

verbose → Kingston was more **verbose** in Chinese than she was in English; she found making conversation in Chinese quite easy.

10.

lucrative → Writing stories is seldom a **lucrative** occupation; the rewards are in personal satisfaction rather than great wealth. Yet Kingston's books are so popular that she has been able to earn a living through her writing.

EXERCISE 2   *Context Clues* 👉

Directions. Scan the definitions in Column A. Then think about how the boldface words are used in the sentences in Column B. To complete the exercise, match each definition in Column A with the correct Vocabulary Word from Column B. Write the letter of your choice on the line provided; then write the Vocabulary Word on the line preceding the definition.

COLUMN A

_____ **11.** word: _____:
n. a mouselike animal that eats insects; a bad-tempered, nagging woman

_____ **12.** word: _____:
adj. profitable; producing money or wealth

_____ **13.** word: _____:
adj. talking too much, especially about unimportant things

_____ **14.** word: _____:
v. to shorten the number of words; to condense

_____ **15.** word: _____:
adj. wordy; using or containing more words than necessary

_____ **16.** word: _____:
v. to call upon a higher power for assistance; to ask or appeal for; to call forth

_____ **17.** word: _____:
n. the quality or condition of being complete or settled; conclusiveness

_____ **18.** word: _____:
adj. without previous thought or preparation; spontaneous

_____ **19.** word: _____:
adj. showing scorn and haughtiness; disdainful; aloof or conceited

_____ **20.** word: _____:
n. a correction; a change in a written text

COLUMN B

(A) One day in the cafeteria, you overhear two students having a casual, **impromptu** discussion about a Chinese folk tale they read in class.

(B) You're curious when you hear that there are two different versions of the story. You wonder if one shorter version has been **abridged** from the original.

(C) Comparing the stories, the students have discovered a few **emendations** to the second version, but the changes are minor.

(D) Most people are **garrulous** at lunch and chat nonstop about trivial things. Why are these students talking about a strange folk tale?

(E) The story is interesting because it **invokes** the legend of Mu Lan, a Chinese woman who disguised herself as a man and earned fame as a warrior.

(F) According to legend, Mu Lan was respected, not because she was a bad-tempered **shrew,** but because she was a brave, admirable woman.

(G) One student is impressed with Mu Lan, but the other seems **supercilious** about the character's efforts. "Why go to all that trouble to become a soldier?" she asks scornfully.

(H) The other student jokes, "Maybe she needed some money—being a famous warrior was probably a **lucrative** job."

(I) You don't really mean to eavesdrop, but the students are so **verbose** that you can't help but pick up a few of their remarks.

(J) You're about to ask a question, but the conversation has an air of **finality** as the students finish their lunch. You'll have to read the story for yourself to find an answer.

EXERCISE 3 *Sentence Completion* ☞

Directions. For each of the following items, circle the letter of the choice that best completes the meaning of the sentence or sentences.

21. In *The Woman Warrior,* Kingston ____, or calls forth, the legend of Mu Lan. She tells the story as she remembers it, without ____.
- (A) finalizes . . . emendation
- (B) abridges . . . finality
- (C) invokes . . . emendation
- (D) emends . . . abridgment
- (E) involves . . . shrews

22. Kingston wasn't ____ as a child, but she did listen carefully to the talk of adults.
- (A) garrulous
- (B) shrewish
- (C) supercilious
- (D) lucrative
- (E) impromptu

23. Many traditional folk tales suggest that women should always be humble, never ____. In some tales Kingston heard, poor families often made ____ exchanges by selling their daughters as slaves.
- (A) lucrative . . . verbose
- (B) impromptu . . . garrulous
- (C) garrulous . . . supercilious
- (D) verbose . . . impromptu
- (E) supercilious . . . lucrative

24. Kingston got the mistaken idea that her parents might sell her. She started throwing ____ tantrums, dropping dishes without warning, and generally acting ____ to show she would make a bad slave.
- (A) impromptu . . . lucrative
- (B) garrulous . . . verbose
- (C) shrewish . . . lucrative
- (D) impromptu . . . shrewish
- (E) lucrative . . . shrewish

25. Kingston was inspired by Mu Lan, who rejected the ____ of age-old rules about women and believed that women should have the last word on how they lived.
- (A) garrulousness
- (B) abridgement
- (C) finality
- (D) emendation
- (E) verbosity

26. As a writer, Kingston ____ the courage and determination of the woman warrior by wielding a pen just as Mu Lan wielded her sword.
- (A) invokes
- (B) finalizes
- (C) emends
- (D) rejects
- (E) abridges

27. In a first draft Kingston lets herself give spontaneous, ____ expression to her thoughts. Although the first version may be ____, the final version is always clear and precise.
- (A) lucrative . . . garrulous
- (B) verbose . . . invoked
- (C) garrulous . . . abridged
- (D) impromptu . . . verbose
- (E) supercilious . . . emended

28. She makes careful ____ in the revision stage of writing until she is satisfied with the story.
- (A) invocations
- (B) emendations
- (C) finality
- (D) abridging
- (E) verbosity

29. Kingston doesn't have a sense of ____ when she completes a draft; she can either ____ the story or develop it further.
- (A) superciliousness . . . abridge
- (B) verbosity . . . emend
- (C) shrewishness . . . invoke
- (D) garrulousness . . . emend
- (E) finality . . . abridge

30. Just as a warrior can't afford to be ____ about her skill, a writer can't afford to be conceited about her abilities. Effort is just as important as talent.
- (A) supercilious
- (B) verbose
- (C) garrulous
- (D) shrewish
- (E) lucrative

MAKING NEW WORDS YOUR OWN

Lesson 10 | CONTEXT: The Literature

Jamaica Kincaid

Two very different worlds come together in the works of American writer Jamaica Kincaid (b. 1949). Born on the island of Antigua in the West Indies, Kincaid brings to her writing the rhythms of West Indian dialects as well as the sounds of American and European English. Kincaid's novel *Annie John* and her short-story collection *At the Bottom of the River* have been widely praised for their unusual depictions of childhood experience and family life in the Caribbean. In her writing, Kincaid focuses on developing complex characters and giving lyrical, dreamlike descriptions of everyday events.

In the exercises below, you will have the opportunity to expand your vocabulary by reading about the works of Jamaica Kincaid. Below are ten Vocabulary Words that will be used in these exercises.

affable	expletive	idiomatic	reciprocate	tawdry
bolster	furor	intangible	subterfuge	wistful

EXERCISE 1 | *Wordbusting*

Directions. Follow these instructions for this word and the nine words on the next page.
- Figure out the word's meaning by looking at its **context**, its **structure**, and its **sound.** Fill in at least one of the three **CSS** boxes. Alternate which boxes you complete.
- Then, look up the word in a dictionary, read all of its meanings, and write the meaning of the word as it is used in the sentence.
- Follow this same process for each of the Vocabulary Words on the next page. You will need to draw your own map for each word. Use a separate sheet of paper.

1.

affable ➡️ In her prose, Jamaica Kincaid isn't concerned with **affability**. She uses frank, even appalling, situations and draws characters who must deal with these trials.

Context:	Structure:	Sound:

Dictionary:

2.

(bolster) →

Jamaica Kincaid's fiction doesn't reinforce stereotypes about Caribbean people; instead, it **bolsters** more complex views of West Indian life.

3.

(expletive) →

Like any good writer with an ear for dialogue, Kincaid creates natural-sounding conversations among her characters, complete with **expletives,** or strong exclamations.

4.

(idiomatic) →

One way that Kincaid acknowledges her roots is by using **idiomatic** expressions unique to West Indian dialects.

5.

(intangible) →

As one critic noted, Kincaid explores the mysterious, undefinable aspects of ordinary experiences. Often, Kincaid captures this **intangible** quality through poetic repetition of words.

6.

(reciprocate) →

Kincaid tells realistic stories about believable characters—characters who feel and love strongly but whose feelings are not always **reciprocated,** or returned.

7.

(subterfuge) →

Yet Kincaid's unusual style isn't a **subterfuge,** or trick, used to escape the conventions of storytelling. Her fiction is genuinely experimental.

8.

(tawdry) →

Her stories of the lives of ordinary people probably wouldn't appeal to someone who likes **tawdry,** flashy, thrill-a-minute story lines.

9.

(wistful) →

Often, the descriptions have a **wistful** quality, especially when the narrator longs for the simple world of her childhood.

10.

(furor) →

Some people have expressed **furor** over the fact that West Indian writers have received too little attention. Their anger and indignation may be justified.

EXERCISE 2 Context Clues ✍

Directions. Scan the definitions in Column A. Then think about how the boldface words are used in the sentences in Column B. To complete the exercise, match each definition in Column A with the correct Vocabulary Word from Column B. Write the letter of your choice on the line provided; then write the Vocabulary Word on the line preceding the definition.

COLUMN A	COLUMN B

COLUMN A

_____ **11.** word: _____:

adj. not capable of being touched; not material; vague or not easily defined

_____ **12.** word: _____:

adj. characteristic of a particular language

_____ **13.** word: _____:

n. an oath or exclamation, usually profane; a word with no meaning of its own, used to complete the pattern of a phrase or sentence

_____ **14.** word: _____:

adj. friendly, cordial, pleasant and easy to talk to; showing friendliness

_____ **15.** word: _____:

n. a long, narrow pillow; anything used as a support; *v.* to prop up, support, or reinforce

_____ **16.** word: _____:

v. to give, do, or take in return; to move with a backward-forward motion

_____ **17.** word: _____:

adj. full of longing; yearning; wishful

_____ **18.** word: _____:

n. frenzied anger; rage; a public uproar or outburst of indignation; great enthusiasm for

_____ **19.** word: _____:

n. a trick, excuse, or deception used to escape something unpleasant

_____ **20.** word: _____:

adj. gaudy; showy and cheap

COLUMN B

(A) Have you ever had a friend who **bolstered** your self-esteem just by thinking you were special?

(B) In Kincaid's story "The Red Girl," the young narrator admires a rebellious red-haired girl who is anything but **affable**. At first, it seems they will never become friends.

(C) The red-haired girl eventually **reciprocates** the narrator's admiration, and the two become friends.

(D) The narrator, Annie John, comes from a strict family and isn't allowed to play with children who act improperly. For example, her mother probably wouldn't let her hang around with someone who uttered rude **expletives**.

(E) Annie John's mother would respond with **furor** if she caught Annie John playing with the Red Girl, who shoots marbles and doesn't brush her teeth.

(F) The Red Girl probably would consider the clothes and jewelry that interest some girls her age to be **tawdry;** she doesn't seem to care at all about such items.

(G) She doesn't have to wash every day or comb her hair. But even more important than these concrete facts, the Red Girl has an **intangible** air of freedom that Annie John envies.

(H) Annie John has a **wistful** desire for the sort of freedom that the Red Girl enjoys.

(I) Because Annie John can't openly associate with the Red Girl, she resorts to **subterfuge** so that she can play marbles with her new friend.

(J) Kincaid's precise description captures the character of the Red Girl in just a few paragraphs, and Annie John's **idiomatic,** everyday way of talking helps characterize her as well.

EXERCISE 3 Sentence Completion ✍

Directions. For each of the following items, circle the letter of the choice that best completes the meaning of the sentence or sentences.

21. You don't need to know West Indian dialects to understand Jamaica Kincaid's _____ expressions. But a brief history of the West Indies might help you appreciate the stories.
(A) affable
(B) tawdry
(C) idiomatic
(D) wistful
(E) intangible

22. After leaving a West Indian island, you might behave more _____ after your pleasant trip to this exotic place and others may _____ your friendliness.
(A) furiously . . . bolster
(B) affably . . . reciprocate
(C) wistful . . . bolster
(D) tawdry . . . reciprocate
(E) bolstered . . . subterfuge

23. Europeans began settling the West Indies in the 1500s. The islands' agricultural riches soon _____ the European economy.
(A) made tawdry
(B) made wistful
(C) reciprocated
(D) made intangible
(E) bolstered

24. A _____ resulted when the French tried to seize Santo Domingo from the Spanish. The Spaniards _____ with a counterattack.
(A) subterfuge . . . bolstered
(B) furor . . . reciprocated
(C) tawdriness . . . reciprocated
(D) furor . . . bolstered
(E) idioms . . . bolstered

25. The West Indies inspired _____ longing in European monarchs. Because the spices and sugar from the islands were so valuable, no _____ was too underhanded in the battle for control.
(A) furious . . . expletive
(B) wistful . . . subterfuge
(C) tawdry . . . bolster
(D) affable . . . reciprocation
(E) reciprocated . . . wistfulness

26. No doubt the native inhabitants of the islands remembered with _____ the era before Columbus's landing.
(A) idioms
(B) bolsters
(C) intangibility
(D) tawdriness
(E) wistfulness

27. By a busy port, a visitor to the West Indies may be surrounded by the sounds of dockhands hurling spicy _____ at one another. Just a few blocks on, the visitor may come across a peaceful seaside shrine.
(A) bolsters
(B) expletives
(C) subterfuges
(D) furors
(E) intangibilities

28. Movies often present _____ images of West Indian life. These films exaggerate the showy aspects of the culture.
(A) laconic
(B) bolstered
(C) wistful
(D) tawdry
(E) intangible

29. The complexity of Caribbean cultures can't be captured in a brief description. Writers like Jamaica Kincaid have devoted whole books to explaining that _____, undefinable quality of the West Indies.
(A) tawdry
(B) affable
(C) intangible
(D) idiomatic
(E) reciprocal

30. If you're interested in _____ your knowledge of West Indian language, you can learn some _____ expressions from reading West Indian writers.
(A) bolstering . . . intangible
(B) reciprocating . . . intangible
(C) reciprocating . . . wistful
(D) bolstering . . . idiomatic
(E) reciprocating . . . idiomatic

Name _____ Date _____ Class _____

MAKING NEW WORDS YOUR OWN

Lesson 11 | CONTEXT: The People

Leonardo, Raphael, Michelangelo, and Donatello: Epic Turtles

Who are Leonardo, Raphael, Michelangelo, and Donatello? If you answered "artists," you're right. But if you answered "turtles," you're right, too! Although they named the turtles after Renaissance artists, cartoonists Peter Alan Laird and Kevin Eastman modeled the once-popular turtles after artists of a different sort—Japanese ninja warriors. These comic-book turtles may seem like unlikely heroes, but they have the strength, courage, and sense of justice common to heroes in every culture. They also have another quality of traditional heroes: They're only human—or, rather, only turtles.

In the following exercises, you will have the opportunity to expand your vocabulary by reading about the Teenage Mutant Ninja Turtles and other heroic figures. These ten Vocabulary Words will be used.

ambivalent	betrothed	consensus	intrepid	sallow
beneficent	congenital	interminable	repugnant	sortie

EXERCISE 1 | *Wordbusting* ☞

Directions. Follow these instructions for this word and the nine words on the next page.
- Figure out the word's meaning by looking at its **context,** its **structure,** and its **sound.** Fill in at least one of the three **CSS** boxes. Alternate which boxes you complete.
- Then, look up the word in a dictionary, read all of its meanings, and write the meaning of the word as it is used in the sentence.
- Follow this same process for each of the Vocabulary Words on the next page. You will need to draw your own map for each word. Use a separate sheet of paper.

1.

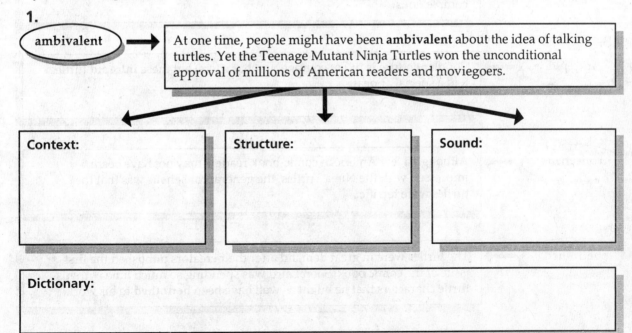

ambivalent → At one time, people might have been **ambivalent** about the idea of talking turtles. Yet the Teenage Mutant Ninja Turtles won the unconditional approval of millions of American readers and moviegoers.

Context:

Structure:

Sound:

Dictionary:

2.

beneficent → These **beneficent** characters dedicate themselves to fighting evil and doing good.

3.

sortie → Heroic figures usually don't fight without a good reason. Likewise, the turtles are sure to launch a **sortie** against villains who cross them.

4.

congenital → The turtles' size, strength, and intelligence aren't **congenital;** the turtles received their powers accidentally instead of being born with them.

5.

interminable → Like all superheroes, the turtles wage an **interminable** battle against evil. They never seem to run out of bad guys to fight.

6.

repugnant → Another important figure in the Ninja Turtle comics is a superintelligent rat who becomes the turtles' teacher. Even people who find rats **repugnant** have come to appreciate this wise character.

7.

sallow → Ordinary people would look **sallow** after years of living in underground tunnels, but the Ninja Turtles maintain their healthy, naturally green complexions.

8.

intrepid → Popular culture is full of courageous characters, but these **intrepid** turtles had a special appeal.

9.

consensus → Although a few American comic-book readers may not have been impressed with the Ninja Turtles, the general **consensus** was that the turtles were terrific.

10.

betrothed → The turtles were in great demand after their creators published the first issue of the comic book. Soon Laird was spending so much time with his turtle characters that he might as well have been **betrothed** to his work.

EXERCISE 2 Context Clues ✍

Directions. Scan the definitions in Column A. Then think about how the boldface words are used in the sentences in Column B. To complete the exercise, match each definition in Column A with the correct Vocabulary Word from Column B. Write the letter of your choice on the line provided, then write the Vocabulary Word on the line preceding the definition.

COLUMN A	COLUMN B

COLUMN A

_____ **11.** word: _____:
adj. present at birth but not hereditary; inborn; having a characteristic so strong as to be part of one's nature

_____ **12.** word: _____:
n. a general agreement or opinion; a majority opinion

_____ **13.** word: _____:
adj. endless; occuring over and over again indefinitely

_____ **14.** word: _____:
adj. grayish yellow in color; sickly pale

_____ **15.** word: _____:
adj. contradictory; offering resistance; distasteful; disgusting

_____ **16.** word: _____:
n. a sudden attack by troops from a defensive position; a single mission of a lone airplane against an enemy

_____ **17.** word: _____:
adj. engaged to be married; *n.* a person who is engaged to be married

_____ **18.** word: _____:
adj. brave or resolute; showing great courage

_____ **19.** word: _____:
adj. kind; charitable; doing good

_____ **20.** word: _____:
adj. having mixed, conflicting, or changing emotions or thoughts toward a person or thing

COLUMN B

(A) If you had polled children in the U.S. about their favorite comic-book heroes, the **consensus** at one time would probably have placed Ninja Turtles high on the list.

(B) Strange-looking as they are, the turtles are too talented and charming to be **repugnant**.

(C) Being **intrepid** isn't the only requirement for a hero. In addition to being brave, a hero must have a strong sense of right and wrong.

(D) The turtles wouldn't seem admirable if they launched an offensive attack against someone for personal gain. Any **sortie** they organize must be in the interest of justice.

(E) Although the turtles received their intelligence and strength from a mysterious green ooze, their pleasant personalities seem to be **congenital**.

(F) People have waged an **interminable** argument about whether the comic book is a literary genre. One reason for the endless debate is that comic books are considered popular entertainment, not art.

(G) Traditionally, epics are long narrative poems that recount the deeds of noble, **beneficent** people.

(H) The heroes of epics are bound to honor and justice, as a husband-to-be might be bound to his **betrothed**.

(I) Since epics usually have a serious tone, some readers are **ambivalent** about whether comic-book heroes can possess epic qualities.

(J) Visually, comic books, with their vivid colors, are very attractive to readers; comic books that feature **sallow** colors might not be as successful.

EXERCISE 3 *Sentence Completion* ☞

Directions. For each of the following items, circle the letter of the choice that best completes the meaning of the sentence or sentences.

21. Although the idea of living in sewers may be _____ to us, the _____ of the turtles is that the sewer suits them just fine.
- (A) interminable . . . ambivalence
- (B) beneficent . . . betrothed
- (C) intrepid . . . consensus
- (D) repugnant . . . consensus
- (E) repugnant . . . sorties

22. An interesting question might be, "Do _____ heroes like the Teenage Mutant Ninja Turtles have a(n) _____ urge to fight evil? That is, are they born heroes?"
- (A) intrepid . . . ambivalent
- (B) betrothed . . . congenital
- (C) interminable . . . ambivalent
- (D) repugnant . . . intrepid
- (E) beneficent . . . congenital

23. Their _____ quality seems to be natural; no one can imagine that the Ninja Turtles, for example, were ever cowardly.
- (A) beneficent
- (B) intrepid
- (C) repugnant
- (D) sallow
- (E) ambivalent

24. However, like the turtles, many superheroes receive extraordinary powers by accident. Some feel _____ about their powers at first; they're not sure they want to be different from ordinary people.
- (A) repugnant
- (B) interminable
- (C) sallow
- (D) beneficent
- (E) ambivalent

25. Cartoon villains usually have _____ faces that reflect their evil natures. For example, in *Captain Planet and the Planeteers,* the villains have a _____, sickly appearance, as if they've breathed too much smog.
- (A) sallow . . . congenital
- (B) repugnant . . . ambivalent
- (C) intrepid . . . repugnant
- (D) repugnant . . . sallow
- (E) congenital . . . intrepid

26. Sometimes, heroes have tragic aspects. A superhero might turn to crime fighting after losing his or her _____ or another loved one, such as a parent.
- (A) betrothed
- (B) repugnance
- (C) ambivalence
- (D) beneficence
- (E) sortie

27. The hero is often a loner who fights criminals single-handedly, like a pilot on a(n) _____ behind enemy lines.
- (A) benificence
- (B) sortie
- (C) consensus
- (D) betrothal
- (E) ambivalence

28. Some might express _____ about whether comic-book characters can be like the heroes of epics. But the general _____ is that crimefighters such as the Ninja Turtles have much in common with legendary heroes.
- (A) consensus . . . sortie
- (B) repugnance . . . consensus
- (C) ambivalence . . . consensus
- (D) beneficance . . . intrepidity
- (E) ambivalence . . . sortie

29. Like epic heroes, comic-book heroes aren't perfect. They're generally _____, but they might show a mean streak now and then.
- (A) repugnant
- (B) beneficent
- (C) intrepid
- (D) sallow
- (E) ambivalent

30. Heroic figures provide almost endless material for reflection. In fact, a discussion on this subject might be _____!
- (A) beneficent
- (B) congenital
- (C) repugnant
- (D) interminable
- (E) intrepid

Name _____ Date _____ Class _____

MAKING NEW WORDS YOUR OWN

Lesson 12 | CONTEXT: The People
W.E.B. DuBois and the NAACP

As a child, W.E.B. DuBois (1868–1963) came to understand African Americans' unequal status in U.S. society firsthand. This realization led him to make the advancement of African Americans his life's work. DuBois cofounded the National Association for the Advancement of Colored People (NAACP), an organization that works to secure civil rights for African Americans and other minority groups. As the editor of *Crisis,* the NAACP's main publication, and as the author of numerous books and essays, DuBois spread his message to thousands of people.

In the following exercises, you will have the opportunity to expand your vocabulary by reading about W.E.B. DuBois. Below are ten Vocabulary Words that will be used in these exercises.

adamant	archives	factious	peremptory	resilient
antagonize	autocrat	frustrate	procrastinate	supplication

EXERCISE 1 — *Wordbusting* 👆

Directions. Follow these instructions for this word and the nine words on the next page.
- Figure out the word's meaning by looking at its **context**, its **structure**, and its **sound**. Fill in at least one of the three **CSS** boxes. Alternate which boxes you complete.
- Then, look up the word in a dictionary, read all of its meanings, and write the meaning of the word as it is used in the sentence.
- Follow this same process for each of the Vocabulary Words on the next page. You will need to draw your own map for each word. Use a separate sheet of paper.

1.

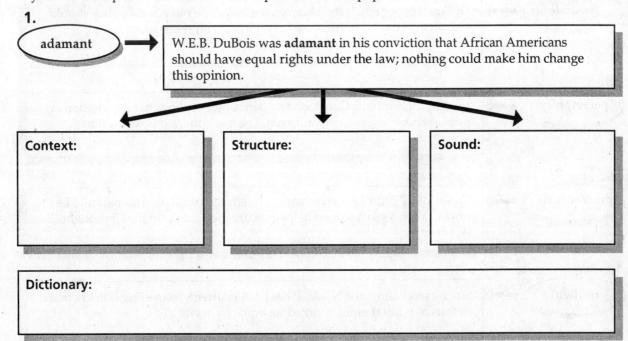

adamant → W.E.B. DuBois was **adamant** in his conviction that African Americans should have equal rights under the law; nothing could make him change this opinion.

Context:

Structure:

Sound:

Dictionary:

Name _____ Date _____ Class _____

2.

antagonize ➤ DuBois criticized Booker T. Washington (1856–1915) for supporting segregation, the policy of separating racial groups. His intention wasn't to **antagonize** Washington, whom he actually admired, but to further the cause of civil rights.

3.

archives ➤ In 1910, DuBois became the editor of *Crisis,* a magazine published by the NAACP. You might find some early issues of the magazine stored away in the **archives** of your local library.

4.

autocrat ➤ Seeking economic solutions to social problems, DuBois embraced the ideal of socialism. Socialism is a communal form of government in which no single **autocrat** holds power over the society.

5.

factious ➤ Some of DuBois's contemporaries may have considered his writing **factious.** Yet DuBois strove to unify African Americans, not to cause conflict among them.

6.

supplication ➤ DuBois knew that loud protest, not meek **supplication,** was necessary to achieve lasting change.

7.

frustrate ➤ DuBois's opponents, who believed the "separate but equal" policy should remain intact, tried to **frustrate** his efforts to end segregation.

8.

peremptory ➤ In 1954, the Supreme Court made a **peremptory** ruling that segregation in public schools was unconstitutional. The law admitted no exceptions.

9.

procrastinate ➤ The NAACP didn't **procrastinate** in its efforts to end discrimination. The organization's swift actions helped secure the passage of the Civil Rights Act of 1957.

10.

resilient ➤ Since its founding, the NAACP has been **resilient,** recovering quickly from defeats as it has steadily worked for equal rights for all.

EXERCISE 2   *Context Clues* ✍

Directions. Scan the definitions in Column A. Then think about how the boldface words are used in the sentences in Column B. To complete the exercise, match each definition in Column A with the correct Vocabulary Word from Column B. Write the letter of your choice on the line provided; then write the Vocabulary Word on the line preceding the definition.

COLUMN A	COLUMN B

COLUMN A

_____ **11.** word: _____:
n. the act of asking humbly and earnestly; a prayer; a petition; an entreaty

_____ **12.** word: _____:
adj. easily springing back to an original form; flexible; recovering quickly; buoyant

_____ **13.** word: _____:
adj. causing disunity, dissension, or disputes; quarrelsome

_____ **14.** word: _____:
n. a ruler with unlimited power; a dictator; a domineering person

_____ **15.** word: _____:
n. a place where public records or historical documents are kept; the records or documents kept in such a place; *v.* to keep or store such records

_____ **16.** word: _____:
v. to prevent from accomplishing; to cause feelings of discouragement

_____ **17.** word: _____:
adj. unbreakable due to hardness; unrelenting; unyielding

_____ **18.** word: _____:
v. to put off until later; to delay without a good reason

_____ **19.** word: _____:
v. to make an enemy of; to oppose or counteract

_____ **20.** word: _____:
adj. arrogant; allowing no denial or refusal; absolute

COLUMN B

(A) Have you ever been **frustrated** or discouraged by rules that seemed unfair?

(B) Maybe you **procrastinated** in speaking your mind, putting off voicing your opinion because you weren't sure you could make a difference.

(C) Sometimes an earnest request is enough to make people change their minds. You can probably think of times when **supplication** helped you get what you wanted.

(D) If you believe strongly in your cause, people may accuse you of having a **peremptory** attitude. Sometimes your single-mindedness can seem like arrogance.

(E) You may also have to risk being **factious** in getting your point across. People are likely to disagree with you and may call you quarrelsome.

(F) W.E.B. DuBois publicly **antagonized** segregationists. For example, he fiercely opposed their idea that African Americans should compromise on the issue of social equality.

(G) People ruled by an **autocrat** have little or no say in government policies. However, in a democracy, the people can bring about changes in legislation.

(H) The NAACP has been **adamant** in its insistence on fair treatment of African Americans. For example, the group was unyielding in its efforts to secure equal rights for African American military personnel during World War II.

(I) Public **archives** contain records that show how the NAACP began influencing legislation in the early 1900s.

(J) You must be **resilient** if you want to change people's beliefs. Be prepared to bounce back and try again if you don't succeed at first.

EXERCISE 3 Sentence Completion ✍

Directions. For each of the following items, circle the letter of the choice that best completes the meaning of the sentence or sentences.

21. You won't have to search any _____ for DuBois's works; you will likely find them on the library's regular shelves.
    (A) resilience
    (B) frustration
    (C) autocrat
    (D) archives
    (E) supplication

22. DuBois strongly opposed _____ legislation that absolutely supported segregation. And, just as _____, he fought against economic inequality.
    (A) adamant . . . autocratically
    (B) peremptory . . . adamantly
    (C) resilient . . . antagonistically
    (D) factious . . . adamantly
    (E) antagonistic . . . peremptorily

23. DuBois pointed out the economic factors that _____ African Americans' efforts to better their condition. He cited undeniable statistics that _____ demonstrated the economic inequality of African Americans.
    (A) frustrated . . . peremptorily
    (B) antagonized . . . frustratedly
    (C) frustrated . . . resiliently
    (D) antagonized . . . resiliently
    (E) procrastinated . . . peremptorily

24. DuBois's presentation of hard facts no doubt _____ people who simply didn't want to face the problem head-on.
    (A) nurtured
    (B) procrastinated
    (C) antagonized
    (D) supplicated
    (E) archived

25. But DuBois's _____ was that his readers examine the facts. He earnestly requested that people stop _____ over the inevitable confrontation over economic injustice.
    (A) antagonism . . . procrastinating
    (B) supplication . . . procrastinating
    (C) frustration . . . antagonizing
    (D) procrastination . . . frustrating
    (E) supplication . . . archiving

26. In _____, the public has little influence in politics. But citizens of the United States can effect legislation through both earnest _____ and organized protest.
    (A) autocracies . . . frustration
    (B) archives . . . supplication
    (C) supplication . . . frustration
    (D) archives . . . antagonism
    (E) autocracies . . . supplication

27. Although DuBois's conclusions might have seemed _____ and divisive, the statistics were _____. It was undeniable that most African American teenagers did not have the opportunity for meaningful work.
    (A) antagonistic . . . factious
    (B) resilient . . . peremptory
    (C) adamant . . . factious
    (D) factious . . . peremptory
    (E) resilient . . . archival

28. The fact that African Americans could recover from such unjust treatment was a testimony to the _____ of the human spirit.
    (A) frustration
    (B) resilience
    (C) adamance
    (D) procrastination
    (E) supplication

29. Although DuBois was probably _____ by obstacles in his attempt to find remedies for a complicated economic situation, he was never completely discouraged.
    (A) procrastinated
    (B) antagonized
    (C) factious
    (D) supplicated
    (E) frustrated

30. Today, thanks to the _____, unyielding efforts of activists like DuBois, the economic rights of minority groups are protected under the law.
    (A) adamant
    (B) antagonistic
    (C) peremptory
    (D) frustrating
    (E) resilient

MAKING NEW WORDS YOUR OWN

Lesson 13 | CONTEXT: The People
Harry S. Truman

Harry S. Truman (1884–1972) was president for two terms during a critical period of international change. His first term began in 1945 at the end of World War II, and his last term ended just before the close of the Korean War. Truman established some of the United States' most important foreign policies, such as the policy to curb Communist expansion and the commitment to provide aid for war-torn countries. Truman's domestic policy, called the Fair Deal, included legislation to end economic discrimination against minority groups.

In the following exercises, you will be given opportunities to expand your vocabulary by reading about Harry S. Truman. Below are ten Vocabulary Words that will be used in these exercises.

exonerate	forgo	incredulous	provocation	secular
expedite	incoherent	plebeian	query	shibboleth

EXERCISE 1 — Wordbusting ✍

Directions. Follow these instructions for this word and the nine words on the next page.
- Figure out the word's meaning by looking at its **context,** its **structure,** and its **sound.** Fill in at least one of the three **CSS** boxes. Alternate which boxes you complete.
- Then, look up the word in a dictionary, read all of its meanings, and write the meaning of the word as it is used in the sentence.
- Follow this same process for each of the Vocabulary Words on the next page. You will need to draw your own map for each word. Use a separate sheet of paper.

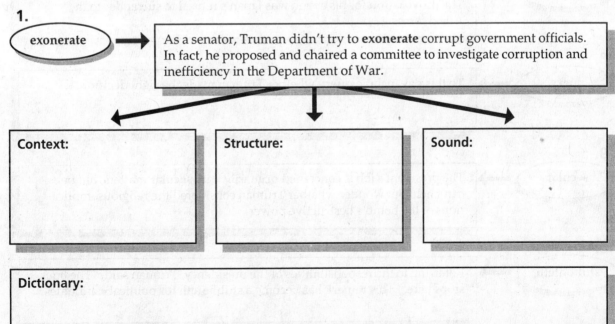

1.

exonerate → As a senator, Truman didn't try to **exonerate** corrupt government officials. In fact, he proposed and chaired a committee to investigate corruption and inefficiency in the Department of War.

Context:

Structure:

Sound:

Dictionary:

2.

expedite ➤ During World War II, this committee helped **expedite** the correction of inefficient, wasteful methods. The committee's swift action may have saved the government billions of dollars.

3.

incoherent ➤ While some politicians twist their speech to the point of being **incoherent**, Truman was well known for his clear, no-nonsense way of speaking.

4.

plebeian ➤ Truman's down-home, colloquial way of talking might have seemed **plebeian** to people who expected a president to be more polished and sophisticated.

5.

forgo ➤ As president, Truman proposed many progressive laws. However, the conservative Congress decided to **forgo** enacting most of Truman's recommendations.

6.

incredulous ➤ The public was **incredulous** when Truman won the 1948 election, since most polls had predicted his defeat.

7.

provocation ➤ Truman went down in history as the president who used the atomic bomb. The **provocation** for his action was Japan's refusal to surrender to the Allied forces.

8.

query ➤ To this day, people **query** whether Truman made the right decision.

9.

secular ➤ The president's job is concerned primarily with **secular** matters, but one can't help but wonder whether Truman considered the religious implications of the bomb's destructive power.

10.

shibboleth ➤ Referring to the responsibilities of the presidency, Truman said, "The buck stops here." This remark has become a **shibboleth** for political candidates.

EXERCISE 2 *Context Clues* ✍

Directions. Scan the definitions in Column A. Then think about how the boldface words are used in the sentences in Column B. To complete the exercise, match each definition in Column A with the correct Vocabulary Word from Column B. Write the letter of your choice on the line provided; then write the Vocabulary Word on the line preceding the definition.

COLUMN A

_____ **11.** word: _____:
adj. impossible to explain or understand

_____ **12.** word: _____:
n. something that stirs up anger or excitement

_____ **13.** word: _____:
n. one of the common people of ancient Rome; a vulgar person; *adj.* common; vulgar; crude

_____ **14.** word: _____:
adj. showing disbelief or doubt; skeptical; disbelieving

_____ **15.** word: _____:
n. a question; *v.* to question; to inquire into

_____ **16.** word: _____:
v. to excuse or clear completely of a charge or accusation; to prove blameless

_____ **17.** word: _____:
adj. worldly or temporal rather than religious or sacred; not belonging to a religious order

_____ **18.** word: _____:
v. to make easier or quicker; to hasten

_____ **19.** word: _____:
n. any use of language, habit, or custom that distinguishes a class; a password; a distinctive slogan used by members of a group

_____ **20.** word: _____:
v. to refrain or abstain from; to go without

COLUMN B

(A) Truman seemed almost **incredulous** when he became president in 1945. He had been vice-president for only twelve weeks before President Franklin D. Roosevelt died unexpectedly.

(B) Because of Roosevelt's sudden death, Truman had to **forgo** the slow, careful training he might have received as vice-president.

(C) World War II was ending when Truman assumed the presidency. His first job was to **expedite,** or hasten, the war's conclusion.

(D) Such complex international issues might have seemed **incoherent** to a less intelligent person.

(E) In Roman society, a vast gulf separated the **plebeian** and the aristocrat, the commoner and the noble. In contrast, any citizen of a modern democracy may seek a position of power.

(F) Judging candidates by their personal merits rather than their social background is a **shibboleth** of American voters.

(G) Truman first received public attention in 1934 when he ran for the U. S. Senate. His ties to a disreputable public figure, Thomas J. Pendergast, were the **provocation** for stinging attacks by the media.

(H) Although the media **queried** Truman's political connections, these questions didn't stop Truman from winning the election.

(I) His record of strict honesty eventually **exonerated** him of charges that he had been corrupted by his association with Pendergast.

(J) The separation of religious and **secular** interests became an issue in the campaign of a later president, John F. Kennedy.

EXERCISE 3 *Sentence Completion* ✍

Directions. For each of the following items, circle the letter of the choice that best completes the meaning of the sentence or sentences.

21. Quotations from presidents often become _____ for their political party. Some presidents, however, may use such slogans to _____ themselves of wrongdoing.
    (A) incoherencies . . . exonerate
    (B) shibboleths . . . exonerate
    (C) queries . . . provoke
    (D) plebeians . . . expedite
    (E) exonerations . . . expedite

22. Some biographers claim that Truman is often misrepresented. These inaccuracies are _____ that stir pro-Truman biographers to set the record straight.
    (A) incredulities
    (B) queries
    (C) exonerations
    (D) plebeians
    (E) provocations

23. For example, you should be _____ when you hear people emphasize Truman's humble, _____ origins. Truman had long associated with highly cultured people.
    (A) plebeian . . . exonerated
    (B) incredulous . . . plebeian
    (C) provocative . . . secular
    (D) forgone . . . secular
    (E) queried . . . incredulous

24. Few politicians today would _____, or pass up, a chance to compare themselves to Harry Truman.
    (A) exonerate
    (B) query
    (C) secularize
    (D) forgo
    (E) expedite

25. President Ronald Reagan had a paperweight that said "The buckaroo stops here." This pun seems meaningless and _____ if you don't know Truman's famous saying.
    (A) incredulous
    (B) incoherent
    (C) secular
    (D) forgone
    (E) plebeian

26. You might be _____ if you learned how different Truman's values were from those of most politicians today. Your surprise may lead you to _____ why so many politicians compare themselves to him.
    (A) incoherent . . . query
    (B) exonerated . . . expedite
    (C) incredulous . . . query
    (D) provoked . . . forgo
    (E) incredulous . . . forgo

27. Candidates may compare themselves to famous presidents to _____ the task of gaining public support. This method may seem _____, or crude, but it often works.
    (A) expedite . . . exonerated
    (B) query . . . secular
    (C) forgo . . . incoherent
    (D) expedite . . . plebeian
    (E) forgo . . . incredulous

28. Politics is a _____, worldly affair, but politicians don't have to _____ expressing their spiritual values. In fact, most voters are interested in a candidate's religious beliefs.
    (A) secular . . . forgo
    (B) plebeian . . . provoke
    (C) secular . . . expedite
    (D) plebeian . . . expedite
    (E) forgone . . . exonerate

29. Presidents never know if history will condemn them for their actions or _____ them of all blame.
    (A) provoke
    (B) forgo
    (C) query
    (D) expedite
    (E) exonerate

30. Often, events that seem _____ at the time become clear later on. By _____ the actions of past leaders, we can develop a more thoughtful plan for the future.
    (A) incoherent . . . exonerating
    (B) incredulous . . . querying
    (C) secular . . . expediting
    (D) incoherent . . . querying
    (E) queried . . . exonerating

Name _____ Date _____ Class _____

MAKING NEW WORDS YOUR OWN

Lesson 14 CONTEXT: The People
Wilt Chamberlain

If asked to name a talented basketball player who has led a team to a world championship, most people would promptly answer, "Michael Jordan!" Of course, they would be right. However, a few older basketball fans might just as quickly and correctly respond, "Wilt Chamberlain!"

After Chamberlain's (1936–1999) first season in professional basketball, he was named Rookie of the Year as well as Most Valuable Player. By the end of his fourteen years in the pro game, he set a professional record for points scored during a career.

In the following exercises, you will have the opportunity to expand your vocabulary by reading about Wilt Chamberlain. Below are ten Vocabulary Words that will be used in these exercises.

blithe	chagrin	filial	intrinsic	proficient
cede	debonair	interpose	precipitate	remission

EXERCISE 1 Wordbusting

Directions. Follow these instructions for this word and the nine words on the next page.
- Figure out the word's meaning by looking at its **context,** its **structure,** and its **sound.** Fill in at least one of the three **CSS** boxes. Alternate which boxes you complete.
- Then, look up the word in a dictionary, read all of its meanings, and write the meaning of the word as it is used in the sentence.
- Follow this same process for each of the Vocabulary Words on the next page. You will need to draw your own map for each word. Use a separate sheet of paper.

1.

blithe → Before Wilt Chamberlain joined the National Basketball Association, he enjoyed a relatively **blithe,** carefree year with the Harlem Globetrotters.

Context:	Structure:	Sound:

Dictionary:

Name _____ Date _____ Class _____

2.

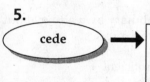

filial → Chamberlain grew up in Philadelphia but attended college in Kansas. **Filial** affection may have made it difficult to go so far from his parents, but Chamberlain wanted to play basketball in the Midwest.

3.

interpose → Chamberlain was such an expert scorer that opponents could rarely **interpose** themselves between him and the basket.

4.

intrinsic → Although Chamberlain worked hard to develop his skills, his talent seemed **intrinsic,** as if from the time he was born he was destined to play basketball.

5.

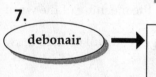

cede → He tried to join a professional team after his junior year in college, but he had to **cede** to the NBA's ruling that he must first play a fourth college season.

6.

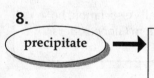

chagrin → Although he might have felt some **chagrin** at first, his play with the Globetrotters was far from disappointing.

7.

debonair → With their newest member, the **debonair** Globetrotters charmed audiences around the world.

8.

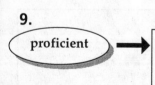

precipitate → The San Francisco Warriors traded Chamberlain to the Philadelphia 76ers in 1967. This event **precipitated** a new degree of success for Chamberlain; he won his first NBA title soon after switching teams.

9.

proficient → Two years later, Chamberlain joined the Los Angeles Lakers. His skill was already legendary, and he quickly made a name for himself as one of the Lakers' most **proficient** players.

10.

remission → In order to play for the Lakers, Chamberlain had to ask to be released from his contract with the 76ers. Chamberlain's **remission** from his contract was fortunate for the Lakers, who hadn't won a championship since 1960.

EXERCISE 2 *Context Clues* ✍

Directions. Scan the definitions in Column A. Then think about how the boldface words are used in the sentences in Column B. To complete the exercise, match each definition in Column A with the correct Vocabulary Word from Column B. Write the letter of your choice on the line provided; then write the Vocabulary Word on the line preceding the definition.

COLUMN A	COLUMN B

COLUMN A

_____ **11.** word: _____:
adj. of or expected from a son or daughter; of a parent's or parents' offspring

_____ **12.** word: _____:
n. a feeling of disappointment, distress, or embarrassment

_____ **13.** word: _____:
v. to yield or give up; to transfer or render title to

_____ **14.** word: _____:
adj. advanced in a particular art or science; skilled; expert; qualified

_____ **15.** word: _____:
v. to cause something to happen; to bring about quickly or suddenly; *adj.* reckless; rash; acting hastily or impulsively

_____ **16.** word: _____:
n. a release from a debt or duty; a lessening of intensity; a diminishing

_____ **17.** word: _____:
v. to put between; to insert between parts; to interject during a conversation; to intervene

_____ **18.** word: _____:
adj. graceful, charming, and smooth; seemingly carefree

_____ **19.** word: _____:
adj. happy; joyful; carefree

_____ **20.** word: _____:
adj. belonging to a thing by its essential nature; inherent

COLUMN B

(A) Chamberlain's professional career was not always joyful. At times he was far from **blithe**.

(B) Chamberlain's greatest opponent, Bill Russell of the Boston Celtics, frequently **interposed** himself between Chamberlain and a championship.

(C) Although Chamberlain played his best, his losses often **precipitated** harsh criticism from the media.

(D) The fierce rivalry with Russell was a cause of **chagrin** for Chamberlain and his fans.

(E) Although even in a post-season tournament he could seem **debonair,** Chamberlain actually had to make a supreme effort to beat Russell on the court.

(F) Some degree of rivalry is **intrinsic** to professional basketball; by its nature the sport is extremely competitive.

(G) Chamberlain's relationship with his coaches could be far from **filial;** he often played the part, not of an obedient son, but of a headstrong maverick.

(H) Because of an injury, Chamberlain wasn't able to play much in the 1969 championship series. Once again, he had to **cede** the championship to Russell.

(I) Chamberlain's **proficient** playing finally paid off in 1972. Overcoming the pain of a fractured wrist, he scored twenty-four points and brought the Lakers the world championship.

(J) This amazing victory brought a swift **remission** of the criticism Chamberlain had endured throughout his career.

EXERCISE 3 *Sentence Completion* ☞

Directions. For each of the following items, circle the letter of the choice that best completes the meaning of the sentence or sentences.

21. Height is _____ quality, one that parents pass on to their children.
(A) a blithe
(B) a precipitate
(C) a chagrined
(D) a proficient
(E) an intrinsic

22. To his parents' _____, Wilt required specially tailored clothes and a special bed. His parents were probably worried about what would happen if their son's growth continued without _____.
(A) precipitation . . . remission
(B) proficiency . . . chagrin
(C) chagrin . . . remission
(D) remission . . . proficiency
(E) blitheness . . . proficiency

23. Chamberlain was so tall that door frames had a way of _____ themselves as he made his way from one room to another.
(A) ceding
(B) interposing
(C) chagrining
(D) remitting
(E) precipitating

24. But Chamberlain showed people that his height was a gift. He was _____ in track, and whoever challenged him on the basketball court eventually had to _____ victory to the towering Wilt.
(A) proficient . . . cede
(B) blithe . . . remit
(C) proficient . . . precipitate
(D) blithe . . . chagrin
(E) filial . . . cede

25. The young Chamberlain felt it was his _____ duty to help out his parents financially whenever he could.
(A) debonair
(B) blithe
(C) precipitate
(D) filial
(E) proficient

26. As a child, Chamberlain made pocket money by selling scraps to junkyards. Once, he found a rug in his basement and sold it for 75¢. Later he was _____ to learn that it was his mother's good rug!
(A) filial
(B) chagrined
(C) debonair
(D) blithe
(E) precipitate

27. Chamberlain said his competitiveness was a(n) _____ quality inherited from his father, to whom he always _____ a win in checkers.
(A) intrinsic . . . chagrined
(B) filial . . . chagrined
(C) precipitate . . . remitted
(D) precipitate . . . ceded
(E) intrinsic . . . ceded

28. Chamberlain worked hard to develop his athletic _____. While his school buddies _____ enjoyed themselves on dates, Chamberlain put in extra hours of practice.
(A) blitheness . . . proficiently
(B) proficiency . . . blithely
(C) remission . . . blithely
(D) blitheness . . . intrinsically
(E) proficiency . . . precipitately

29. Chamberlain's rise to stardom might have seemed _____, but he had worked steadily toward that goal since college.
(A) filial
(B) chagrined
(C) precipitate
(D) proficient
(E) interposed

30. Chamberlain was capable of being _____, but when he couldn't charm a coach into seeing things his way, he was quick to take the offensive.
(A) debonair
(B) chagrined
(C) proficiency
(D) filial
(E) unremitting

MAKING NEW WORDS YOUR OWN

Lesson 15 | CONTEXT: The People

Elvis and the Beatles: When England Met the United States

Rock-and-roll, a remarkably popular style of music, developed from big band, rhythm and blues, and country and western—the main styles of United States popular music in the 1940s and the early 1950s.

Rock-and-roll began in the U.S. and was popularized by Elvis Presley (1935–1977). By the early 1960s, rock-and-roll had swept across England; the Beatles came to enjoy the same superstar status there that Presley held in the U.S. Eventually, Beatlemania crossed the Atlantic.

In the following exercises, you will have the opportunity to expand your vocabulary by reading about Elvis Presley and the Beatles. Below are ten Vocabulary Words that will be used in these exercises.

acquiesce	assail	brunt	palliate	predecessor
altercation	beleaguer	deprecate	phalanx	redress

EXERCISE 1 Wordbusting

Directions. Follow these instructions for this word and the nine words on the next page.
- Figure out the word's meaning by looking at its **context**, its **structure**, and its **sound**. Fill in at least one of the three **CSS** boxes. Alternate which boxes you complete.
- Then, look up the word in a dictionary, read all of its meanings, and write the meaning of the word as it is used in the sentence.
- Follow this same process for each of the Vocabulary Words on the next page. You will need to draw your own map for each word. Use a separate sheet of paper.

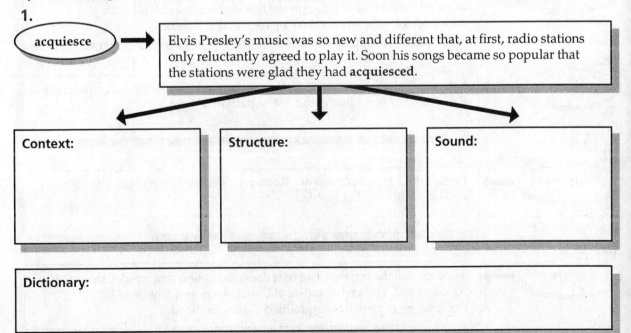

1.

acquiesce → Elvis Presley's music was so new and different that, at first, radio stations only reluctantly agreed to play it. Soon his songs became so popular that the stations were glad they had **acquiesced**.

Context:

Structure:

Sound:

Dictionary:

2.

altercation ➡️ When Presley first sang on television, his performing style delighted teenagers but shocked many of their parents. One can imagine that a few **altercations** occurred between harassed television broadcasters and complaining viewers.

3.

phalanx ➡️ A **phalanx** of people always gathered wherever tickets to a Presley concert were being sold. These fans were united by their love of Presley's music.

4.

beleaguer ➡️ Presley was constantly **beleaguered** by pushy crowds, but he learned to be good-natured about the harassment.

5.

assail ➡️ Feverish fans often surrounded Presley to demand his autograph. They didn't really mean to attack him, although he probably felt sometimes as if he were being **assailed**.

6.

brunt ➡️ Because he was more in the spotlight than lesser-known performers, Presley had to bear the **brunt** of public criticism against rock-and-roll music.

7.

deprecate ➡️ Of course, not everyone in the 1950s **deprecated** rock-and-roll. Millions of people expressed their approval of the new music by attending rock-and-roll concerts and buying rock-and-roll records.

8.

palliate ➡️ Young people's eagerness to hear more and more rock-and-roll music was like a thirst or fever that could not be **palliated**.

9.

predecessor ➡️ Presley did have **predecessors**—other musicians who had developed a rock-and-roll style before him.

10.

redress ➡️ Rock-and-roll historians need to **redress** the notion that Presley invented rock-and-roll. The earlier music of Chuck Berry and Antoine "Fats" Domino, for example, also qualified as rock-and-roll.

EXERCISE 2 *Context Clues* 👈

Directions. Scan the definitions in Column A. Then think about how the boldface words are used in the sentences in Column B. To complete the exercise, match each definition in Column A with the correct Vocabulary Word from Column B. Write the letter of your choice on the line provided; then write the Vocabulary Word on the line preceding the definition.

COLUMN A

_____ **11.** word: _____:
v. to ease without curing; to alleviate; to make (a crime or offense) appear less serious; to lessen the intensity of something

_____ **12.** word: _____:
v. to attack violently; to assault; to attack with arguments, words, or questions

_____ **13.** word: _____:
n. an angry argument

_____ **14.** word: _____:
n. a formation of massed soldiers; a closely united group

_____ **15.** word: _____:
n. a person who precedes another in an office or a position

_____ **16.** word: _____:
v. to give in to or consent to without protest and without enthusiasm

_____ **17.** word: _____:
v. to express strong disapproval of something; to plead against; to belittle

_____ **18.** word: _____:
v. to besiege or surround with troops; to beset; to harass

_____ **19.** word: _____:
n. the main shock or force of a blow or attack; the heaviest part of an accusation or attack

_____ **20.** word: _____:
n. a correction; a reparation; a relief; *v.* to set something right; to remedy

COLUMN B

(A) The Beatles weren't exactly **beleaguered** with offers when they started out. But they didn't give up just because they weren't being surrounded by record companies eager to record them.

(B) The Beatles' manager, Brian Epstein, finally discovered a record company that would **acquiesce** to give the group a recording contract. After the Beatles became famous, many companies regretted having turned them down.

(C) In the early 1960s, long hair on men generally met with disapproval. Thus, some people **deprecated** the Beatles' longish hairstyles.

(D) Have you ever had an **altercation** with someone about your appearance? For example, have you argued about whether you had the right to wear your hair a certain way?

(E) The Beatles' catchy music and charming personalities helped **palliate** the disapproval they received from some members of the older generation.

(F) The Beatles cheerfully bore the **brunt** of the criticism directed at them.

(G) Every time they made a public appearance, the Beatles risked being **assailed** by overly enthusiastic admirers. Fortunately, the frenzy of Beatlemania seldom led to violence.

(H) Often, a **phalanx** of police officers lined up in front of the stage was the only barrier between the Beatles and their hysterical fans.

(I) The group sometimes needed **redress** from the adoration of their public. They were relieved when they could snatch a moment of privacy now and then.

(J) The Beatles had no major **predecessors** in their country; they were the very first English rock stars.

EXERCISE 3 Sentence Completion 👉

Directions. For each of the following items, circle the letter of the choice that best completes the meaning of the sentence or sentences.

21. It's 1964, and you've been _____ your parents for permission to attend the Beatles' first American concert. Finally they _____ to your harassment and reluctantly agree to let you go.

(A) assailing . . . redress
(B) redressing . . . palliate
(C) beleaguering . . . acquiesce
(D) assailing . . . deprecate
(E) beleaguering . . . palliate

22. They don't _____ you with angry arguments about why you shouldn't go, but they do express some concern about the crowd at the concert getting out of hand.

(A) alter
(B) assail
(C) redress
(D) palliate
(E) acquiesce

23. You _____ their fears by reassuring them that you and your friends will look out for each other. In fact, you will stay as close together as a _____ of soldiers.

(A) deprecate . . . phalanx
(B) acquiesce . . . brunt
(C) assail . . . predecessor
(D) beleaguer . . . redress
(E) palliate . . . phalanx

24. "But you might be _____ by a violent mob of crazed Beatles fans!" your older sister says disapprovingly. You don't appreciate her _____ remark.

(A) assailed . . . deprecating
(B) deprecated . . . beleaguering
(C) redressed . . . acquiescing
(D) palliated . . . deprecating
(E) beleaguered . . . acquiescing

25. As your _____ in going to rock concerts, she feels she's earned the right to comment on your plans.

(A) phalanx
(B) deprecation
(C) assailant
(D) predecessor
(E) redress

26. Before you can go to the concert, you and your friends must _____ a problem: None of you has a car. The problem is solved when your sister reluctantly _____ to your pleas that she drive you to the concert hall.

(A) palliate . . . redresses
(B) redress . . . acquiesces
(C) palliate . . . deprecates
(D) redress . . . assails
(E) beleaguer . . . acquiesces

27. At the concert, your first sight of the Beatles takes your breath away, as if you've just received the _____ of a blow.

(A) redress
(B) predecessor
(C) altercation
(D) phalanx
(E) brunt

28. At first, you and your friends _____ the annoying screams of the crowd. But when Paul McCartney starts singing, you join in the joyful shouting.

(A) redress
(B) acquiesce
(C) palliate
(D) deprecate
(E) assail

29. You're relieved that the crowd doesn't get too rowdy; no one has_____ the stage, and you haven't seen any serious _____ between members of the audience.

(A) assailed . . . altercations
(B) beleaguered . . . acquiescence
(C) deprecated . . . predecessors
(D) acquiesced . . . altercations
(E) assailed . . . predecessors

30. When you wake up, you have to _____ to the realization that you dreamed the whole concert. You fell asleep listening to an old Beatles album!

(A) assail
(B) beleaguer
(C) acquiesce
(D) redress
(E) deprecate

62 LESSON 15

MAKING NEW WORDS YOUR OWN

Lesson 16 — CONTEXT: The People

The Immigrants of Ellis Island

Immigrants have been coming to the U.S. for hundreds of years, but it is the image of Ellis Island around 1900 that stands as the strongest symbol of the immigrant experience. The majority of these immigrants were Europeans escaping overpopulation, poverty, and persecution.

Ellis Island had been closed as an immigration center for thirty years before restoration began in 1983. Since the building was reopened to the public in 1990, millions of people have visited Ellis Island.

In the following exercises, you will have the opportunity to expand your vocabulary by reading about immigrants to the United States. Below are ten Vocabulary Words that will be used in these exercises.

bulwark	exodus	insidious	martyr	repression
coalition	heinous	invidious	peripheral	waive

EXERCISE 1 — Wordbusting

Directions. Follow these instructions for this word and the nine words on the next page.
- Figure out the word's meaning by looking at its **context,** its **structure,** and its **sound.** Fill in at least one of the three **CSS** boxes. Alternate which boxes you complete.
- Then, look up the word in a dictionary, read all of its meanings, and write the meaning of the word as it is used in the sentence.
- Follow this same process for each of the Vocabulary Words on the next page. You will need to draw your own map for each word. Use a separate sheet of paper.

1.

bulwark → In the following sentences, a student tells about her great-grandfather, who came to Ellis Island as a young man. Alone, without the **bulwark** of his family to depend on for support, he made a life for himself in the U.S.

Context:	Structure:	Sound:

Dictionary:

2.
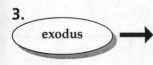

Before the United States had entered World War I, a **coalition** of nations had already formed against the Central Powers.

3.
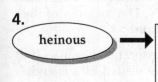

My great-grandfather, Josef, came to the United States from Europe to put the bloodshed of Europe's battlefields behind him. He joined the **exodus** of people—sometimes five thousand a day—who fled from Europe.

4.
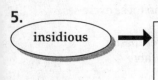

My great-grandfather had not experienced the hateful persecution that led many Europeans to escape their homelands. Yet he sympathized with the **heinous** treatment they had experienced.

5.

My great-grandfather had friends who were denied entry into the United States because of trachoma, an **insidious** eye disease that often did not show symptoms until too late.

6.
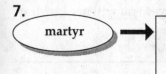

Life in New York City was often a struggle for poor immigrants like Josef. Barely surviving, they could not help but feel some ill will toward wealthy people who made an **invidious** display of their riches.

7.
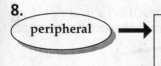

Some people died helping others escape persecution in Europe and come to the United States. Such people, who sacrificed everything for their cause, might be considered **martyrs**.

8.
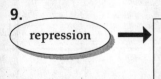

It was impossible for any chief European power to remain **peripheral** during World War I. Almost everyone was involved in or affected by the war.

9.
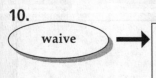

It is easy to imagine that Josef, and others like him, might have experienced some **repression** of those war memories. For many, the memories probably returned at different moments during their lives.

10.

To be granted United States citizenship, my great-grandfather had to **waive** all allegiance to his former homeland. Declaring his sole loyalty to the United States was a very emotional experience for him.

EXERCISE 2 *Context Clues* ✍

Directions. Scan the definitions in Column A. Then think about how the boldface words are used in the sentences in Column B. To complete the exercise, match each definition in Column A with the correct Vocabulary Word from Column B. Write the letter of your choice on the line provided; then write the Vocabulary Word on the line preceding the definition.

COLUMN A	COLUMN B

_____ **11.** word: _____:

n. an alliance, usually of nations, political parties, or factions; a temporary union

(A) War was not the only thing that led Europeans to immigrate to the United States. **Repression** of their rights forced many to flee to the freedom found in this country.

_____ **12.** word: _____:

adj. sly; treacherous; working in a hidden but dangerous way

(B) The **exodus** from Europe also resulted from poverty, overcrowding, and persecution.

_____ **13.** word: _____:

n. the holding back or subduing; suppression; pushing painful ideas or memories into the subconscious (in psychiatry)

(C) Also, not all immigrants were escaping **heinous,** or vile, conditions in their homelands. Some simply hoped to make a new start in the land of opportunity.

_____ **14.** word: _____:

adj. away from the central part; on the edge; only slightly concerned with the important part; unessential

(D) The walls of Ellis Island must have seemed like a protecting **bulwark** to immigrants after their hazardous journey across the sea.

_____ **15.** word: _____:

n. one who is persecuted, tortured, or killed for refusing to renounce religious principles; one who sacrifices for the sake of a belief or cause; *v.* to torture or put to death for refusing to deny a belief or faith

(E) World War I ended soon after the United States joined the **coalition** of nations united against the Central Powers, and immigration gradually declined.

(F) Immigrants at Ellis Island often found that they had to **waive** their claim to their family names; immigration officials frequently assigned immigrants new, usually English-sounding names.

_____ **16.** word: _____:

n. a wall of earth used for defense; a person or thing that gives support or protection

(G) When the Nazis rose to power, many Jewish Germans immigrated to the United States because they saw that conditions were getting much worse for Jews. These were not **peripheral** concerns. Indeed, Germany's persecution of Jews resulted in more than six million deaths.

_____ **17.** word: _____:

n. a departure, usually of a great number of people

_____ **18.** word: _____:

adj. likely to cause ill will or envy; hateful

(H) Some sympathetic Germans became **martyrs** when they gave their lives to help Jews escape the country.

(I) Sadly, after escaping persecution at home, some immigrants experienced a more **insidious** form of discrimination in the United States. Although not always expressed outright, this discrimination led to some immigrants being denied jobs.

_____ **19.** word: _____:

v. to relinquish, usually a claim, right, or privilege; to defer or delay

_____ **20.** word: _____:

adj. abominable; grossly wicked and hateful; vile

(J) Although some Americans were guilty of **invidious** treatment of immigrants, many others worked to create goodwill among all Americans.

EXERCISE 3 *Sentence Completion* ☞

Directions. For each of the following items, circle the letter of the choice that best completes the meaning of the sentence or sentences.

21. For some, only the most ____ conditions, such as war, are enough to drive them from the supportive ____ of their homes.
- (A) insidious . . . peripheral
- (B) heinous . . . bulwarks
- (C) invidious . . . bulwarks
- (D) heinous . . . exodus
- (E) insidious . . . exodus

22. Other emigrants may pull up their roots when they are experiencing ____. This suppression might be politically or ethnically motivated.
- (A) coalition
- (B) martyrdom
- (C) waiver
- (D) repression
- (E) bulwark

23. Unrealistic expectations of wealth are the ____ side of the American dream. Some immigrants feel that they've been slyly deceived about the economic opportunities in the United States.
- (A) heinous
- (B) invidious
- (C) insidious
- (D) martyred
- (E) waived

24. Today, about 15 percent of immigrants eventually ____, or give up, their right to stay in the United States.
- (A) claim
- (B) exercise
- (C) martyr
- (D) coalesce
- (E) waive

25. A mass ____ from Germany took place in the mid 1800s. Millions left Germany for the U.S., partly because of the uneasy ____, or union, of political factions in Germany.
- (A) exodus . . . coalition
- (B) repression . . . martyrdom
- (C) coalition . . . exodus
- (D) martyrs . . . bulwark
- (E) bulwark . . . coalition

26. The Vietnam War brought a wave of Vietnamese immigrants. Some were only ____ involved in the conflict and left before the killing began. They foresaw a slow, ____ communist takeover.
- (A) coalition . . . invidious
- (B) exodus . . . heinous
- (C) peripherally . . . insidious
- (D) bulwark . . . insidious
- (E) coalition . . . heinous

27. In 1921, the United States established an immigration quota and ____ some emigrants' entry into the country. Many emigrants must have seen the delay as an ____ act of ill will.
- (A) martyred . . . heinous
- (B) martyred . . . insidious
- (C) waived . . . invidious
- (D) waived . . . martyred
- (E) martyred . . . invidious

28. These quotas, which were considered ____, or vile, by many people, were made less restrictive in 1965.
- (A) repressive
- (B) waived
- (C) coalitionist
- (D) martyred
- (E) heinous

29. People who remain in war-torn countries to help their families, instead of joining the mass ____ of emigrants, are often considered ____ because of their sacrifices.
- (A) coalition . . . martyrs
- (B) exodus . . . bulwarks
- (C) coalition . . . bulwarks
- (D) repression . . . martyrs
- (E) exodus . . . martyrs

30. Some argue that immigrants are the ____, the supporting backbone of the U.S.
- (A) peripheral
- (B) bulwark
- (C) repression
- (D) martyrs
- (E) exodus

Name _____ Date _____ Class _____

MAKING NEW WORDS YOUR OWN

Lesson 17 | CONTEXT: The People

Wynton Marsalis: Jazz's Neotraditionalist

Since its birth in New Orleans shortly after the turn of the century, the uniquely U.S. musical form
called jazz has reinvented itself again and again. In the 1960s, jazz became increasingly experimental,
appealing to smaller audiences. In the 1970s, jazz became widely popular again in a form called
fusion, but many purists felt that this blend of jazz and rock compromised jazz's integrity. A new
generation of musicians have repopularized traditional jazz. Foremost among these, called
neotraditionalists, is New Orleans-born trumpet player Wynton Marsalis (b. 1961).

In the following exercises, you will have the opportunity to expand your vocabulary by reading about
Wynton Marsalis and jazz. Below are ten Vocabulary Words that will be used in these exercises.

affinity	audacious	deign	epicure	ingratiate
array	convivial	derogatory	fastidious	oscillate

EXERCISE 1 | *Wordbusting* ✍

Directions. Follow these instructions for this word and the nine words on the next page.
- Figure out the word's meaning by looking at its **context**, its **structure**, and its **sound**. Fill in at least
  one of the three **CSS** boxes. Alternate which boxes you complete.
- Then, look up the word in a dictionary, read all of its meanings, and write the meaning of the word
  as it is used in the sentence.
- Follow this same process for each of the Vocabulary Words on the next page. You will need to draw
  your own map for each word. Use a separate sheet of paper.

1.

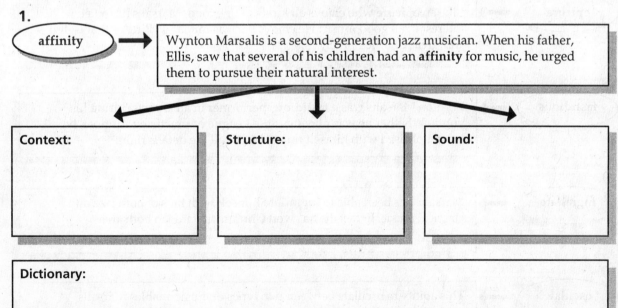

affinity → Wynton Marsalis is a second-generation jazz musician. When his father,
Ellis, saw that several of his children had an **affinity** for music, he urged
them to pursue their natural interest.

Context:

Structure:

Sound:

Dictionary:

2.

array →

Ellis Marsalis founded a jazz program for up-and-coming young musicians at the New Orleans Center for the Creative Arts. His program has produced an impressive **array** of talent, including Harry Connick, Jr., and Ellis's own sons, Branford and Wynton.

3.

audacious →

Wynton quickly proved to be an **audacious** talent in both jazz and classical music; his bold style first stunned audiences when he made his debut at the age of fourteen with the New Orleans Philharmonic.

4.

convivial →

Jazz was born in the dance halls of New Orleans. In that city's **convivial** French Quarter, where the atmosphere is always festive, you still can hear jazz being played in the old tradition.

5.

deign →

Some celebrity musicians wouldn't **deign** to appear on a children's television show, but Wynton Marsalis didn't consider it beneath him to make an appearance on *Sesame Street*.

6.

derogatory →

Because music education is important to him, Marsalis approves of such public television appearances. But he takes a **derogatory** view of musicians who bow to the media's wishes merely to achieve financial success.

7.

epicure →

Like an **epicure** who enjoys all kinds of fine food, Marsalis has a keen interest in all good music: He enjoys Bach as much as "Bird"—that is, the jazz great Charlie Parker.

8.

fastidious →

Wynton Marsalis was a **fastidious** performer in all aspects during his youth. Whether he was playing Little League or practicing trumpet, he wasn't pleased with himself unless he got all the details right.

9.

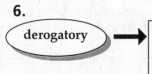

Marsalis has been able to **ingratiate** himself with fans of both jazz and classical music. In fact, he has won Grammy awards in both areas.

10.

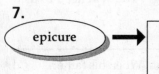

This ability to **oscillate** between two types of music enables Marsalis to continually bring a fresh perspective to both musical forms.

EXERCISE 2 — *Context Clues* ✍

Directions. Scan the definitions in Column A. Then think about how the boldface words are used in the sentences in Column B. To complete the exercise, match each definition in Column A with the correct Vocabulary Word from Column B. Write the letter of your choice on the line provided; then write the Vocabulary Word on the line preceding the definition.

COLUMN A	COLUMN B

COLUMN A

_____ **11.** word: _____:
adj. disparaging; belittling; meant to show an unfavorable opinion

_____ **12.** word: _____:
adj. fond of eating and drinking with friends; festive; social

_____ **13.** word: _____:
v. to grant or agree condescendingly to do something; stoop

_____ **14.** word: _____
n. a natural attraction or liking for a person or a thing; a close relationship

_____ **15.** word: _____:
adj. hard to please; easily disgusted; overly dainty

_____ **16.** word: _____:
v. to move back and forth like a pendulum; to vary between two or more opinions, thoughts, or actions; to vacillate

_____ **17.** word: _____:
adj. fearlessly daring; bold; insolent; contemptuous of decorum

_____ **18.** word: _____:
n. a person who has refined tastes in eating and drinking

_____ **19.** word: _____:
v. to bring oneself into someone's good graces or favor

_____ **20.** word: _____:
n. an orderly arrangement of persons or objects; splendid dress; *v.* to set in proper order (especially soldiers); to dress or adorn

COLUMN B

(A) Marsalis's first **affinity** was for classical music; he didn't develop a strong attraction to jazz until he had established himself as a classical trumpeter.

(B) Marsalis's musical talent was forged not in the **convivial** atmosphere of a New Orleans dance hall but in the highly disciplined environment of the New Orleans Center for the Creative Arts.

(C) Critics **oscillate** in their judgments of Marsalis. One moment they praise him for his enormous talent, and the next they condemn him for his brash comments.

(D) Many people thought he was rude to publicly criticize Miles Davis, a sacred figure to many jazz fans. Marsalis himself attributes his **audacious** comments to immaturity.

(E) Few musicians, especially young ones, would dare to make **derogatory** comments about such a well-loved figure.

(F) But Marsalis is a **fastidious** individual. He believes that it is not enough for a musician to be talented; he demands that a musician also have personal integrity.

(G) A well-publicized argument occurred when Wynton's brother, Branford, joined forces with rock star Sting. Wynton himself would not have **deigned** to play in such a commercial venture.

(H) Marsalis now regrets some of the remarks he made when he was younger. They certainly did not help to **ingratiate** him with other jazz musicians or jazz critics.

(I) Like most young jazz performers today, Marsalis shuns drugs, cigarettes, and alcohol. If he has a weakness, it might be for clothing; he seems to indulge himself in high fashion much as an **epicure** indulges in fine food and drink.

(J) Marsalis's strong sense of personal style shows in both his music and his appearance. He often performs **arrayed** in designer clothing.

Name _____ Date _____ Class _____

Directions. For each of the following items, circle the letter of the choice that best completes the meaning of the sentence or sentences.

21. Nina, Coleman, and Doug are spending a _____ afternoon eating and listening to recordings. Coleman collects CDs, which are _____ neatly on a shelf in his room.
(A) derogatory . . . oscillated
(B) fastidious . . . ingratiated
(C) convivial . . . arrayed
(D) audacious . . . deigned
(E) epicurean . . . derided

22. Coleman has developed an _____ for jazz. Doug is _____ about Coleman's latest purchase. "How can you like that stuff? To me, jazz sounds like a bunch of people making mistakes and pretending it's music."
(A) affinity . . . derogatory
(B) oscillation . . . fastidious
(C) audaciousness . . . convivial
(D) epicure . . . ingratiating
(E) array . . . oscillating

23. "That's a pretty _____ comment. I can't believe you would dare to say that; you play guitar so well yourself—NOT!"
(A) convivial
(B) epicurean
(C) fastidious
(D) audacious
(E) ingratiating

24. Nina, who is an _____ of snack food, stops indulging herself in raw cauliflower long enough to side with Coleman. "I think jazz is great. It's just that it's an acquired taste, like cauliflower."
(A) array
(B) epicure
(C) affinity
(D) ingratiation
(E) conviviality

25. Nina has succeeded in _____ herself with Coleman, so he decides to show his approval with a generous offer.
(A) oscillating
(B) deigning
(C) arraying
(D) ingratiating
(E) deriding

26. "You can use my new Miles Davis CD—just don't scratch it." Coleman is _____ about keeping his CDs in good shape.
(A) fastidious
(B) epicurean
(C) ingratiating
(D) oscillating
(E) derogatory

27. "What?" says Nina. "I can't believe you would _____ to let me borrow your CD. I'm honored that you condescend to let me!"
(A) oscillate
(B) array
(C) forbid
(D) ingratiate
(E) deign

28. Coleman sways with laughter, _____ back and forth like a pendulum. "Am I that bad? Can I _____ myself with you guys again? I'll try to learn to be lovable."
(A) ingratiating . . . deign
(B) oscillating . . . ingratiate
(C) deigning . . . oscillate
(D) oscillating . . . array
(E) ingratiating . . . oscillate

29. Nina smiles. "The one who really needs to learn something is Doug. His _____ comment has insulted me. Jazz is an important part of my heritage."
(A) epicurean
(B) arrayed
(C) derogatory
(D) oscillating
(E) convivial

30. "I confess! I got a Marsalis CD, and I like it. He's _____, he's bold, he's daring! I was just playing devil's advocate." To the unique sound of Miles Davis's trumpet, Coleman and Nina _____ swat Doug with a pillow.
(A) epicurean . . . fastidiously
(B) fastidious . . . audaciously
(C) deigning . . . convivially
(D) audacious . . . convivially
(E) oscillating . . . audaciously

Name _____ Date _____ Class _____

MAKING NEW WORDS YOUR OWN

Lesson 18 | CONTEXT: The People
Crimefighters

Although there are no easy solutions to the crime rate in the U.S., each community has a system for preventing and combatting crime. Thousands of people devote their lives to fighting crime. A police officer in a patrol car is probably the most familiar image of a crimefighter. Within a city's police department, alone, many different jobs are performed to aid the process of crimefighting. Some crimefighters work in the court system or the correctional system; still others work through federal agencies such as the Federal Bureau of Investigation.

In the exercises below, you will have the opportunity to expand your vocabulary by reading about American crimefighters. Below are ten Vocabulary Words that will be used in these exercises.

bandy	efficacious	felony	imperious	rationalize
degenerate	equestrian	flay	malevolent	relent

EXERCISE 1 — Wordbusting ✍

Directions. Follow these instructions for this word and the nine words on the next page.
- Figure out the word's meaning by looking at its **context,** its **structure,** and its **sound.** Fill in at least one of the three **CSS** boxes. Alternate which boxes you complete.
- Then, look up the word in a dictionary, read all of its meanings, and write the meaning of the word as it is used in the sentence.
- Follow this same process for each of the Vocabulary Words on the next page. You will need to draw your own map for each word. Use a separate sheet of paper.

1.

(bandy) → It's the beginning of class, when you usually **bandy** jokes and small talk back and forth with the other students for a few minutes until your teacher tells you it's time to stop chatting.

Context:	Structure:	Sound:

Dictionary:

2.
degenerate →
But today your class has a speaker, and your teacher has asked you to act like polite, dignified human beings—not, she added jokingly, like **degenerates** with low moral standards.

3.
efficacious →
Her request was **efficacious**. Long before Sergeant Sharon Lamont walks into the room, the class is completely silent.

4.
equestrian →
Sergeant Lamont is an **equestrian,** or mounted, police officer; unfortunately, she couldn't bring her horse to your class!

5.
felony →
She's come to answer your questions about law enforcement and to talk about careers in police work. One student asks a question about the difference between **felonies** and less serious crimes.

6.
flay →
Sgt. Lamont explains that a misdemeanor, though less serious than a felony, is still a crime; for example, cruelly **flaying** an animal is a misdemeanor in the eyes of the law, even though it is a serious offense in the eyes of most people.

7.
imperious →
Sgt. Lamont hopes to change the image of police officers as **imperious** people who act arrogant and overbearing because of their badges.

8.
malevolent →
Certainly, police are not **malevolent;** their job is to help others, not to show ill will toward them.

9.
rationalize →
No dedicated, caring police officer would try to **rationalize,** or explain away, the use of unnecessary force.

10.
relent →
Generally, it is a good thing for the police when a suspect **relents** from trying to escape. The officers don't have to use force when suspects give themselves up.

EXERCISE 2 · Context Clues ✍

Directions. Scan the definitions in Column A. Then think about how the boldface words are used in the sentences in Column B. To complete the exercise, match each definition in Column A with the correct Vocabulary Word from Column B. Write the letter of your choice on the line provided; then write the Vocabulary Word on the line preceding the definition.

COLUMN A	COLUMN B
_____ **11.** word: _____: *v.* to strip off the skin, as by whipping; to scold or criticize severely	(A) "What causes people to commit serious crimes?" a student asks. "Are hardened criminals just people who've **degenerated** to a point where they have no sense of right and wrong?"
_____ **12.** word: _____: *n.* a crime of such seriousness (such as murder, kidnapping, or burglary) that it is punishable by a severe sentence	(B) "That's a good question—why would someone willingly commit a **felony,** such as kidnapping or murder? Criminologists try to find the answer to that question."
_____ **13.** word: _____: *adj.* producing the desired effect; effective	(C) Sgt. Lamont continues, "Criminology is the study of crime, criminals, and criminal behavior. By learning about the reasons for crime, a criminologist may discover **efficacious** methods of rehabilitating criminals—methods that really work."
_____ **14.** word: _____: *v.* to explain in a manner that is false but seems reasonable; to devise self-serving but false reasons; to explain away	(D) "Many criminologists argue that we can't **rationalize** a criminal justice system that punishes people without rehabilitating them. While we give reasonable-sounding explanations, the same offenders keep winding up back in prison."
_____ **15.** word: _____: *v.* to decline in physical, mental, or moral qualities; *n.* a person having low moral standards; *adj.* having grown worse or deteriorated	(E) The same student asks, "But are all violent criminals **malevolent** people? Do they really wish evil on others?"
_____ **16.** word: _____: *adj.* domineering; overbearing; arrogant	(F) Just then another student, impatient to speak, interrupts in a rude, **imperious** manner.
_____ **17.** word: _____: *v.* to give in or yield to something; to become less harsh	(G) The teacher **flays** her by way of a scolding look.
_____ **18.** word: _____: *adj.* wishing harm or evil to others; showing or having ill will toward others; spiteful	(H) After a moment we begin to **bandy** again, tossing questions, answers, and opinions back and forth.
_____ **19.** word: _____: *n.* a horseback rider; *adj.* pertaining to horses or the riding of horses	(I) Someone asks, "Why are some police patrols on horseback? What's the point of **equestrian** police?"
_____ **20.** word: _____: *v.* to toss back and forth; to exchange; to discuss lightly	(J) You all want to know, but just now the bell rings. Reluctantly, you **relent** to the constraints of time.

Name _____ Date _____ Class _____

Directions. For each of the following items, circle the letter of the choice that best completes the meaning of the sentence or sentences.

21. After lunch, you _____ with the sergeant about careers in crimefighting. The exchange is _____; she achieves her purpose of showing you the many different careers.

(A) degenerate . . . malevolent
(B) rationalize . . . relentless
(C) bandy . . . efficacious
(D) flay . . . equestrian
(E) relent . . . imperious

22. She explains that some police officers investigate serious crimes, or _____.

(A) degenerates
(B) equestrians
(C) malevolences
(D) felonies
(E) rationalisms

23. Other officers in the juvenile division refer young offenders to counselors. If a young person is merely misguided but not _____, counseling may help keep the person from _____ into a hardened criminal.

(A) malevolent . . . degenerating
(B) efficacious . . . flaying
(C) equestrian . . . bandying
(D) relentless . . . degenerating
(E) imperious . . . relenting

24. Patrol officers like Sergeant Lamont are _____ in looking out for people in their area, or beat. They constantly stay alert for any sign of trouble.

(A) imperious
(B) degenerate
(C) equestrian
(D) malevolent
(E) relentless

25. The _____, or mounted, police usually patrol city parks. They take good care of their horses; an officer would never _____ a horse or harm it in any other way.

(A) efficacious . . . bandy
(B) equestrian . . . rationalize
(C) malevolent . . . relent
(D) equestrian . . . flay
(E) imperious . . . flay

26. The sergeant enjoys being _____; she jokes that it's easy to look imposing and _____ sitting on a tall, majestic horse!

(A) a rationalization . . . equestrian
(B) an equestrian . . . imperious
(C) a degenerate . . . malevolent
(D) a felony . . . relentless
(E) an equestrian . . . degenerate

27. It's the police department's job to deal with crime expertly and _____. However, the sergeant points out, ordinary citizens shouldn't use this fact to _____ ignoring a crime when they see it.

(A) efficaciously . . . rationalize
(B) malevolently . . . degenerate
(C) rationally . . . relent
(D) relentlessly . . . flay
(E) imperiously . . . bandy

28. Each police station has a central dispatch office that you can call to report crimes in progress. It's important not to _____ with the operators since they don't have time for such exchanges.

(A) degenerate
(B) rationalize
(C) flay
(D) bandy
(E) relent

29. Even the most _____ criminal, intent on doing harm, may give up, or _____, on learning that the police are on the way.

(A) imperious . . . degenerate
(B) equestrian . . . relent
(C) efficacious . . . flay
(D) degenerate . . . rationalize
(E) malevolent . . . relent

30. The sergeant points out that although police officers don't always need college degrees, it would be a false _____ to end one's studies for that reason alone.

(A) degenerate
(B) equestrian
(C) rationalization
(D) malevolence
(E) felony

MAKING NEW WORDS YOUR OWN

Lesson 19 | CONTEXT: The People

Walt Disney's Imagination

When Walt Disney (1901–1966) began his career as a commercial artist, he couldn't have known that his work would someday capture the imagination of the entire world. Neither could he have known that he would build an entertainment empire from a single cartoon creation—a funny-looking mouse! After featuring Mickey Mouse in the first "talking" cartoon in the 1920s, Disney made a vast fortune from sales of endlessly popular Mickey Mouse products. Disney became a pioneer of cartoon animation and also created Disneyland, the world's first theme park, and several other parks in the U.S. and abroad.

In the following exercises you will have the opportunity to expand your vocabulary by reading about Walt Disney. Below are ten Vocabulary Words that will be used in these exercises.

abash	auspicious	demeanor	immemorial	purport
allure	deference	guise	integral	syndicate

EXERCISE 1 *Wordbusting*

Directions. Follow these instructions for this word and the nine words on the next page.
- Figure out the word's meaning by looking at its **context**, its **structure**, and its **sound**. Fill in at least one of the three **CSS** boxes. Alternate which boxes you complete.
- Then, look up the word in a dictionary, read all of its meanings, and write the meaning of the word as it is used in the sentence.
- Follow this same process for each of the Vocabulary Words on the next page. You will need to draw your own map for each word. Use a separate sheet of paper.

1.

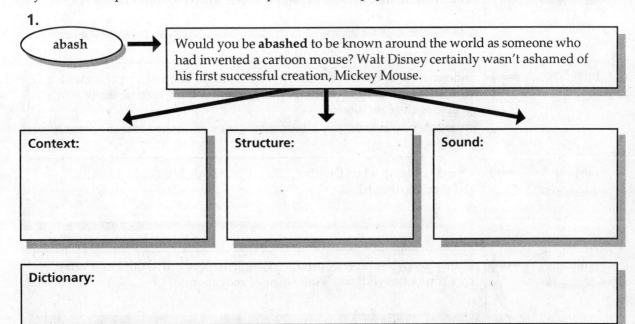

abash → Would you be **abashed** to be known around the world as someone who had invented a cartoon mouse? Walt Disney certainly wasn't ashamed of his first successful creation, Mickey Mouse.

Context:

Structure:

Sound:

Dictionary:

2.

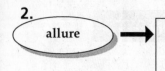 **allure** ➤ It is hard to resist the **allure** of Mickey. He is so charming that he was chosen as the trademark for Walt Disney Productions.

3.

 **auspicious** ➤ Beginning with his first appearance in the 1923 cartoon *Steamboat Willie*, Mickey Mouse's immense popularity marked him as Disney's most **auspicious** character.

4.

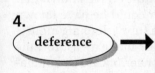 **deference** ➤ The character was originally called Mortimer Mouse. In **deference** to his wife, Disney followed her suggestion of changing the name to Mickey.

5.

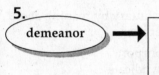 **demeanor** ➤ In addition to the name, the **demeanor** of the cartoon character changed over the years. Eventually, he came to look and act like the Mickey Mouse we know today.

6.

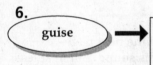 **guise** ➤ Over the years, millions of children donned the black mouse-ear caps, the **guise** of a Mickey Mouse Club member.

7.

 **immemorial** ➤ Disney's cartoon characters seem to have been around since time **immemorial;** we can hardly imagine a time when they didn't exist.

8.

 **integral** ➤ Indeed, these cartoon characters have become an **integral** part of our culture. People of all ages recognize them, and they have become familiar to people of all generations.

9.

 **purport** ➤ Or did you gasp when Dumbo, who **purported** that he could fly, actually did soar into the air?

10.

syndicate ➤ Disney's movies were not produced single-handedly by Walt Disney, but by a corporate **syndicate,** Walt Disney Productions.

EXERCISE 2 *Context Clues* 👆

Directions. Scan the definitions in Column A. Then think about how the boldface words are used in the sentences in Column B. To complete the exercise, match each definition in Column A with the correct Vocabulary Word from Column B. Write the letter of your choice on the line provided; then write the Vocabulary Word on the line preceding the definition.

COLUMN A

_____ **11.** word: _____:
v. to claim to be or do something; *n.* the apparent purpose or main idea of something

_____ **12.** word: _____:
n. outward behavior; manner of conduct; bearing

_____ **13.** word: _____:
n. a group of persons or companies united to carry out some enterprise or business; *v.* to form such an association

_____ **14.** word: _____:
v. to make uneasy or ashamed; to embarrass

_____ **15.** word: _____:
n. outward appearance; a costume; a style of dress

_____ **16.** word: _____:
n. charm; *v.* to fascinate; to tempt with something desirable

_____ **17.** word: _____:
adj. marked by signs of success or good fortune; favorable

_____ **18.** word: _____:
adj. reaching back beyond the bounds of memory; extremely old

_____ **19.** word: _____:
n. a yielding in judgment, opinion, or wishes to another; courteous respect

_____ **20.** word: _____:
adj. pertaining to a part of the whole; complete; essential

COLUMN B

(A) Although Disney's first full-length film didn't premiere until 1937, his influence seems to have been shaping popular culture since time **immemorial**.

(B) Disney's extraordinary success was not pulled from thin air. His ideas were like the pieces of a puzzle and were the product of his hard work and extraordinary vision, all **integral** ingredients in the whole of his success.

(C) **Abashed** by the idea of just making money, Disney was an artist who had to create things to be happy.

(D) Millions of Disney's fans are grateful, however, that he and several associates made the decision to **syndicate** themselves because the decision allowed Disney's artistry to reach an ever-widening audience.

(E) In an interview, Disney recalled the **auspicious** day when he first had the idea for a new kind of amusement park. Disneyland, the world's first theme park, was the direct result of that vision.

(F) Disney's **demeanor** in photographs is that of a modest, good-humored man.

(G) The recollections of his friends suggest that this image was not just a **guise** but was a true reflection of his character.

(H) Disney's brother, who was also a business partner, referred to Walt with **deference**. At the opening of the second theme park, Disney World, he expressed his opinion that Disney was a genius.

(I) Disney was keenly sensitive to the wishes of the American public, and he knew the **allure** of his entertaining cartoons.

(J) At the time of Disney's death in 1966, his company, Walt Disney Productions, **purported** to have touched the lives of more than 800 million people around the world.

EXERCISE 3 Sentence Completion ✍️

Directions. For each of the following items, circle the letter of the choice that best completes the meaning of the sentence or sentences.

21. When I was five years old, I went with my family to Disney World. I don't _____ to remember much about the trip, but I do know it was _____ event of my young life.
    (A) syndicate . . . an immemorial
    (B) purport . . . an auspicious
    (C) defer . . . an immemorial
    (D) demean . . . an integral
    (E) purport . . . a deferential

22. Out of _____ to our wishes, our parents agreed to take my brother and me to Disney World that summer. They _____ to share our joy, but they really weren't looking forward to the drive.
    (A) demeanor . . . purported
    (B) deference . . . abashed
    (C) purport . . . syndicated
    (D) deference . . . purported
    (E) guise . . . abashed

23. Now that I think of it, we didn't even have to ask; our mom seemed to have an un-canny understanding of the _____ of Disney World. Perhaps she was tempted by it also.
    (A) purport
    (B) allure
    (C) syndicate
    (D) demeanor
    (E) guise

24. The drive took two days, and my brother and I fought a lot in the car. Our parents kept reminding us to watch our _____, so we tried to maintain a _____ of civility.
    (A) demeanor . . . guise
    (B) purport . . . demeanor
    (C) guise . . . syndicate
    (D) deference . . . purport
    (E) demeanor . . . purport

25. Finally the _____ moment arrived—we were at Disney World!
    (A) integral
    (B) alluring
    (C) immemorial
    (D) auspicious
    (E) deferential

26. My first impression was of a tour guide who was dressed as Prince Charming. His impressive elegance was only part, yet an _____ one, of my overall enjoyment of Disney World.
    (A) auspicious
    (B) integral
    (C) deferential
    (D) purported
    (E) abashed

27. As a child I wasn't easily _____, so I didn't feel embarrassed at having my picture taken with a tour guide in the _____ of Minnie Mouse.
    (A) abashed . . . deference
    (B) auspicious . . . demeanor
    (C) abashed . . . guise
    (D) deferred . . . guise
    (E) auspicious . . . demeanor

28. She said something, but I couldn't hear her through the costume. My parents ex-plained the _____ of her comment: She thought I was cute!
    (A) allure
    (B) deference
    (C) purport
    (D) auspiciousness
    (E) syndicate

29. I blushed, as any kid would have done. Since time _____, children have been _____ by compliments.
    (A) immemorial . . . abashed
    (B) auspicious . . . abashed
    (C) alluring . . . purport
    (D) immemorial . . . purport
    (E) auspicious . . . immemorial

30. The Disney _____ is a company that knows how to please children. I enjoyed every single ride at the park!
    (A) integral
    (B) deference
    (C) syndicate
    (D) demeanor
    (E) guise

MAKING NEW WORDS YOUR OWN

Lesson 20 | CONTEXT: The People

Susan B. Anthony and Gloria Steinem

Writer and lecturer Susan B. Anthony (1820–1906) was one of the most important leaders in the early women's rights movement. Along with Elizabeth Cady Stanton (1815–1902), she helped found the National Woman Suffrage Association.

Born more than a hundred years after Susan B. Anthony, Gloria Steinem (b. 1934) became a spokesperson for the feminist movement in the late 1960s. Steinem, who helped found *Ms.* magazine, continues to work for women's rights.

In the following exercises, you will have the opportunity to expand your vocabulary by reading about Susan B. Anthony and Gloria Steinem. These ten Vocabulary Words will be used.

| arbitrary | bureaucracy | inane | premeditated | scapegoat |
| browbeat | contraband | politic | proxy | transient |

EXERCISE 1 *Wordbusting*

Directions. Follow these instructions for this word and the nine words on the next page.
- Figure out the word's meaning by looking at its **context,** its **structure,** and its **sound.** Fill in at least one of the three **CSS** boxes. Alternate which boxes you complete.
- Then, look up the word in a dictionary, read all of its meanings, and write the meaning of the word as it is used in the sentence.
- Follow this same process for each of the Vocabulary Words on the next page. You will need to draw your own map for each word. Use a separate sheet of paper.

1.

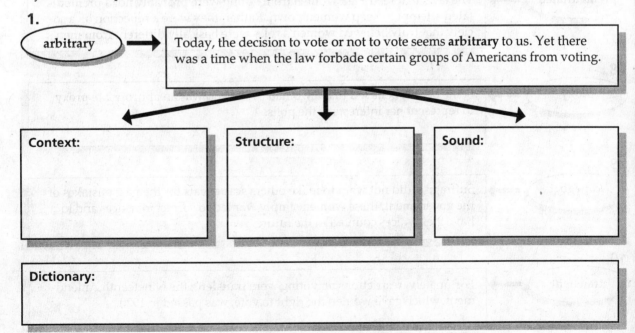

arbitrary → Today, the decision to vote or not to vote seems **arbitrary** to us. Yet there was a time when the law forbade certain groups of Americans from voting.

Context:

Structure:

Sound:

Dictionary:

2.

browbeat →

It's unimaginable today that someone would be **browbeaten** for wanting to exercise the right to vote. Yet in the early twentieth century, women and African Americans were often frightened off from voting even after they had gained the legal right to do so.

3.

bureaucracy →

Government **bureaucracies** were often inefficient in protecting these voters. Government officials were not able to guarantee the voters' legal rights.

4.

contraband →

Would you exercise your right to vote if you couldn't do so openly—if you had to smuggle your ballot in like **contraband**?

5.

inane →

In hindsight, we can see that laws and attitudes restricting voting were **inane**. Yet not everyone in the early 1900s saw the pointlessness and stupidity of them.

6.

politic →

When the women's suffrage movement began, many elected officials did not consider it **politic,** or in their own best interests, to support the cause.

7.

premeditated →

The laws that restricted women from voting were probably not a **premeditated** attempt to keep women down. Rather, they were a reflection of a society that truly believed women's roles were basically different from men's.

8.

proxy →

Some people believed that a woman's husband was an appropriate **proxy** to represent her interests at the polls.

9.

scapegoat →

Suffragists did not want to make others **scapegoats** for the past mistakes of the government; these women simply wanted to correct injustices and to have their voices counted in the future.

10.

transient →

Fortunately, restrictions on voting were **transient;** the Nineteenth Amendment, which gave women the right to vote, was passed in 1920.

EXERCISE 2 Context Clues ✍

Directions. Scan the definitions in Column A. Then think about how the boldface words are used in the sentences in Column B. To complete the exercise, match each definition in Column A with the correct Vocabulary Word from Column B. Write the letter of your choice on the line provided; then write the Vocabulary Word on the line preceding the definition.

COLUMN A	COLUMN B

COLUMN A

_____ **11.** word: _____:
n. smuggled goods

_____ **12.** word: _____:
adj. wise in looking out for one's own interests; prudent; shrewd

_____ **13.** word: _____:
adj. senseless; pointless; stupid

_____ **14.** word: _____:
n. a person who is given the authority to act or stand in for another; written proof of such authority

_____ **15.** word: _____:
n. the collection of departments of appointed officials through which a government is run; inflexible governmental procedures

_____ **16.** word: _____:
adj. based on one's own wishes; not fixed by rules; absolute, despotic

_____ **17.** word: _____:
adj. lasting or used for a short time only; not permanent; fleeting; *n.* a person or thing that has no settled place

_____ **18.** word: _____:
adj. planned or plotted; closely considered beforehand; deliberate

_____ **19.** word: _____:
v. to frighten with a stern manner of harsh words; to bully

_____ **20.** word: _____:
n. a person or thing who takes the blame for the mistakes or crimes of others

COLUMN B

(A) The National Woman Suffrage Association, and later the National American Woman Suffrage Association, battled the government **bureaucracy** to win the vote for women.

(B) The organization's deliberate, carefully **premeditated** efforts helped bring about the passage of the Nineteenth Amendment.

(C) Susan B. Anthony was elected president of the organization in 1892. The choice wasn't **arbitrary,** but rather was based on Anthony's outstanding record of achievements.

(D) Anthony and other suffragists didn't try to **browbeat** the government into granting women the vote; however, they did work tirelessly to change public opinion.

(E) Many suffragists went to jail for their efforts. Clearly, they were more concerned with furthering their cause than with being **politic,** or acting solely out of personal interest.

(F) Anthony's intelligence and purposefulness were obvious to everyone who heard her speak. Even those who disagreed with her could not accuse her of being **inane**.

(G) The suffragist magazine *The Revolution* supported so many unpopular causes that it was treated as **contraband**; one can imagine that some readers had to smuggle the magazine into their homes.

(H) Some people were so opposed to women's rights that they made the suffragists **scapegoats** and blamed them for the moral decline of American society.

(I) *The Revolution* was **transient** due to financial problems. The magazine was forced to fold after only two years.

(J) Anthony was so well trusted and respected that the suffragists let her be a **proxy** to represent their views.

Name _____ Date _____ Class _____

EXERCISE 3 *Sentence Completion* ☞

Directions. For each of the following items, circle the letter of the choice that best completes the meaning of the sentence or sentences.

21. The other day, you made a thoughtless, _____ remark about the women's rights movement. The comments seemed to be made _____, as if on a whim, so you decided to set the record straight.
    (A) inane . . . transiently
    (B) contraband . . . politically
    (C) bureaucratic . . . arbitrarily
    (D) inane . . . arbitrarily
    (E) bureaucratic . . . transiently

22. Your _____, carefully chosen remarks strongly impressed your listener.
    (A) arbitrary
    (B) premeditated
    (C) contraband
    (D) transient
    (E) inane

23. You convinced your listener that most feminists are not merely looking for _____ on which to hang the blame for the problems of women.
    (A) browbeaters
    (B) inanities
    (C) scapegoats
    (D) politics
    (E) contraband

24. You pointed out that feminists have worked to promote change through the official channels of the government _____.
    (A) inanity
    (B) scapegoat
    (C) proxy
    (D) contraband
    (E) bureaucracy

25. For example, in 1977, President Carter chose Gloria Steinem to sit on the National Committee on the Observance of International Women's Year. His choice was not _____; it was carefully _____, or thought out, based on her impressive reputation.
    (A) bureaucratic . . . politic
    (B) browbeaten . . . premeditated
    (C) arbitrary . . . premeditated
    (D) inane . . . politic
    (E) transient . . . arbitrary

26. As a woman, Steinem feels very strongly about the interests and rights of all women. But in her pursuit of civil and equal rights, she must be _____ and not offend anyone who might help her cause.
    (A) premeditated
    (B) transient
    (C) browbeaten
    (D) arbitrary
    (E) politic

27. Thanks to the women's rights movement, legally, women can no longer be _____, or bullied, for holding jobs that were formerly held only by men. And women should no longer have to hide their views like smugglers carrying _____.
    (A) inane . . . bureaucracy
    (B) browbeaten . . . contraband
    (C) browbeaten . . . scapegoats
    (D) premeditated . . . contraband
    (E) inane . . . proxies

28. Like any special-interest group, the women's rights movement has appointed a few _____ to represent the views of many.
    (A) proxies
    (B) contraband
    (C) scapegoats
    (D) bureaucracies
    (E) inanities

29. Clearly, the movement is not _____; it is likely to continue for a long time.
    (A) arbitrary
    (B) proxied
    (C) transient
    (D) premeditated
    (E) politic

30. Many people have strong opinions about women's rights. The best speakers on the subject express thoughtful, objective views, not _____, _____ ones.
    (A) transient . . . bureaucratic
    (B) inane . . . arbitrary
    (C) arbitrary . . . proxied
    (D) politic . . . premeditated
    (E) premeditated . . . transient

82 LESSON 20

MAKING NEW WORDS YOUR OWN

Lesson 21 | CONTEXT: The Land
John Muir

John Muir (1838–1914) was born in Scotland, but he spent most of his life in the United States. He helped start the conservation movement in the U.S., and throughout his long, active life, Muir worked to preserve nature's beauty. He even guided President Theodore Roosevelt (1858–1919) through California's Yosemite Valley. As a result of his time with the president, his extensive writing, and his work with the Sierra Club, Muir was able to convince Roosevelt and others to preserve many areas, including forests in Colorado, Yosemite National Park, and acres of redwoods now named Muir Woods.

In the following exercises, you will have the opportunity to expand your vocabulary by reading about John Muir. Below are ten Vocabulary Words that will be used in these exercises.

assay	diverge	fiord	subside	unremitting
augment	faction	inherent	taint	vogue

EXERCISE 1 — Wordbusting

Directions. Follow these instructions for this word and the nine words on the next page.
- Figure out the word's meaning by looking at its **context,** its **structure,** and its **sound.** Fill in at least one of the three **CSS** boxes. Alternate which boxes you complete.
- Then, look up the word in a dictionary, read all of its meanings, and write the meaning of the word as it is used in the sentence.
- Follow this same process for each of the Vocabulary Words on the next page. You will need to draw your own map for each word. Use a separate sheet of paper.

1.

(assay) →

> As Muir traveled the country, he assessed the threat that destructive uses of the land posed to different species of plants. For example, in California he **assayed** the destructive effect that improper sheep grazing had on wildflowers.

Context:

Structure:

Sound:

Dictionary:

2.

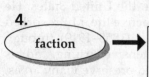

Because Muir thought Americans did not pay enough attention to nature, he wanted to **augment** people's appreciation of beautiful landscapes.

3.

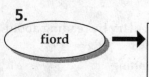

When it came to the issue of redwood forests, Muir saw his ideas of preservation **diverge** from those of business people who wanted to cut down the redwoods for lumber.

4.

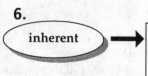

Even though people in the conservation movement agree on basic issues, there are **factions** within the movement because different people want different things.

5.

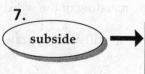

For example, some might argue that the stark beauty of a **fiord** should be easily accessible to tourists, and others might say the inlet and its surrounding cliffs should be reserved for the fish and wildlife that live there.

6.

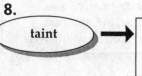

Muir's dedication to nature was an **inherent** part of his personality. From the time he was a small child, he loved to escape to the seashore and revel in the beauty he found there.

7.

Muir's interest in nature never **subsided;** he spent much of his time outdoors up until his death.

8.

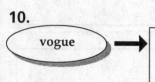

The pattern of preservation begun by Muir has ensured that certain areas have remained **untainted**. Thanks to Muir, attempts to commercialize and spoil many unique areas have been thwarted.

9.

unremitting

His dedication to preservation was consistent and **unremitting**.

10.

vogue

Muir was a pioneer in many ways. He championed conservation long before it was fashionable, or in **vogue**.

EXERCISE 2 *Context Clues*

Directions. Scan the definitions in Column A. Then think about how the boldface words are used in the sentences in Column B. To complete the exercise, match each definition in Column A with the correct Vocabulary Word from Column B. Write the letter of your choice on the line provided; then write the Vocabulary Word on the line preceding the definition.

<table>
<tr><td>

COLUMN A

_____ **11.** word: _____:
n. style; fashion; popularity

_____ **12.** word: _____:
n. a group of people within a larger group, usually causing conflict or disagreement; a selfish or quarrelsome group

_____ **13.** word: _____:
n. an analysis (especially of ore) to determine composition; *v.* to assess or put to a test; to attempt or try

_____ **14.** word: _____:
n. a trace of something bad or harmful, or of contamination or infection; *v.* to infect, corrupt, poison; to spoil; to besmear (someone's name or reputation); to stain

_____ **15.** word: _____:
v. to move or extend in different directions from a common point; to differ in opinion

_____ **16.** word: _____:
adj. inborn, basic, native

_____ **17.** word: _____:
n. a long, narrow inlet of the sea, with steep cliffs rising alongside

_____ **18.** word: _____:
adj. never stopping or slackening; unceasing; constant

_____ **19.** word: _____:
v. to increase; to make greater; to enlarge

_____ **20.** word: _____:
v. to sink or fall to a lower level; to become less active; to wane

</td><td>

COLUMN B

(A) When John Muir was twenty-two years old, his life began to **diverge** from the life of his family. He left the family farm and headed out in a new direction.

(B) He began his lifelong journey to **augment** both his own and other people's understanding of the natural world.

(C) Muir began to travel widely because he realized that the need to study nature was an **inherent** part of who he was; he could no more change his interest than he could change his eye color.

(D) Muir wrote about the earth differently than another **faction** of authors did; he disagreed with those writers who saw nature as an enemy.

(E) He did, however, think nature was unforgiving when people made mistakes—something that must have made a lot of sense to people who had sailed through a narrow Alaskan **fiord** and had seen the threatening cliffs that surrounded them.

(F) His reputation isn't **tainted** today. People admire his dedication to preserving the land.

(G) Muir also developed and tested scientific theories. By recording ice movements, he worked to **assay** his idea that the Yosemite area had once been covered by a glacier.

(H) When he decided to embark on a campaign to save the Yosemite area, Muir was prepared for people's resistance to his plan. He knew that such ideas were not in **vogue**.

(I) Because of his **unremitting** commitment to preservation, even in the face of equally relentless cattlemen and ranchers, Muir eventually triumphed.

(J) While objections to land preservation have not **subsided** today, Muir serves as a role model for everyone who would continue to fight for nature.

</td></tr>
</table>

EXERCISE 3 Sentence Completion ✍

Directions. For each of the following items, circle the letter of the choice that best completes the meaning of the sentence or sentences.

21. Leaving the open sea to sail through a narrow _____ is the type of awe-inspiring experience that led Muir to his _____ commitment to preservation. Muir worked unceasingly to protect such rare beauty.
    - (A) fiord . . . tainted
    - (B) vogue . . . unremitting
    - (C) assay . . . inherent
    - (D) fiord . . . unremitting
    - (E) faction . . . augmented

22. In Muir's day, there were basically only two _____ involved in the conflict over land use. These groups _____ on one major issue—whether to preserve or develop land.
    - (A) factions . . . subsided
    - (B) assays . . . diverged
    - (C) factions . . . diverged
    - (D) fiords . . . assayed
    - (E) inherents . . . remitted

23. Muir _____ the idea that overuse of land destroyed wildlife. One way he tested this theory was by observation.
    - (A) subsided
    - (B) diverged
    - (C) unremitted
    - (D) augmented
    - (E) assayed

24. Muir's writings _____ our society's understanding of how we interact with nature. The current environmental-awareness _____, or fashion, owes Muir a large debt.
    - (A) diverged . . . inherent
    - (B) augmented . . . vogue
    - (C) subsided . . . unremitting
    - (D) assayed . . . vogue
    - (E) remitted . . . faction

25. One wonders if Muir ever saw a landscape he didn't like. Did he think beauty was _____ in all of nature?
    - (A) unremitting
    - (B) augmented
    - (C) assayed
    - (D) vogue
    - (E) inherent

26. Anti-environmentalists' efforts have not _____; in fact, as more old-growth forests are cut down, those who never stop fighting for forests' preservation must sometimes feel that their fight is _____.
    - (A) subsided . . . unremitting
    - (B) diverged . . . unremitting
    - (C) subsided . . . augmented
    - (D) assayed . . . divergent
    - (E) augmented . . . inherent

27. Muir demonstrated early in his life the love of nature that later prompted him to work to keep it free from _____ and destruction.
    - (A) vogue
    - (B) factions
    - (C) augmentation
    - (D) taint
    - (E) diverging

28. John Muir's friendship with Gifford Pinchot ended when their views _____. Pinchot's loyalty was to civilization; Muir's was to pure wilderness.
    - (A) augmented
    - (B) assayed
    - (C) diverged
    - (D) remitted
    - (E) subsided

29. Many believe that Muir influenced President Theodore Roosevelt to _____ wilderness preservation.
    - (A) augment
    - (B) assay
    - (C) subside
    - (D) diverge
    - (E) factionalize

30. Battles over conservation remind us that there are many _____ of the population that depend on the land and that each group has opinions on how best to use it.
    - (A) fiords
    - (B) assays
    - (C) vogues
    - (D) diverges
    - (E) factions

MAKING NEW WORDS YOUR OWN

Lesson 22 | CONTEXT: The Land
Thoreau's Walden Pond

What's so special about a little pond in Concord, Massachusetts? The American naturalist Henry David Thoreau (1817–1862) made Walden Pond famous as the setting for his book *Walden, or Life in the Woods*. Thoreau was a rebel in his time—an independent thinker who decided to find out for himself what life was all about. Few of his contemporaries could understand why he gave up the comforts of town life to spend two years alone in the woods. One who did recognize Thoreau's genius, however, was Ralph Waldo Emerson (1803–1882), the poet and philosopher.

In the following exercises, you will have the opportunity to expand your vocabulary by reading about Henry David Thoreau. Below are ten Vocabulary Words that will be used in these exercises.

abstain	credence	entity	idyll	prototype
catharsis	dissipate	entomology	omnivorous	tepid

EXERCISE 1 — Wordbusting

Directions. Follow these instructions for this word and the nine words on the next page.
- Figure out the word's meaning by looking at its **context,** its **structure,** and its **sound.** Fill in at least one of the three **CSS** boxes. Alternate which boxes you complete.
- Then, look up the word in a dictionary, read all of its meanings, and write the meaning of the word as it is used in the sentence.
- Follow this same process for each of the Vocabulary Words on the next page. You will need to draw your own map for each word. Use a separate sheet of paper.

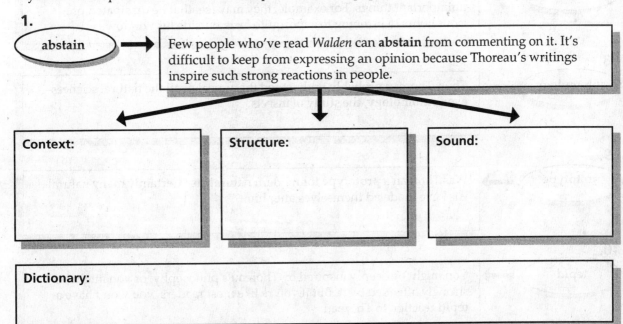

1.

abstain → Few people who've read *Walden* can **abstain** from commenting on it. It's difficult to keep from expressing an opinion because Thoreau's writings inspire such strong reactions in people.

Context:

Structure:

Sound:

Dictionary:

2.

catharsis ➔ One reason to read literature is that it can bring about a **catharsis**. You may experience a purifying release of emotions when you read *Walden*.

3.

credence ➔ Thoreau believed that it was possible to be happy living a simple life in the woods. He gave **credence** to the idea that simpler is better.

4.

idyll ➔ Just as peaceful country life is the subject of an **idyll**, life in the woods is the subject of Thoreau's *Walden*.

5.

omnivorous ➔ Thoreau was **omnivorous** in his study of nature; he eagerly took in everything around him.

6.

entity ➔ Thoreau seemed to believe that every **entity** in the world, from a mosquito to a human being, was worth noticing and studying.

7.

dissipate ➔ Some readers may get the impression that Thoreau wasted his time on unimportant things. For example, they may feel that he **dissipated** precious hours in listening to a mosquito buzz outside his window.

8.

entomology ➔ Thus, Thoreau probably understood the appeal of all the natural sciences— even **entomology**, the study of insects.

9.

prototype ➔ Was Thoreau a **prototype** for modern naturalists? Certainly many naturalists have modeled themselves after him.

10.

tepid ➔ You might be deeply inspired by Thoreau's philosophy, or you might be strongly offended by it. But if you're like most readers, you won't have a **tepid** reaction to Thoreau.

EXERCISE 2 — *Context Clues*

Directions. Scan the definitions in Column A. Then think about how the boldface words are used in the sentences in Column B. To complete the exercise, match each definition in Column A with the correct Vocabulary Word from Column B. Write the letter of your choice on the line provided; then write the Vocabulary Word on the line preceding the definition.

COLUMN A

_____ **11.** word: _____:

v. to choose to do without; to refrain from

_____ **12.** word: _____:

n. the branch of zoology that deals with insects

_____ **13.** word: _____:

adj. slightly warm; lukewarm; lacking warmth of feeling or enthusiasm

_____ **14.** word: _____:

n. an original model on which subsequent forms are based; a standard example

_____ **15.** word: _____:

n. belief; acceptance as valid or true

_____ **16.** word: _____:

adj. eating every kind of food, both animal and vegetable; eagerly taking in everything

_____ **17.** word: _____:

n. a short description of peaceful country life; a scene suitable for such a work

_____ **18.** word: _____:

n. a purging; a purifying by ridding of emotions, especially through the experience of art

_____ **19.** word: _____:

v. to spread in every direction; to scatter; to waste

_____ **20.** word: _____:

n. a being; something with independent existence, either in actuality or in one's mind; a discrete unit

COLUMN B

(A) Like an **omnivorous** animal eating every kind of food, Thoreau was hungry for all kinds of knowledge.

(B) Walden Pond, the rural setting for Thoreau's intellectual journey, was peaceful enough to be the subject of an **idyll**.

(C) For two years Thoreau **abstained** from contact with the hustle and bustle of ordinary life. But he didn't refrain from his favorite activity, writing.

(D) Journal writing was often a **catharsis** for Thoreau; he poured out his feelings onto paper.

(E) Taken separately, Thoreau's journal entries might have looked like random, unconnected scribblings. Yet Thoreau eventually unified them into a single **entity**, *Walden*.

(F) The important insights that Thoreau gained at Walden lend **credence** to his idea that contact with nature refreshes the mind and spirit.

(G) Later generations judged Thoreau to be a great man, but his neighbors thought of him as an extremely impractical person. They couldn't understand why he **dissipated** his energies on pursuits that didn't make any money.

(H) They were probably amazed that he spent so much time on **entomology**. "Why bother studying insects?" they might have asked.

(I) In the 1840s, Thoreau refused to pay his state taxes because Massachusetts didn't oppose slavery. His refusal to obey a law he didn't believe in has been held up as a **prototype**, or standard example, of civil disobedience.

(J) It would have been easier to pay the tax than to spend a night in jail as Thoreau did. But rather than live a **tepid**, halfhearted life, Thoreau chose to stand up for his beliefs, no matter what the consequences.

EXERCISE 3 Sentence Completion ☞

Directions. For each of the following items, circle the letter of the choice that best completes the meaning of the sentence or sentences.

21. Today, Concord is not quite the _____ setting that Thoreau enjoyed in the 1800s. But the city has kept Walden Pond peaceful by making it a nature preserve.

(A) prototypical
(B) tepid
(C) omnivorous
(D) dissipated
(E) idyllic

22. In the 1980s, Thoreau's admirers fought to keep developers from putting a tall building near Walden Pond. The developers agreed to _____ from building there.

(A) dissipate
(B) abstain
(C) waste
(D) create
(E) indulge

23. Bathing in Walden Pond in the early spring must have been a sort of _____ for Thoreau; far from _____, the water is so cold that it could drive out every troubled thought and feeling from a person's head.

(A) credence . . . tepid
(B) catharsis . . . omnivorous
(C) catharsis . . . tepid
(D) credence . . . idyllic
(E) prototype . . . omnivorous

24. In the early morning, Thoreau was _____, taking in every sight and sound. He gave _____ to the idea that morning is a time for refreshing the senses.

(A) omnivorous . . . idyll
(B) tepid . . . credence
(C) omnivorous . . . credence
(D) idyllic . . . dissipation
(E) dissipated . . . entity

25. Thoreau thought that a person's energies tend to _____, or become scattered, during the day.

(A) abstain
(B) dissipate
(C) become tepid
(D) be idyllic
(E) give credence

26. Like a careful _____ studying a textbook _____ of an ant colony, Thoreau studied Walden Pond as a model community.

(A) entity . . . credence
(B) entomologist . . . idyll
(C) prototype . . . entomology
(D) entomologist . . . prototype
(E) entity . . . catharsis

27. In "Walden—1954," E. B. White doesn't _____ from giving his opinion of *Walden.* White's excellent reputation as a critic gives _____ to his claim that *Walden* is one of the greatest works of American literature.

(A) abstain . . . credence
(B) abstain . . . tepidness
(C) dissipate . . . idyll
(D) dissipate . . . credence
(E) abstain . . . catharsis

28. White points out that *Walden* is not just a peaceful _____ on the joys of rural life; it also includes social criticism.

(A) prototype
(B) credence
(C) entomology
(D) catharsis
(E) idyll

29. Thoreau was a sort of _____ for people who want to trade worldly cares for a peaceful life with nature. Thoreau is an excellent model of someone who created a simple life in an _____ setting.

(A) prototype . . . omnivorous
(B) credence . . . omnivorous
(C) prototype . . . idyllic
(D) entity . . . idyllic
(E) idyll . . . entomological

30. Thoreau believed each person was a unique _____. He said his own mission was "to observe what transpires, not in the street, but in the mind and heart of me!"

(A) catharsis
(B) abstinence
(C) entity
(D) credence
(E) entomology

MAKING NEW WORDS YOUR OWN

Lesson 23 | CONTEXT: The Land

Loren Eiseley's Spiritual Ecology

As an anthropologist, naturalist, and writer, Loren Eiseley (1907–1977) bridged the gap between science and poetry. Eiseley completed demanding scientific training and a great deal of hands-on fieldwork as an anthropologist; yet he always maintained a questioning spirit and a sense of awe for the mystery of life. Eiseley's ecology was based on his wide knowledge of the earth's history, as well as on his philosophical view of humanity. In the simplest terms, Eiseley believed that before we could understand our relationship to the environment, we had to understand ourselves.

In the following exercises, you will have the opportunity to expand your vocabulary by reading about Loren Eiseley. Below are ten Vocabulary Words that will be used in these exercises.

apprise	bestow	correlate	enormity	recrimination
austere	camaraderie	elation	exhaustive	undermine

EXERCISE 1 *Wordbusting* ✍

Directions. Follow these instructions for this word and the nine words on the next page.
- Figure out the word's meaning by looking at its **context,** its **structure,** and its **sound.** Fill in at least one of the three **CSS** boxes. Alternate which boxes you complete.
- Then, look up the word in a dictionary, read all of its meanings, and write the meaning of the word as it is used in the sentence.
- Follow this same process for each of the Vocabulary Words on the next page. You will need to draw your own map for each word. Use a separate sheet of paper.

1.

(apprise) ➡ In his essay "The Naturalist's Vision," Loren Eiseley **apprises,** or informs, readers about the threat that humanity poses to the earth.

Context:

Structure:

Sound:

Dictionary:

2.

 **austere** ➤ Eiseley echoes philosopher Francis Bacon's stern caution about the dangers of knowledge without wisdom. Despite his **austere** warning, Eiseley also reminds us of humanity's rich potential.

3.

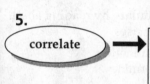 **bestow** ➤ Eiseley argues that the world was forever changed when humankind was **bestowed** with the power of reasoning. This gift sets us apart from all other creatures of the earth.

4.

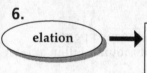 **camaraderie** ➤ As reasoning animals, we humans lost a certain **camaraderie** with other living things—that is, we no longer have the same fellowship with them.

5.

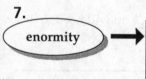 **correlate** ➤ Is it possible to **correlate** scientific study of the earth with a spiritual sense of the miracle of creation? Eiseley believed it was not only possible but also necessary to put the two in relation to each other.

6.

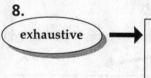 **elation** ➤ In his essay, Eiseley seems to suggest that we should not feel too much **elation** about the progress our species has made. Before we feel joyful about our triumphs, we should look at what we might have lost along the way.

7.

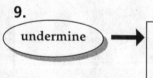 **enormity** ➤ Eiseley's essay points out a contrast between the **enormity** of our harmful effect on the planet and the goodness of our most precious gift, the human imagination.

8.

exhaustive ➤ For a more **exhaustive** description of Eiseley's philosophy, you might read his first book, *The Immense Journey*. He takes readers on a journey from prehistoric Earth to the future of the human race, leaving nothing out in between.

9.

undermine ➤ Eiseley points out that humanity has not been careful in its application of scientific knowledge. The cost of this lack of caution is an **undermined**, unstable, and threatened planet.

10.

 **recrimination** ➤ Eiseley was known for his criticism of the strict scientific method most anthropologists used. Some fellow scientists responded with **recriminations** and accused Eiseley, in turn, of not being a true scientist.

EXERCISE 2 *Context Clues* 👉

Directions. Scan the definitions in Column A. Then think about how the boldface words are used in the sentences in Column B. To complete the exercise, match each definition in Column A with the correct Vocabulary Word from Column B. Write the letter of your choice on the line provided; then write the Vocabulary Word on the line preceding the definition.

COLUMN A	COLUMN B

_____ **11.** word: _____:

n. extreme wickedness; outrageousness; vastness

_____ **12.** word: _____:

n. the spirit of goodwill, loyalty, and understanding among friends; good fellowship

_____ **13.** word: _____:

v. to inform; to notify; to give notice to

_____ **14.** word: _____:

n. the act of making an accusation in return; a counteraccusation

_____ **15.** word: _____:

adj. leaving out nothing; thorough, comprehensive

_____ **16.** word: _____:

v. to dig from beneath; to wear away and weaken the supports of; to weaken or injure, especially by guileful means

_____ **17.** word: _____:

n. high spirits; a feeling of exaltation due to relief or triumph

_____ **18.** word: _____:

adj. stern; strict; severe in appearance or manner; plain or simple

_____ **19.** word: _____:

n. one of two related things, especially if one implies the other; *v.* to bring into mutual relation with another thing

_____ **20.** word: _____:

v. to confer or present as a gift or an honor; to apply or dedicate for a purpose

(A) Your science teacher has just **apprised** you of your next assignment: an essay about a well-known scientist. After being informed about the assignment, you decide to research the life of Loren Eiseley.

(B) You discover that the young Eiseley was very withdrawn and cautious around people. Perhaps young Eiseley's personality was **undermined** partly by an unhappy family life.

(C) Although generally shy and lonely, Eiseley did have some **camaraderie** with other children. For example, he had a good friend named "Rat" with whom he often went exploring.

(D) His family's life style was **austere;** they could afford little beyond the plain necessities.

(E) In his autobiography, *All the Strange Hours,* Eiseley explained that the vastness of the Great Plains helped shape his character. He was moved by the **enormity** of the Nebraska landscape.

(F) In his poetry, he would **correlate** his abstract ideas with imagery of the Great Plains. This balanced relationship between the general and the specific was important in all of his writing.

(G) As a child, Eiseley **bestowed** great effort on teaching himself to read. In fact, he was so dedicated to it that he was reading long before most children start to learn.

(H) Eiseley taught himself to read after his half-brother read *Robinson Crusoe* to him. Imagine his **elation** when he could finally read it himself!

(I) In college, Eiseley once wrote a poem on an exam instead of the required essay. He indirectly accused the professor of choosing a boring topic; yet instead of responding with a **recrimination,** the teacher gave Eiseley an "A."

(J) Eiseley led such a full life that an **exhaustive** account of it would take hours, but at least you've learned a few interesting parts.

EXERCISE 3 Sentence Completion

Directions. For each of the following items, circle the letter of the choice that best completes the meaning of the sentence or sentences.

21. In 1931, after taking part in several archaeological digs, Loren Eiseley was accepted to the South Party of the Morrill Paleontological Expedition. His _____ at such an honor must have been great.

(A) enormity
(B) correlation
(C) elation
(D) bestowal
(E) recrimination

22. He took part in the South Party's _____ field expeditions in Nebraska. The thorough examination of fossil records was a strict, _____ discipline.

(A) exhaustive . . . elated
(B) austere . . . undermined
(C) recriminating . . . exhaustive
(D) exhaustive . . . austere
(E) recriminating . . . elated

23. Eiseley joked that he might turn into a yucca plant. Spending days on the bare, _____ hillsides may suggest its _____ as something taking root in the ground.

(A) austere . . . correlate
(B) exhaustive . . . correlate
(C) austere . . . apprise
(D) exhaustive . . . bestow
(E) undermined . . . bestow

24. Eiseley _____ much energy on anthropology, eventually earning a Ph.D.

(A) apprised
(B) elated
(C) recriminated
(D) correlated
(E) bestowed

25. In 1948, he began a book that would take readers on a journey through time. Because of the _____ of the subject, Eiseley took ten years to complete *The Immense Journey.*

(A) elation
(B) exhaustion
(C) apprisal
(D) enormity
(E) correlation

26. Some publishers were cautious about the book, perhaps because it seemed too _____, or comprehensive. But later, when the book became a bestseller, they were probably _____.

(A) elated . . . undermined
(B) exhaustive . . . elated
(C) austere . . . bestowed
(D) exhaustive . . . apprised
(E) elated . . . exhausted

27. In his book, Eiseley _____ the development of mammals to that of flowering plants. He _____, or informs, us that one could not exist without the other.

(A) exhausts . . . bestows
(B) apprises . . . exhausts
(C) correlates . . . apprises
(D) bestows . . . apprises
(E) recriminates . . . bestows

28. Eiseley aimed _____ at scientists who accused him of being unscientific; he, in turn, accused them of ignoring culture.

(A) elation
(B) correlations
(C) austerity
(D) recriminations
(E) apprisals

29. Humans are the only animals _____ with self-consciousness. Eiseley believes this awareness isn't entirely a gift and can actually be _____ to humans. The loneliness and challenges of the human journey make some humans more troubled about life.

(A) bestowed . . . undermining
(B) correlated . . . elate
(C) bestowed . . . correlate
(D) apprised . . . recriminate
(E) apprised . . . undermining

30. Eiseley must have felt a sort of _____ with earlier naturalists, such as Thoreau. Both took a similar, mystical approach to nature.

(A) austerity
(B) recrimination
(C) elation
(D) undermining
(E) camaraderie

MAKING NEW WORDS YOUR OWN

Lesson 24 | CONTEXT: The Land

Urban Landscapes—The New City

Cities have changed a great deal over the past one hundred years, and the next hundred years promise even more change. In 1900, only 15 percent of the population lived in cities; in the year 2000, nearly half of the world's population lived in urban areas. There will be many changes in our daily lives as we deal with the growing urban world.

In the following exercises, you will have the opportunity to expand your vocabulary by reading about the modern city. Below are ten Vocabulary Words that will be used in these exercises.

accost	furtive	permeate	populace	rapacious
appraisal	mercenary	pernicious	proletarian	recalcitrant

EXERCISE 1 Wordbusting ✍

Directions. Follow these instructions for this word and the nine words on the next page.
- Figure out the word's meaning by looking at its **context,** its **structure,** and its **sound.** Fill in at least one of the three **CSS** boxes. Alternate which boxes you complete.
- Then, look up the word in a dictionary, read all of its meanings, and write the meaning of the word as it is used in the sentence.
- Follow this same process for each of the Vocabulary Words on the next page. You will need to draw your own map for each word. Use a separate sheet of paper.

1.

(accost) → In the hustle and bustle of the modern city, it is not uncommon for a stranger to **accost** you on the street with a request for directions or a sales pitch.

Context:	Structure:	Sound:

Dictionary:

2.

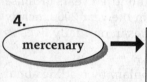

Realizing that new experiences are not necessarily bad can lead to a positive **appraisal** of life in the city—crowds and all.

3.

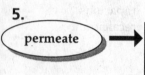

First-time visitors to the city may try to hide their excitement by casting only **furtive** glances at the awesome skyscrapers.

4.

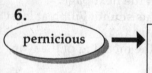

In the city, there are **mercenary** people who take advantage of others in need of housing or food by making them pay much more than the goods are worth; but most people, like people everywhere, are apt to be kind and generous.

5.

The fast pace of city life **permeates** every activity and place; you can sense the excitement everywhere you go.

6.

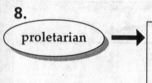

If urban planners do their jobs well, **pernicious** problems, like pollution that refuses to go away, will be solved.

7.

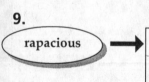

Perhaps the most exciting aspect of a city is the ethnically and racially diverse **populace** that inhabits it. Such diversity reflects the promise the city holds for people of all cultures and backgrounds.

8.

While most people were farmers when the population was centered in the countryside, we have a more varied workforce in cities, from **proletarian** workers to artists to wealthy bankers.

9.

rapacious

All these different people living close to one another means that cooperation and fairness is needed in the city; there is no room for **rapacious** people who try to take more than their share.

10.

recalcitrant

While some cities have resisted modernization, even the most **recalcitrant** communities eventually recognize that urban planners can help improve living conditions.

EXERCISE 2 *Context Clues* 👈

Directions. Scan the definitions in Column A. Then think about how the boldface words are used in the sentences in Column B. To complete the exercise, match each definition in Column A with the correct Vocabulary Word from Column B. Write the letter of your choice on the line provided; then write the Vocabulary Word on the line preceding the definition.

COLUMN A

_____ **11.** word: _____:
adj. stealthy; secretive; sneaky

_____ **12.** word: _____:
adj. desiring money only; greedy; *n.* a paid soldier who will fight for any country for money

_____ **13.** word: _____:
v. to pass through openings or pores; to penetrate; to spread throughout

_____ **14.** word: _____:
v. to approach someone and speak first

_____ **15.** word: _____:
n. the masses; the common people; a population

_____ **16.** word: _____:
adj. greedy; plundering

_____ **17.** word: _____:
adj. stubbornly disobedient; defiant; difficult to deal with

_____ **18.** word: _____:
n. an expert valuation; an assessment; an estimate of quality or quantity

_____ **19.** word: _____:
adj. of or belonging to the working class; *n.* a person belonging to the working class

_____ **20.** word: _____:
adj. very harmful; highly injurious; evil; causing moral harm

COLUMN B

(A) Two hundred years ago, the world's **populace** was relatively small, and most people worked on farms.

(B) There were few opportunities to earn money, but one of these was to be hired as a **mercenary** in the wars of other countries.

(C) People mostly worked just to feed themselves; these **proletarians** did not have much money.

(D) In the nineteenth century, during the Industrial Revolution, machines began to make peoples' lives easier and opened up opportunities. Greed led some **rapacious** businesspeople to build vast fortunes at the expense of others. But many people became wealthy through honest labor.

(E) The rapid growth of cities around the turn of the century took on the energy of a steam train that would not be stopped; even the most **recalcitrant** city dwellers were swept up in the changes.

(F) The use of reinforced concrete changed the face of contemporary architecture as bigger and taller buildings began to **permeate** the landscape of most cities.

(G) One of the most serious urban problems at the turn of the century was the **pernicious** illnesses of people living in overpopulated sections of the cities.

(H) Epidemics of typhoid and other contagious diseases devastated entire communities. These diseases were a **furtive** enemy; without warning, they entered and spread through neighborhoods.

(I) Today, most urban planners include sunlight and trees in their designs. Few would dare **accost** a city dweller with a proposal that left out either of these elements.

(J) Many improvements have been made in urban living. If you make a careful **appraisal** of city life, your assessment may reveal that in some ways city life is better today than ever before.

Name _____ Date _____ Class _____

EXERCISE 3 Sentence Completion ✍

Directions. For each of the following items, circle the letter of the choice that best completes the meaning of the sentence or sentences.

21. The inhabitants of cities in the United States are not like those in other parts of the world; the mix of cultures makes the U.S. _____ unique.
  - (A) proletarian
  - (B) populace
  - (C) mercenary
  - (D) appraisal
  - (E) rapaciousness

22. Many people wanted to claim political control over the cities, but the most _____ and _____ people were the ones who took advantage of others to gain power.
  - (A) proletarian . . . pernicious
  - (B) rapacious . . . mercenary
  - (C) furtive . . . recalcitrant
  - (D) appraised . . . permeated
  - (E) populated . . . furtive

23. Although many immigrants arrived legally in the early twentieth century, later laws restricting immigration forced others to sneak into the country _____.
  - (A) perniciously
  - (B) mercenarily
  - (C) rapaciously
  - (D) furtively
  - (E) recalcitrantly

24. Although many have moved to the city, a longing for rural life _____ the country. This widespread attitude is not realistic, but it _____ refuses to fade from the public consciousness.
  - (A) accosts . . . rapaciously
  - (B) permeates . . . furtively
  - (C) populates . . . perniciously
  - (D) appraises . . . proletarian
  - (E) permeates . . . recalcitrantly

25. During the Industrial Revolution, cities were home to a huge _____ workforce that worked for low wages.
  - (A) pernicious
  - (B) mercenary
  - (C) furtive
  - (D) populace
  - (E) proletarian

26. The _____ of high crime rates in many U.S. cities threatens peoples' lives every day.
  - (A) rapaciousness
  - (B) perniciousness
  - (C) recalcitrancy
  - (D) furtiveness
  - (E) appraisal

27. Urban landscapes do, however, offer positive experiences, including a widely varied _____. A careful _____ of city life shows the value of living with many different kinds of people.
  - (A) proletariat . . . appraisal
  - (B) populace . . . appraisal
  - (C) rapaciousness . . . accosting
  - (D) perniciousness . . . furtiveness
  - (E) mercenariness . . . permeated

28. Being _____ by unfamiliar cultures and faced with new experiences can be unsettling to a new arrival in the city.
  - (A) appraised
  - (B) permeated
  - (C) accosted
  - (D) populated
  - (E) mercenary

29. Urban renewal often threatens older neighborhoods, and people who have lived in them for a long time can be _____ about the changes. They resent the _____ of developers whose main concern is profit, not people.
  - (A) mercenary . . . proletarians
  - (B) furtive . . . populace
  - (C) pernicious . . . permeability
  - (D) recalcitrant . . . rapaciousness
  - (E) proletarian . . . furtiveness

30. An important part of urban development is land _____, which tells people the value of their property.
  - (A) rapaciousness
  - (B) permeability
  - (C) appraisal
  - (D) furtiveness
  - (E) recalcitrance

98 LESSON 24

MAKING NEW WORDS YOUR OWN

Lesson 25 | CONTEXT: The Land

Changes in the Literary Landscape of the United States

The Industrial Revolution had a great impact on the growth of the United States and on American culture and literature. Critic Leo Marx noted images of industrialization in the writings of early American writers Ralph Waldo Emerson (1803–1882), Henry David Thoreau (1817–1862), and Nathaniel Hawthorne (1804–1864). Marx believes that these writers' works reflect a new development in American culture—a conflict between technology and the American landscape.

In the following exercises, you will have the opportunity to expand your vocabulary by reading about writers' views of the changing American landscape. These ten Vocabulary Words will be used.

acquisition	brusque	microcosm	tenacity	ulterior
alleviate	debacle	rigorous	thwart	wily

EXERCISE 1 *Wordbusting*

Directions. Follow these instructions for this word and the nine words on the next page.
- Figure out the word's meaning by looking at its **context,** its **structure,** and its **sound.** Fill in at least one of the three **CSS** boxes. Alternate which boxes you complete.
- Then, look up the word in a dictionary, read all of its meanings, and write the meaning of the word as it is used in the sentence.
- Follow this same process for each of the Vocabulary Words on the next page. You will need to draw your own map for each word. Use a separate sheet of paper.

1.

(acquisition) ⟶ The **acquisition** of the technology of the steam engine was essential to the expansion of the United States; having the means to build a railway was the key to industrial development.

Context:

Structure:

Sound:

Dictionary:

2.

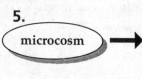

The inconvenience of long-distance travel was **alleviated** by the railroads because trains could quickly cover many miles.

3.

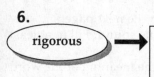

The introduction of technology such as trains led to a **brusque** change in American life: Landscapes were suddenly transformed, people traveled to the cities, and industry increased.

4.

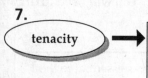

Although technology provided the means to develop the western United States, it also caused a **debacle** in the way we treated the land and the environment.

5.

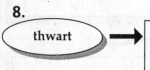

Understanding the threat of technology to the landscape, writers such as Hawthorne, Emerson, and Thoreau observed and wrote about tiny, natural communities as **microcosms** of the larger world.

6.

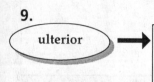

The importance these early writers placed on nature led to their **rigorous** defense of the land and severe criticism of technology as the world became more mechanized.

7.

Thoreau demonstrated much **tenacity** when he left society to live in a cabin on Walden Pond. There, he steadfastly pursued a life of solitude and closeness to nature.

8.

Thoreau feared that the railroad and accompanying urban growth would **thwart** the American ideal of living close to the land.

9.

Hawthorne seems to have had an **ulterior** motive in using railroad imagery in his fiction; critics claim he was really examining new cultural changes and tensions.

10.

A **wily** writer, Hawthorne often used seemingly innocent imagery in his stories to suggest slyly hidden meanings.

EXERCISE 2 *Context Clues* 🖎

Directions. Scan the definitions in Column A. Then think about how the boldface words are used in the sentences in Column B. To complete the exercise, match each definition in Column A with the correct Vocabulary Word from Column B. Write the letter of your choice on the line provided; then write the Vocabulary Word on the line preceding the definition.

COLUMN A	COLUMN B

COLUMN A

_____ **11.** word: _____:
adj. abrupt in manner or speech; blunt

_____ **12.** word: _____:
n. a miniature world; a small system or community regarded as representative of a larger world

_____ **13.** word: _____:
n. the act of obtaining something, especially as an addition to a larger collection; something obtained

_____ **14.** word: _____:
n. a sudden collapse or overthrow; an overwhelming defeat; a rout

_____ **15.** word: _____:
adj. crafty; sly; guileful; full of trickery or stratagems

_____ **16.** word: _____:
adj. beyond what is seen or expressed; intentionally concealed in order to deceive

_____ **17.** word: _____:
v. to calm; to ease suffering of the body or mind

_____ **18.** word: _____:
n. perseverance; persistence; cohesiveness

_____ **19.** word: _____:
v. to oppose; to keep from doing something; to obstruct or hinder

_____ **20.** word: _____:
adj. very strict; exact; difficult and demanding; severe; strenuous

COLUMN B

(A) Images of nature have always been used to describe the spirit of the United States, and as each new land **acquisition** expanded its borders, different geographies were added to the landscape.

(B) Writers like Hawthorne and Thoreau spent much of their time in the American countryside. There, they might examine the **microcosm** of a beehive or an anthill as a reflection of life on a grand scale.

(C) Even as the U.S. became more industrialized, these writers maintained a strict, **rigorous** use of nature images to reflect the national consciousness.

(D) Gradually, images of industry began to invade the writers' landscape, and Hawthorne began to write of the locomotive's "shriek" piercing the serenity of nature—a **debacle** to those who sought peace and quiet in the country.

(E) The **brusque** nature of a life governed by the abrupt rhythms of machines was a rich topic for these writers.

(F) The **tenacity** of Hawthorne's and Thoreau's commitment to images of nature tells us how important it was for them to preserve nature from technology.

(G) Hawthorne and Thoreau were skilled, even **wily**, writers. Both devised sly strategies to convey to the nation the importance of the land.

(H) Technology threatened to destroy nature as an image; Thoreau worked to **thwart** this by writing of natural locations that were separate from any sense of history.

(I) Perhaps Thoreau and Hawthorne wrote such stories because they believed nature could help **alleviate** the sufferings of a world dominated by machines.

(J) In any case, expressing concern about industrialization was often the **ulterior** motive hidden behind the stories and essays Hawthorne and Thoreau wrote.

EXERCISE 3 *Sentence Completion* ✍

Directions. For each of the following items, circle the letter of the choice that best completes the meaning of the sentence or sentences.

21. To calculate the overall effect of this country's _____ of the railroad, one could study the _____ of a small town to see how changes in delivery schedules affected daily life.

(A) thwarting . . . tenacity
(B) acquisition . . . microcosm
(C) alleviating . . . debacle
(D) wiliness . . . rigorousness
(E) acquisition . . . brusqueness

22. Most people thought that technology would _____ many hardships of daily life.

(A) alleviate
(B) thwart
(C) acquire
(D) make brusque
(E) make wily

23. Hawthorne and Thoreau used train imagery as a disruptive force, one with the potential of _____ nature.

(A) alleviating
(B) thwarting
(C) acquiring
(D) appeasing
(E) congratulating

24. The vast American landscape _____ attempts at industrialization since it was too large to cover. However, supporters of technology found creative, sometimes _____ ways to mechanize the country.

(A) alleviated . . . tenacious
(B) thwarted . . . ulterior
(C) debacle . . . rigorous
(D) thwarted . . . wily
(E) brusque . . . acquisition

25. Hawthorne's hidden, _____ motive in using themes of loss and anxiety in his stories may have been to comment on what happens to people once life becomes more _____ and less fluid.

(A) microcosmic . . . rigorous
(B) tenacious . . . wily
(C) brusque . . . tenacious
(D) ulterior . . . brusque
(E) thwarted . . . rigorous

26. These writers were _____ in their persistent use of machine images as a way to write about the changing American landscape.

(A) rigorous
(B) wily
(C) tenacious
(D) brusque
(E) ulterior

27. Emerson tended to view technology not as _____, or disaster, for the natural world, but as a sign of humans' power over the world.

(A) a debacle
(B) a microcosm
(C) an acquisition
(D) an alleviation
(E) a rigorousness

28. In *Walden*, Thoreau writes about living in the woods _____, or strictly, following Emerson's instructions on how to "correctly" live. Thoreau saw his home in the woods as _____ that reflected the truths of the whole world.

(A) tenaciously . . . an acquisition
(B) rigorously . . . a microcosm
(C) wily . . . a debacle
(D) brusquely . . . a tenaciousness
(E) rigorously . . . a brusqueness

29. The literature of Thoreau and Emerson is not just about society's _____ of technology; it is also about how life in the U.S. took on a new shape because of machines.

(A) alleviation
(B) debacle
(C) rigorousness
(D) acquisition
(E) microcosm

30. Industrialization was not the _____ feared by some, nor was it the cure-all hoped for by others.

(A) acquisition
(B) brusqueness
(C) debacle
(D) microcosm
(E) alleviation

MAKING NEW WORDS YOUR OWN

Lesson 26 | CONTEXT: The Land

Gary Snyder: A Poet Responds to the Environment

Gary Snyder (b. 1930) has a rich store of personal experiences to draw on for his poems. He has been a logger, a timber scaler, a forest-fire lookout, and a seaman on a tanker. After studying anthropology at Reed College and Oriental languages at the University of California at Berkeley, he lived in Japan for a number of years. Snyder has published many books of poems, including translations of Japanese poetry. Snyder has also been an active conservationist since the late 1960s, and his poetry often reflects his love of the wilderness and his deep respect for the environment.

In the following exercises, you will have the opportunity to expand your vocabulary by reading about Gary Snyder. Below are ten Vocabulary Words that will be used in these exercises.

arduous	enthrall	impetuous	oracular	sluice
deluge	grandiose	insatiable	platitude	synchronize

EXERCISE 1   *Wordbusting* ✍

Directions. Follow these instructions for this word and the nine words on the next page.
- Figure out the word's meaning by looking at its **context,** its **structure,** and its **sound.** Fill in at least one of the three **CSS** boxes. Alternate which boxes you complete.
- Then, look up the word in a dictionary, read all of its meanings, and write the meaning of the word as it is used in the sentence.
- Follow this same process for each of the Vocabulary Words on the next page. You will need to draw your own map for each word. Use a separate sheet of paper.

1.

(arduous) → Gary Snyder's poems sound so natural that one can hardly believe writing is an **arduous** task for him. Yet Snyder puts much effort into crafting his poems.

Context:	**Structure:**	**Sound:**

Dictionary:

2.
deluge → Snyder often **deluges** the reader with a flood of rich images.

3.
enthrall → You might be **enthralled** by his poem "Riprap," with its spellbinding blend of abstract ideas and vivid sensory details.

4.
grandiose → Snyder's poems might seem **grandiose** if they weren't firmly grounded in physical experience. His down-to-earth attitude, as well as his sense of humor, helps keep the poems from sounding stuffy.

5.
impetuous → Some of his poems have a slow, deliberate rhythm; others are **impetuous,** as if the poet had galloped full speed to the end of a thought.

6.
insatiable → Snyder's poems reveal an **insatiable** thirst for experiences of the natural world. For example, he describes a simple walk as if he can't get enough of the sights and sounds around him.

7.
oracular → Some of his poems are quite **oracular**—so brief and mysterious that the reader gets only a fragment of an image.

8.
platitude → In writing about himself as a poet, Snyder has explained that he holds very basic values, including a deep respect for the land. He doesn't express these sentiments in **platitudes,** or trite sayings, but rather through striking, original images.

9.
sluice → The artificial structure of poetry provides a passage for the flow of ideas, much as a **sluice** conducts the flow of water.

10.
synchronize → According to Snyder, a poet must look two ways at once: toward the human world and toward the natural world. It is not always easy to **synchronize,** or coordinate, the two experiences.

EXERCISE 2 *Context Clues* ✍

Directions. Scan the definitions in Column A. Then think about how the boldface words are used in the sentences in Column B. To complete the exercise, match each definition in Column A with the correct Vocabulary Word from Column B. Write the letter of your choice on the line provided; then write the Vocabulary Word on the line preceding the definition.

COLUMN A	COLUMN B

COLUMN A

_____ **11.** word: _____:
adj. moving with great force or speed; acting hastily, rashly, or on impulse

_____ **12.** word: _____:
v. to cause to occur at the same time; to cause to agree in rate or speed; to coordinate

_____ **13.** word: _____:
adj. difficult; requiring much effort; laborious

_____ **14.** word: _____:
n. a dull or commonplace remark made as if it were a new idea; a trite saying

_____ **15.** word: _____:
adj. incapable of being satisfied; greedy

_____ **16.** word: _____:
adj. grand or great in scope, effect, or intent; magnificent; having an affected or absurd notion of splendor; pompous

_____ **17.** word: _____:
v. to captivate; to charm; to keep spellbound

_____ **18.** word: _____:
n. a channel for conducting water; a floodgate; *v.* to wash off with a rush of water

_____ **19.** word: _____:
adj. wise and prophetic; brief and mysterious (remarks)

_____ **20.** word: _____:
n. a great flood; a heavy rainfall; a great amount of something; *v.* to flood; to overwhelm

COLUMN B

(A) A beginning poet often expresses commonplace ideas as if they were new. One way to avoid writing **platitudes** is to focus on personal experiences instead of general truths.

(B) Poets don't have to be **oracular;** in other words, they don't have to say incredibly wise things all the time.

(C) Instead of starting with a **grandiose** statement about life, you might begin a poem with a simple, ordinary detail from your experience.

(D) Gary Snyder begins his poem "The Walk" by saying that it's Sunday and he doesn't have to work. What follows is a **deluge** of concrete images—a flood of specific details about his walk to Benson Lake.

(E) Snyder runs together some of the sentences so that one image flows directly into another. It is as if someone opened a **sluice**—except words pour through the floodgate instead of water.

(F) The speaker's walk is **arduous;** he struggles over huge boulders along a creek bed and almost loses his footing.

(G) The pace of the poem seems to be **synchronized** with the pace of the walk. Thus, the reader moves along at the same rate as the walker, pausing at some places and rushing ahead at others.

(H) Looking down into a dark lake, the speaker seems **enthralled** by some shining trout. They captivate him until he turns his attention to other sights.

(I) On an impulse, he takes a swim when he finally reaches the camp again. Who wouldn't take the **impetuous** leap when faced with a cool stream after a long, dusty walk?

(J) The speaker in "The Walk" has an **insatiable** curiosity about his surroundings. He seems to drink in everything he sees along the way.

EXERCISE 3   *Sentence Completion* ✍

Directions. For each of the following items, circle the letter of the choice that best completes the meaning of the sentence or sentences.

21. How can poets aid the _____ labors of conservationists? Does it seem _____, or affected, for a poet to hope that his words can change the world?

  (A) arduous . . . insatiable
  (B) grandiose . . . insatiable
  (C) grandiose . . . oracular
  (D) arduous . . . grandiose
  (E) synchronized . . . arduous

22. The phrase "the pen is mightier than the sword" has become _____. Yet this cliché reveals the power of writing.

  (A) a deluge
  (B) a platitude
  (C) a sluice
  (D) a synchronization
  (E) an oracle

23. A poet can _____ a reader with just a few well-chosen words. Once you're captivated by a poem, you may become _____ and read all of the poet's work.

  (A) enthrall . . . arduous
  (B) sluice . . . insatiable
  (C) deluge . . . arduous
  (D) synchronize . . . impetuous
  (E) enthrall . . . insatiable

24. Gary Snyder doesn't _____ readers with direct political statements. Instead of overwhelming readers, he expresses his views about the environment gently.

  (A) deluge
  (B) sluice
  (C) enthrall
  (D) synchronize
  (E) satiate

25. Snyder's conservationist views are tied to his appreciation for the sweeping, _____ beauty of nature. It's not difficult to see how these two ideas might be _____, or expressed at the same time, in a poem.

  (A) grandiose . . . enthralled
  (B) impetuous . . . synchronized
  (C) arduous . . . deluged
  (D) grandiose . . . synchronized
  (E) oracular . . . deluged

26. In the poem "Oil," Snyder doesn't _____ blurt out his opinion that the world is too dependent on oil. Instead, in the last stanza he gives a brief, almost _____ image of nations crazed by their need for oil.

  (A) arduously . . . oracular
  (B) impetuously . . . oracular
  (C) grandiosely . . . synchronized
  (D) arduously . . . arduous
  (E) insatiably . . . enthralled

27. Snyder sees natural beauty in everyday acts—even as he _____ dirt from his hands after gardening.

  (A) satiates
  (B) deluges
  (C) synchronizes
  (D) sluices
  (E) enthralls

28. Like Emerson and Thoreau, Snyder expresses his knowledge of the mysteries of nature. His poetry has _____ quality; it is full of the wisdom he's learned from the land.

  (A) a grandiose
  (B) an arduous
  (C) an impetuous
  (D) an oracular
  (E) an insatiable

29. It has become a _____ to say that _____ greed for energy sources threatens the environment. Yet this commonplace idea is not believed by everyone.

  (A) platitude . . . insatiable
  (B) sluice . . . insatiable
  (C) grandiosity . . . arduous
  (D) platitude . . . enthralling
  (E) grandiosity . . . impetuous

30. Snyder has received a flood of praise for his books of poetry. This _____ suggests that many people share his concern.

  (A) grandiosity
  (B) deluge
  (C) platitude
  (D) sluice
  (E) synchronization

MAKING NEW WORDS YOUR OWN

Lesson 27 | CONTEXT: The Land

The Western Frontier

The western frontier of the United States was relatively untouched by Easterners until the discovery of gold and silver drew people to the far west and homesteaders pushed back borders in search of farmland. Since the West seemed uncivilized to the settlers, new social and political structures were invented. These structures defined the frontier in a whole new way. Chief Running Bear reminds us, however, that American Indians adapted to land, instead of adapting the land to their own use.

In the following exercises, you will have the opportunity to expand your vocabulary by reading about the western frontier. Below are ten Vocabulary Words that will be used in these exercises.

abate	effete	inure	propagate	stint
contrition	indolence	presumptuous	protract	wrest

EXERCISE 1 *Wordbusting* ✍

Directions. Follow these instructions for this word and the nine words on the next page.
- Figure out the word's meaning by looking at its **context**, its **structure**, and its **sound**. Fill in at least one of the three **CSS** boxes. Alternate which boxes you complete.
- Then, look up the word in a dictionary, read all of its meanings, and write the meaning of the word as it is used in the sentence.
- Follow this same process for each of the Vocabulary Words on the next page. You will need to draw your own map for each word. Use a separate sheet of paper.

1.

(abate) → Debates over whether the expansion into the western frontier was positive haven't **abated**. The topic is still heatedly discussed today.

Context:	Structure:	Sound:

Dictionary:

2.

contrition ➤ Many people express **contrition** for the terrible way American Indians were treated by settlers.

3.

effete ➤ Judged against the work ethic of an alien culture, American Indians were incorrectly perceived as being **effete**.

4.

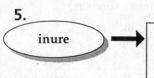 ➤ Often, a homesteader justified taking American Indians land by noting their **indolence** and by claiming that only settlers would work hard enough to make the land produce.

5.

inure ➤ To be sure, people who moved to the western frontier withstood many hardships. They had to **inure** themselves to their harsh environment to survive.

6.

presumptuous ➤ However, it would be **presumptuous** to claim that the settlers suffered while American Indians led comfortable lives; both battled against their harsh environment.

7.

propagate ➤ In fact, both populations adopted similar strategies to survive. For example, they both depended on wildlife to **propagate** at high rates because large numbers of young animals would guarantee good hunting for years.

8.

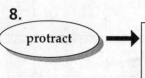 ➤ Anyone living off the land needed to stay healthy and strong; to **protract** an illness over any length of time by not taking care of oneself was asking for trouble.

9.

stint ➤ It was also important to take care of the animals, such as horses and cattle, so the settlers wouldn't have to **stint** on food. Animals were not only used for food; they also helped till the soil for planting crops.

10.

wrest ➤ Indeed, everyone—American Indian or miner or homesteader—had to **wrest** a living from land that was not overly generous.

EXERCISE 2 *Context Clues* ✍

Directions. Scan the definitions in Column A. Then think about how the boldface words are used in the sentences in Column B. To complete the exercise, match each definition in Column A with the correct Vocabulary Word from Column B. Write the letter of your choice on the line provided; then write the Vocabulary Word on the line preceding the definition.

COLUMN A	COLUMN B
_____ **11.** word: _____: *n.* laziness; tendency to avoid work	(A) When settlers headed west, they did not want to **protract** their journeys; they wanted to arrive at their destinations as soon as possible.
_____ **12.** word: _____: *v.* to twist or pull away by force; to seize power; to extract by persistent effort	(B) This impatience was not because of an **indolence** or unwillingness to work; the settlers knew that hard work awaited them.
_____ **13.** word: _____: *v.* to produce offspring; to reproduce; to spread (an idea or belief)	(C) They knew that they would have to serve a certain **stint** before their homesteads could begin to produce enough food. The length of time it would require depended on the soil and climate, among other conditions.
_____ **14.** word: _____: *n.* remorse for wrongdoing; repentance; sorrow for one's sins	(D) Today it would seem **presumptuous** to arrive at a place and build a new society without asking the current inhabitants' permission, but settlers in the 1800s felt it was their right to displace American Indian populations.
_____ **15.** word: _____: *v.* to limit to a certain quantity, usually small; *n.* a limit; an assigned task; a specified amount of time spent doing something	(E) Homesteaders kept moving west partly in search of farmland; poor farming techniques had quickly turned the once-fertile land left behind into **effete**, barren stretches.
_____ **16.** word: _____: *v.* to reduce in amount, degree, or intensity; to lessen; to decrease	(F) Miners kept moving in search of gold or silver. They had to **inure** themselves to constant change as each mine was gradually exhausted.
_____ **17.** word: _____: *adj.* acting without permission or right; arrogant	(G) As more people moved west, stories began to trickle east about life on the frontier; writers like Bret Harte helped **propagate** many ideas that are now the mythology of the West.
_____ **18.** word: _____: *v.* to prolong; to draw out; to lengthen in time	(H) Some individuals of the Wild West, such as "Buffalo Bill" Cody, became myths themselves. One hundred years later, it takes a great effort to **wrest** the truth from the fabulous, fictional stories of the mythical West.
_____ **19.** word: _____: *adj.* no longer able to produce; worn-out; lacking vigor or moral courage; decadent	(I) However, since these stories are now part of American mythology, it's unlikely that any of the tall-tale-tellers would feel **contrition** over their stretching of the truth.
_____ **20.** word: _____: *v.* to accustom or habituate, usually to something undesirable	(J) Americans' fascination with unknown lands will probably never **abate;** just look at how the mystery of outer space now attracts people.

EXERCISE 3 *Sentence Completion* 👈

Directions. For each of the following items, circle the letter of the choice that best completes the meaning of the sentence or sentences.

21. Many settlers ____ believed that they had a right to American Indian lands. To support this arrogant attitude, many ____, or spread, false stories about the Indians.
    - (A) contritely . . . protracted
    - (B) indolently . . . wrested
    - (C) presumptuously . . . propagated
    - (D) effetely . . . inured
    - (E) protractedly . . . abated

22. Some writers and government officials falsely portrayed American Indians as ____ and ____, just the opposite of the moral and hardworking pioneers.
    - (A) presumptuous . . . contrite
    - (B) stinted . . . inured
    - (C) indolent . . . abated
    - (D) protracted . . . propagated
    - (E) indolent . . . effete

23. Today, many citizens express ____ for the mistreatment of American Indians. People now realize the ____ of saying one culture is superior to another.
    - (A) presumptuousness . . . protractedness
    - (B) effeteness . . . indolence
    - (C) contrition . . . propagation
    - (D) indolence . . . contrition
    - (E) contrition . . . presumptuousness

24. Pioneers ____ themselves to hardship. They learned to go without things like sugar or new clothes.
    - (A) abated
    - (B) wrested
    - (C) inured
    - (D) protracted
    - (E) propagated

25. The homesteaders who settled in the rocky plains of Texas faced a(n) ____ battle to ____ a living from the harsh, dry land; they had to work long hours to realize any return on their efforts.
    - (A) propagated . . . protract
    - (B) protracted . . . abate
    - (C) effete . . . inure
    - (D) indolent . . . wrest
    - (E) protracted . . . wrest

26. Lack of control over climate caused many "dust bowl" settlements to fail, but irrigation has finally allowed crops to ____.
    - (A) protract
    - (B) propagate
    - (C) inure
    - (D) wrest
    - (E) abate

27. When the mining of gold and silver in western mines ____, once-thriving mining towns became ghost towns.
    - (A) abated
    - (B) wrested
    - (C) protracted
    - (D) propagated
    - (E) inured

28. In 1871, more than four hundred thousand cattle were driven from Texas to Kansas. Cowboys served long ____ on the trails herding the cattle there for shipment to the East.
    - (A) indolence
    - (B) effetes
    - (C) stints
    - (D) propagation
    - (E) contrition

29. Chief Standing Bear claimed that the meditation and reflection of American Indians was not laziness or ____ behavior, but a process of joining with the universe.
    - (A) propagated
    - (B) presumptuous
    - (C) protracted
    - (D) contrite
    - (E) indolent

30. One frontier myth that will never ____ in importance is the story of Johnny Appleseed. Stories of this roving orchard planter continue to intrigue readers.
    - (A) inure
    - (B) abate
    - (C) propagate
    - (D) protract
    - (E) wrest

110 LESSON 27

MAKING NEW WORDS YOUR OWN

Lesson 28 | CONTEXT: The Land

Environmental Ethics in the United States

For thousands of years, debates about morality have focused solely on the rights of human beings and on our duties to each other. Now, for the first time in the Western world, large numbers of people are talking about the rights of nonhumans—animals, plants, inanimate objects such as rivers and mountains, and the earth as a whole. This view was anticipated in the nineteenth century by people like Henry David Thoreau (1817–1862) and John Muir (1838–1914). At the time, they were not taken seriously, but today, the idea that we owe something to the environment is no longer viewed as foolish or eccentric.

In the following exercises, you will have the opportunity to expand your vocabulary by reading about environmental ethics. Below are ten Vocabulary Words that will be used in these exercises.

abominable	defile	fallible	insular	vegetate
concerted	encroach	innocuous	panacea	vilify

EXERCISE 1 | Wordbusting ✍

Directions. Follow these instructions for this word and the nine words on the next page.
- Figure out the word's meaning by looking at its **context,** its **structure,** and its **sound.** Fill in at least one of the three **CSS** boxes. Alternate which boxes you complete.
- Then, look up the word in a dictionary, read all of its meanings, and write the meaning of the word as it is used in the sentence.
- Follow this same process for each of the Vocabulary Words on the next page. You will need to draw your own map for each word. Use a separate sheet of paper.

1.

(abominable) → Animal rights activists say that the way animals are treated in many research laboratories is **abominable,** but their opponents argue that the suffering of some animals results in medical breakthroughs that benefit humans.

Context:	Structure:	Sound:

Dictionary:

2.

concerted → Most environmentalists agree that the problems facing the planet will be solved only if all countries join together and make a **concerted** attempt to tackle these problems.

3.

defile → When we **defile** the earth, we spoil it, not just for ourselves, but also for future generations.

4.

encroach → Industrial and commercial development projects can **encroach** on the territory of wild animals. Some environmentalists view these intrusions as a form of trespass.

5.

fallible → Because human beings are **fallible,** we often make mistakes in calculating the effects of our actions on the environment.

6.

innocuous → Something that seems **innocuous** today may have a harmful impact on the environment tomorrow.

7.

insular → Environmentalists believe that no country can afford to be **insular** in its attitude to the world's environmental problems; these problems are global and cannot be isolated in any one region.

8.

panacea → Environmentalists do not offer their new ethic as a **panacea** that will solve all our environmental problems overnight.

9.

vegetate → Environmental activists view themselves as people who are not content to **vegetate,** or sit passively, in front of their television sets while the fate of the earth hangs in the balance.

10.

vilify → Animal rights activists complain that some journalists **vilify** them by painting a very unfavorable picture of them as a foolish and extreme fringe group.

112 LESSON 28

EXERCISE 2 *Context Clues* ✍

Directions. Scan the definitions in Column A. Then think about how the boldface words are used in the sentences in Column B. To complete the exercise, match each definition in Column A with the correct Vocabulary Word from column B. Write the letter of your choice on the line provided; then write the Vocabulary Word on the line preceding the definition.

COLUMN A	COLUMN B
_____ **11.** word: _____: *n.* a supposed remedy for all diseases or problems; a cure-all	(A) Environmentalists are not the only ones who are filled with disgust at the sight of a coastline **defiled** by an oil spill.
_____ **12.** word: _____: *adj.* capable of erring or making a mistake	(B) Protecting endangered species requires a **concerted** effort from environmentalists, businesspeople, and politicians. They must all work together to save endangered species.
_____ **13.** word: _____: *adj.* mutually agreed upon; done together; combined	(C) Those who argue for animal rights reject the **insular** attitude that considers only the welfare of human beings. This attitude, they claim, is as narrow-minded as racism.
_____ **14.** word: _____: *v.* to abuse verbally; to slander; to speak badly of	(D) Regulating industrial practices can reduce but not stop the damage to the environment. Since human beings are **fallible**, mistakes are always possible.
_____ **15.** word: _____: *v.* to intrude gradually upon the property or rights of another; to trespass	(E) Every citizen has a choice, say the environmentalists: One can **vegetate** and hope that others will protect the earth or one can fight to save our planet.
_____ **16.** word: _____: *adj.* harmless; having no injurious or adverse effects; lacking impact	(F) The pollution in some cities is **abominable**. Anyone who wants to know how unpleasant it can be should walk around Los Angeles on a muggy day.
_____ **17.** word: _____: *adj.* detestable; horrid; vile; totally unpleasant	(G) The idea that things we do intrude on the rights of animals has been around for some time; however, the idea that it is also possible to **encroach** on the rights of plants is relatively new.
_____ **18.** word: _____: *adj.* having to do with islands or life on an island; isolated; narrow-minded	(H) Few environmentalists believe that science will provide a **panacea** for all our environmental ills. Science, they point out, causes as well as cures our problems.
_____ **19.** word: _____: *v.* to grow or sprout as a plant does; to lead a monotonous, inactive life	(I) Critics of environmentalists argue that their seemingly **innocuous** proposal to respect the environment may have an ill effect on economic growth.
_____ **20.** word: _____: *v.* to spoil; to make disgusting	(J) Environmentalists often speak very badly of those in positions of power; but some say it would make more sense for them to **vilify** the ordinary people whose day-to-day habits create environmental problems.

EXERCISE 3 · *Sentence Completion* 👉

Directions. For each of the following items, circle the letter of choice that best completes the meaning of the sentence or sentences.

21. Some defenders of animal rights predict that the _____ of those who reject nonhumans' rights will come to seem as _____ as the narrow-mindedness of those who once made the same vile claim about people of different races.

    (A) insularity . . . abominable
    (B) panacea . . . concerted
    (C) encroachment . . . fallible
    (D) panacea . . . insular
    (E) abomination . . . innocuous

22. Thoreau was one of the first to criticize the _____, or intrusion, of industrial society upon areas of natural beauty.

    (A) vilification
    (B) vegetation
    (C) abomination
    (D) encroachment
    (E) panacea

23. Many things that originally were thought to be _____ have turned out to be environmental hazards.

    (A) fallible
    (B) concerted
    (C) innocuous
    (D) insular
    (E) abominable

24. If we _____ our wilderness areas, we spoil them for generations to come. This is why environmentalists sometimes _____, or heap abuse on, those they hold responsible.

    (A) vilify . . . defile
    (B) defile . . . vilify
    (C) encroach . . . vegetate
    (D) concert . . . defile
    (E) abominate . . . encroach

25. No one expects to discover _____ for all our environmental problems. They are too complex to allow a simple solution.

    (A) an abomination
    (B) a vilification
    (C) an encroachment
    (D) an insularity
    (E) a panacea

26. Some environmentalists believe that if all nations unite in _____ effort, the quality of life will improve worldwide.

    (A) an innocuous
    (B) a fallible
    (C) a pessimistic
    (D) a concerted
    (E) an abominable

27. Mistakes made by researchers, especially in the field of nuclear energy, have taught us that science can be .

    (A) abominable
    (B) insular
    (C) innocuous
    (D) concerted
    (E) fallible

28. Opponents of the environmental groups have sometimes been able to join together to run _____ campaign aimed at _____ and ridiculing environmentalists.

    (A) an insular . . . vegetating
    (B) a fallible . . . encroaching
    (C) an abominable . . . defiling
    (D) an innocuous . . . vegetating
    (E) a concerted . . . vilifying

29. Animals kept by research laboratories can do nothing except _____ in small cages. But it is not always possible to find cures to diseases in ways that are _____ to laboratory animals.

    (A) vegetate . . . abominable
    (B) defile . . . fallible
    (C) encroach . . . innocuous
    (D) vegetate . . . innocuous
    (E) vilify . . . insular

30. Few habitats on earth have been left untouched. Even the _____ ecosystems of places like Hawaii have been _____ on by the search for minerals or fuel.

    (A) concerted . . . vegetated
    (B) insular . . . vegetated
    (C) insular . . . encroached
    (D) innocuous . . . defiled
    (E) fallible . . . vilified

MAKING NEW WORDS YOUR OWN

Lesson 29 | CONTEXT: The Land

George Washington Carver: Agricultural Pioneer

If you've ever enjoyed peanut butter or sweet-potato pie, you have George Washington Carver to thank! Carver (1864–1943) was an African American botanist and agricultural researcher who revolutionized agriculture in the South. After convincing southern farmers to grow peanuts and sweet potatoes in addition to their cotton crops, he went on to invent dozens of new ways to use these plants. Carver, who was born a slave, was world famous by the time of his death.

In the following exercises, you will have the opportunity to expand your vocabulary by reading about George Washington Carver. Below are ten Vocabulary Words that will be used in these exercises.

attrition	bilateral	flail	impunity	stoic
baleful	entourage	haggard	somnolent	vanquish

EXERCISE 1 *Wordbusting* ✍

Directions. Follow these instructions for this word and the nine words on the next page.
- Figure out the word's meaning by looking at its **context,** its **structure,** and its **sound.** Fill in at least one of the three **CSS** boxes. Alternate which boxes you complete.
- Then, look up the word in a dictionary, read all of its meanings, and write the meaning of the word as it is used in the sentence.
- Follow this same process for each of the Vocabulary Words on the next page. You will need to draw your own map for each word. Use a separate sheet of paper.

1.

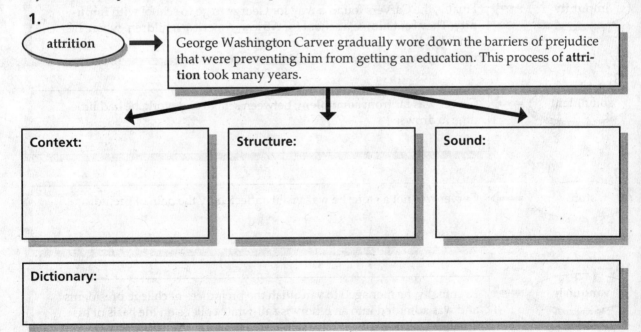

attrition → George Washington Carver gradually wore down the barriers of prejudice that were preventing him from getting an education. This process of **attrition** took many years.

Context:

Structure:

Sound:

Dictionary:

2.

Carver's future seemed dark and unpromising, especially after the **baleful** event of his mother being kidnapped by night raiders when he was just a baby.

3.

Carver was saved by the family his mother had worked for, and a **bilateral,** completely mutual affection developed between George and the Carvers, who also took in his older brother Jim.

4.

Carver wasn't allowed in the Missouri town's all-white school. He must have felt sad watching a more fortunate child walk to school with an **entourage** of friends.

5.

Carver was too frail to work in the fields as his brother did. He couldn't harvest or **flail** grain, so the Carvers gave him lighter work to do in the house.

6.
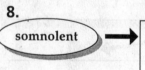
Thus, Carver didn't become **haggard** from overwork; he had energy left to receive what little education the Carvers could give him.

7.
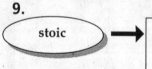
Finally, the Carvers found a way for George to go to school with **impunity**. They sent him to a school for African American children, where he wouldn't be punished for entering the classroom.

8.
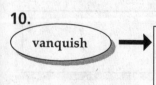
Carver was far from **somnolent;** between school and work, he had little time to drowse.

9.

stoic

Carver was not a **stoic;** he was visibly affected by the pain of prejudice.

10.

vanquish

Eventually, he managed to **vanquish** the prejudices of college presidents and was admitted into an otherwise all-white college on the basis of his intelligence and skills.

EXERCISE 2 *Context Clues*

Directions. Scan the definitions in Column A. Then think about how the boldface words are used in the sentences in Column B. To complete the exercise, match each definition in Column A with the correct Vocabulary Word from Column B. Write the letter of your choice on the line provided; then write the Vocabulary Word on the line preceding the definition.

COLUMN A	**COLUMN B**
_____ **11.** word: _____: *n.* a manual tool used for threshing grain; *v.* to beat or strike at something (as if threshing grain)	(A) At Iowa State College, Carver became so popular that he constantly had an **entourage** of friends around him.
_____ **12.** word: _____: *n.* a person who appears unaffected by pain or pleasure; *adj.* unaffected by pain or pleasure; impassive	(B) Although he had to work at menial jobs to pay for his schooling, he did not become **haggard;** he bloomed in an environment of learning.
_____ **13.** word: _____: *adj.* untamed, unruly; looking worried, tired, or exhausted	(C) Students and professors alike treated him with respect and granted him **impunity** from the sort of discrimination he had so often experienced.
_____ **14.** word: _____: *v.* to conquer; to defeat; to overcome	(D) Carver revealed an unusual talent for growing things; he was able to **vanquish** almost any problem that prevented a healthy, thriving crop.
_____ **15.** word: _____: *adj.* ominous; dire; sinister	(E) He was familiar with the features of many plants; for example, he could easily recognize a plant by the **bilateral** symmetry of the sides of a leaf.
_____ **16.** word: _____: *adj.* sleepy; drowsy; tending to bring on sleepiness	(F) In 1896, Carver became the first African American to earn a graduate degree in agriculture. Afterward, he did not rest or become **somnolent,** but quickly sought work.
_____ **17.** word: _____: *n.* the attendants, followers, or associates of a person	(G) Carver did not have to **flail** at the barriers of prejudice or beat down any doors to find a job. Booker T. Washington offered him a position as head of Tuskegee Institute's agriculture department.
_____ **18.** word: _____: *adj.* having two sides (often symmetrical); undertaken by and affecting two sides equally; mutually binding	(H) Nor did Carver have to rely on **attrition** to open a position for him; the agriculture department was new, so there was no former head whose retirement Carver's position might have depended on.
_____ **19.** word: _____: *n.* freedom from punishment, penalty, or other harm	(I) Instead of just directing his students on how to till soil, Carver drove a plow alongside them. He was **stoic** about this task, and did not let on if his frail body ached from the effort.
_____ **20.** word: _____: *n.* the act of rubbing away, wearing down, or weakening due to friction; loss of personnel due to retirement or death	(J) The closing of Tuskegee Institute would have been a **baleful** circumstance for its students. Carver helped avoid such a dire event by gaining the college official recognition from the United States government.

EXERCISE 3 *Sentence Completion* 👈

Directions. For each of the following items, circle the letter of the choice that best completes the meaning of the sentence or sentences.

21. Carver faced a _____, or dire, problem: The agriculture department could not afford to buy fertilizer. Carver _____ this problem by using other ways to nurture crops.
    (A) haggard . . . flailed
    (B) baleful . . . vanquished
    (C) bilateral . . . flailed
    (D) somnolent . . . vanquished
    (E) stoic . . . vanquished

22. Carver and his _____ of students piled together leaves, weeds, and vegetable peelings to form a rich compost heap. He was the first to promote organic gardening.
    (A) impunity
    (B) attrition
    (C) somnolence
    (D) stoic
    (E) entourage

23. All the steps of producing a crop—from tilling soil to _____, or threshing, grain— involve hard work. Farmers have little time for _____, or drowsing.
    (A) vanquishing . . . stoicism
    (B) flailing . . . somnolence
    (C) vanquishing . . . impunity
    (D) vanquishing . . . balefulness
    (E) flailing . . . haggardness

24. However, Carver's students endured the work _____, with little complaint. Soon, the school's land was yielding record numbers of sweet potatoes.
    (A) haggardly
    (B) balefully
    (C) somnolently
    (D) bilaterally
    (E) stoically

25. Carver pursued with _____ his mission to educate Southern farmers. Far from resenting the intrusion, the _____, overworked farmers gladly took his advice.
    (A) impunity . . . haggard
    (B) attrition . . . stoic
    (C) entourage . . . somnolent
    (D) somnolence . . . bilateral
    (E) impunity . . . baleful

26. Carver soon had a _____, equal relationship with the farmers; they sought him out as often as he sought them out.
    (A) somnolent
    (B) stoic
    (C) bilateral
    (D) haggard
    (E) baleful

27. Carver worked to change the notion that cotton was the South's only reliable cash crop. Throughout the slow process of _____, he convinced farmers to plant peanuts and sweet potatoes as well.
    (A) impunity
    (B) attrition
    (C) entourage
    (D) somnolence
    (E) flailing

28. Carver might have fallen into a _____ lifestyle after he stopped teaching in 1910. Instead, he energetically set out to _____ an important problem: How could the South use its new crops?
    (A) baleful . . . flail
    (B) bilateral . . . vanquish
    (C) stoic . . . flail
    (D) somnolent . . . vanquish
    (E) haggard . . . flail

29. Having converted their fields to peanut patches, the farmers now faced a _____ situation: They couldn't sell the peanuts.
    (A) bilateral
    (B) baleful
    (C) somnolent
    (D) haggard
    (E) stoic

30. Carver's solution was to _____ and grind the peanuts into a powder and then extract the peanut oil from the meal. In other words, he made peanut butter!
    (A) become stoical
    (B) become baleful
    (C) flail
    (D) overcome somnolence
    (E) vanquish

118 LESSON 29

Name _____ Date _____ Class _____

MAKING NEW WORDS YOUR OWN

Lesson 30 | CONTEXT: The Land

Frederick Law Olmsted and the Design of Public Parks

Even if you've never heard of Frederick Law Olmsted (1822–1903), you've probably enjoyed the fruits of his brilliant labors. Olmsted was one of America's first and greatest landscape architects. His most famous landscape designs include Central Park in New York City and the United States Capitol grounds in Washington, D.C. In addition, Olmsted fought to have California's Yosemite Valley declared America's first national park.

In the following exercises, you will have the opportunity to expand your vocabulary by reading about Frederick Law Olmsted. Below are ten Vocabulary Words that will be used in these exercises.

| abut | askew | gradation | indigenous | orient |
| arable | gird | incise | nurture | solstice |

EXERCISE 1 *Wordbusting* ☞

Directions. Follow these instructions for this word and the nine words on the next page.
• Figure out the word's meaning by looking at its **context,** its **structure,** and its **sound.** Fill in at least one of the three **CSS** boxes. Alternate which boxes you complete.
• Then, look up the word in a dictionary, read all of its meanings, and write the meaning of the word as it is used in the sentence.
• Follow this same process for each of the Vocabulary Words on the next page. You will need to draw your own map for each word. Use a separate sheet of paper.

1.

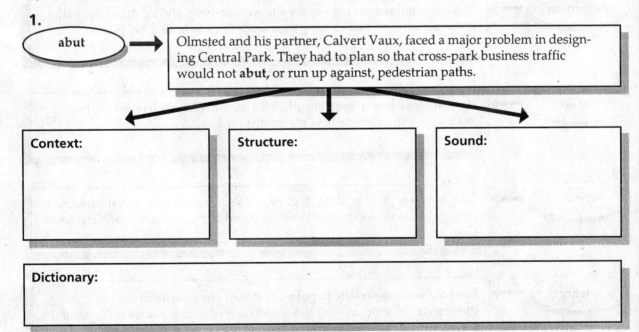

abut

Olmsted and his partner, Calvert Vaux, faced a major problem in design-ing Central Park. They had to plan so that cross-park business traffic would not **abut,** or run up against, pedestrian paths.

Context:

Structure:

Sound:

Dictionary:

MAKING NEW WORDS YOUR OWN   **119**

2.
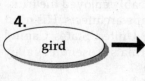
arable

Another basic problem was the 850-acre site chosen for the park. Far from **arable,** the barren soil seemed almost impossible to cultivate.

3.
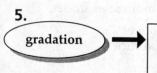
askew

The planners also had to make sure that the areas of the park balanced one another by being laid out in pleasing lines. If something was **askew,** it would take away from the park's beauty.

4.
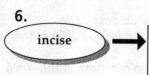
gird

Miles of paths **girded** the various areas of the park so that the public could walk around each area and enjoy its beauty.

5.
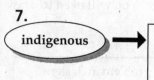
gradation

The **gradations** in the construction progressed slowly, and people came to watch each stage of the process.

6.
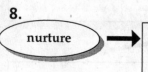
incise

To solve the traffic problem, Olmsted and Vaux decided to **incise** four strips across the park. By cutting deep into the land, they created four business roads that ran below the level of the park.

7.
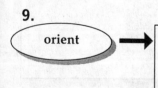
indigenous

The trees **indigenous** to the park site were scrubby and unattractive, so the construction crew had to bring thousands of trees from other places.

8.

nurture

It wasn't easy to **nurture** transplanted vegetation on such poor soil, but with some extra care the new plants survived.

9.

orient

Like an **orient** pearl lending its glow to its surroundings, Central Park lent great luster to the increasingly crowded, industrialized center of New York City.

10.

solstice

Central Park is especially popular on at least one **solstice** of the year. On the first day of summer, you can see all sorts of people enjoying the natural setting.

EXERCISE 2 Context Clues 👈

Directions. Scan the definitions in Column A. Then think about how the boldface words are used in the sentences in Column B. To complete the exercise, match each definition in Column A with the correct Vocabulary Word from Column B. Write the letter of your choice on the line provided; then write the Vocabulary Word on the line preceding the definition.

COLUMN A

_____ **11.** word: _____:
adj. fit for plowing and planting; suitable for cultivation; tillable

_____ **12.** word: _____:
v. to fasten or put a belt or girdle around; to prepare for action; to surround

_____ **13.** word: _____:
v. to cut into; to carve; to engrave

_____ **14.** word: _____:
n. a series of systematic steps or stages; a gradual change from one stage, tone, or shade to another; a transitional stage

_____ **15.** word: _____:
adj. and *adv.* lopsided; awry; not in line

_____ **16.** word: _____:
v. to touch at one end or edge; to join at a boundary

_____ **17.** word: _____:
n. a pearl with great luster; *adj.* lustrous; sparkling; *v.* to position with respect to the points of the compass; to adapt to circumstances

_____ **18.** word: _____:
adj. native to an area; originating in the region or country where found

_____ **19.** word: _____:
v. to bring up; to care for; to feed and nourish; *n.* the act of bringing up and caring for someone

_____ **20.** word: _____:
n. the time of the year when the sun is either farthest north or farthest south of the equator; the first day of summer or winter

COLUMN B

(A) Frederick Law Olmsted didn't change all at once from a good-natured, aimless young man into the country's most famous landscape architect. There were a number of **gradations** in his development.

(B) Olmsted probably inherited his love for beautiful landscapes from his father, who made an extra effort to **nurture,** or bring up, Olmsted after the death of Olmsted's mother.

(C) His father showed him many of the natural wonders of the United States, such as Niagara Falls, as one might show off the **orient** luster of a rare pearl.

(D) Olmsted never did well in his studies; one can imagine he preferred to spend the summer **solstice** roaming the countryside instead of spending the longest day of the year in a stuffy room with one of his tutors.

(E) However, he probably had too much respect for nature to **incise** his name on a tree trunk with a pocketknife, as many children like to do.

(F) Exploring a swamp when he was fourteen, Olmsted touched some poison sumac, a dangerous plant that's **indigenous** to swampy areas.

(G) The poison sumac damaged Olmsted's eyes so badly that his father lost all hope of sending him to Yale. Instead, he tried to **gird,** or prepare, his son for a practical occupation.

(H) After several failed ventures, Olmsted acquired a plot of **arable** land on Staten Island and began farming the fertile soil.

(I) Olmsted became infatuated with Mary Perkins, a young woman who lived near his farm. Although her family's land didn't actually **abut** his, the two homes were close enough that he saw her often.

(J) The straight line to a happy future with Perkins that Olmsted envisioned was thrown **askew** when he realized that his brother was in love with her, too.

EXERCISE 3 Sentence Completion ✍

Directions. For each of the following items, circle the letter of the choice that best completes the meaning of the sentence or sentences.

21. After Olmsted's brother died, Olmsted looked after Mary and ____ her three children. He eventually married her and adopted the children as his own.
    - (A) oriented
    - (B) incised
    - (C) abutted
    - (D) girded
    - (E) nurtured

22. Olmsted became famous in New York City for his prize-winning plan to turn barren land into a green, ____ public park.
    - (A) askew
    - (B) arable
    - (C) incised
    - (D) indigenous
    - (E) orient

23. Olmsted admired how well-tended and ____ Europe's public parks were. He believed that something was ____ about the planning in American cities.
    - (A) incised . . . nurturing
    - (B) abutted . . . orient
    - (C) incised . . . askew
    - (D) nurtured . . . askew
    - (E) girded . . . orient

24. Olmsted didn't ____, or prepare, himself for action right away. The opportunity to plan a public park presented itself by chance.
    - (A) abut
    - (B) gird
    - (C) incise
    - (D) orient
    - (E) nurture

25. While having tea in a hotel, Olmsted's seat ____ that of a planner of Central Park. At the planner's side, Olmsted was able to cut into the conversation as easily as he ____ the steak on his plate.
    - (A) girded . . . incised
    - (B) gradated . . . nurtured
    - (C) abutted . . . incised
    - (D) nurtured . . . gradated
    - (E) oriented . . . nurtured

26. The planner was impressed with Olmsted's knowledge of the ____, or steps, involved in constructing and operating a large public park.
    - (A) gradations
    - (B) incisions
    - (C) girders
    - (D) solstice
    - (E) nurturing

27. Olmsted quickly ____ himself to the topic, as one might position oneself with respect to north and south on the winter or summer ____.
    - (A) gradated . . . orient
    - (B) oriented . . . gradation
    - (C) nurtured . . . solstice
    - (D) incised . . . orient
    - (E) oriented . . . solstice

28. Olmsted had many skills necessary to build a public park: He knew how to make infertile land ____ and how to transplant plants that weren't ____ to an area.
    - (A) orient . . . arable
    - (B) askew . . . nurturing
    - (C) arable . . . indigenous
    - (D) askew . . . arable
    - (E) arable . . . orient

29. After he became superintendent, Olmsted's ____ enabled him to cut through tangled political intrigues.
    - (A) orientation
    - (B) gradation
    - (C) arability
    - (D) incisiveness
    - (E) nurturing

30. After Central Park was finished, Olmsted quickly ____ himself for further action. His ambitions might once have been ____, but in his later years he made up for any youthful wrongheadedness.
    - (A) nurtured . . . arable
    - (B) girded . . . askew
    - (C) oriented . . . arable
    - (D) nurtured . . . abutted
    - (E) girded . . . abutted

Why We Practice Analogies

Practice with analogies develops proficiency in logic. To answer analogy questions correctly, you analyze two words and identify the relationship between them; then you identify another pair of words that has the same relationship. In addition, when you study analogies, you think about the precise meanings of words and fix these definitions in your memory. Finally, studying word analogies will help you to gain higher scores on national tests that include multiple-choice analogy questions. The new Scholastic Aptitude Test-I Verbal Reasoning Test, for example, includes analogy questions.

Understanding Word Analogies

A word analogy is a comparison between two pairs of words. Here's how word analogies are written:

Example 1   FIND : LOCATE :: lose : misplace

The colon (:) stands for the phrase "is related to." Here's how to read the relationships in Example 1:

> FIND [is related to] LOCATE
> lose [is related to] misplace

The double colon [::] between the two pairs of words stands for the phrase "in the same way that." Here is how to read the complete analogy:

> FIND [is related to] LOCATE
> [in the same way that]
> lose [is related to] misplace

Here is another way:

> FIND is to LOCATE as lose is to misplace.

A properly constructed analogy, then, tells us that the relationship between the first pair of words is the same as the relationship between the second pair of words. In Example 1, *find* and *locate* are synonyms, just as *lose* and *misplace* are synonyms.

Let's look at another example:

Example 2   GIFT : JOY :: grief : tears

What's the relationship here? A *gift* causes *joy,* just as *grief* causes *tears*. A cause-and-effect relationship links the two pairs of words in Example 2. To help you identify the relationships expressed in analogies, we have designed the chart on page 124. No chart, of course, could include all possible relationships between words, but these twelve relationships are frequently presented. You should familiarize yourself with these relationships.

TYPES OF ANALOGIES		
RELATIONSHIP	**EXAMPLE**	**EXPLANATION**
Synonym	DRY : ARID :: lost : mislaid	*Dry* is similar in meaning to *arid*, just as *lost* is similar in meaning to *mislaid*.
Antonym	KIND : CRUEL :: happy : sad	*Kind* is the opposite of *cruel*, just as *happy* is the opposite of *sad*.
Part and Whole	CHAPTER : BOOK :: fender : automobile	A *chapter* is a part of a *book*, just as a *fender* is a part of an *automobile*.
	POEM : STANZAS :: play : acts	A *poem* is composed of *stanzas*, just as a *play* is composed of *acts*.
Characteristic Quality	MIRROR : SMOOTH :: sandpaper : rough	*Mirrors* are characteristically *smooth*, just as *sandpaper* is characteristically *rough*.
Classification	POLKA : DANCE :: frog : amphibian	A *polka* may be classified as a *dance*, just as a *frog* may be classified as an *amphibian*.
	BIRD : CARDINAL :: house : igloo	A *cardinal* is classified as a *bird*, just as an *igloo* is classified as a *house*.
Cause and Effect	GIFT : JOY :: rain : flood	A *gift* can cause *joy*, just as *rain* can cause a *flood*.
	TEARS : SADNESS :: smiles : joy	*Tears* are an effect of *sadness*, just as *smiles* are an effect of *joy*.
Function	KNIFE : CUT :: shovel : dig	The function of a *knife* is to *cut*, just as the function of a *shovel* is to *dig*.
Location	FISH : SEA :: moose : forest	A *fish* can be found in the *sea*, just as a *moose* can be found in a *forest*.
Degree	CHUCKLE : LAUGH :: whimper : cry	*Chuckle* and *laugh* have similar meanings, but differ in degree in the same way that *whimper* and *cry* have similar meanings but differ in degree.
Performer and Related Object	CASHIER : CASH :: plumber : pipe	A *cashier* works with *cash*, just as a *plumber* works with *pipe*.
Performer and Related Action	AUTHOR : WRITE :: chef : cook	You expect an *author* to *write*, just as you expect a *chef* to *cook*.
Action and Related Object	BOIL : EGG :: throw : ball	You *boil* an *egg*, just as you *throw* a *ball*. (In these items, the object always receives the action.)

A Process for Solving Analogies

Your job in solving multiple-choice analogy questions is to identify the relationship between the first two words and then to find the pair of words that has the most similar relationship. Here are four hints to help you:

Hint #1.   Eliminate choices that represent relationships that do not match the relationship between the capitalized words.

Hint #2.   Eliminate choices that have vague relationships. Remember, the original relationship will always be clear. So, too, will the answer's relationship.

Hint #3.   Eliminate word pairs that express the same relationship as the capitalized pair, but appear in the opposite word order.

Hint #4.   If you can not determine the relationship between two words, try reading them backward. Remember that a cause-and-effect relationship, for example, exists whether the pair is written *Cause* : *Effect* or *Effect* : *Cause*.

Here's a process that will help you with analogy questions:

Answering Analogy Questions: A 3-Step Method
1.   Identify the relationship between the capitalized pair of words.
2.   Look for that relationship in the pairs of words in the answer choices. Eliminate those that do not have that relationship.
3.   Choose the pair of words whose relationship and word order match those of the capitalized pair.

Let's apply this pattern to a sample question in Example 3.

Example 3   FISH : SEA ::

    (A)   sun : star
    (B)   hero : villain
    (C)   moose : forest
    (D)   spacesuit : astronaut
    (E)   garage : car

1.   *Identify the relationship.* It is location; a *fish* can be found in the *sea*.
2.   *Eliminate choices.* Choice A has a relationship of classification; the *sun* is a *star*. Choice B has two opposites; *hero* is an antonym for *villain*. Choice D consists of a performer (*astronaut*) and a related object (*spacesuit*). None of these choices match.
3.   *Choose the correct answer.* Choices C and E both have location relationships: A *moose* can be found in a *forest,* and a *car* can be found in a *garage.* But Choice E could only be correct if the words appeared in the opposite order— *car* : *garage.* So Choice C must be correct.

A Final Word

Analogies are easier to tackle if you approach them with flexibility. Allow yourself to discover the relationship between the first pair of words and to explore the relationships between the words in the answer choices. Keep in mind that some words can represent more than one part of speech and that most words have multiple meanings. Remember, these little verbal puzzles are a test of your ability to demonstrate flexibility as well as logic.

CONNECTING NEW WORDS AND PATTERNS

Lesson 1   ANALOGIES

Directions. For each of the following items, choose the lettered pair of words that expresses a relationship that is most similar to the relationship between the pair of capitalized words. Write the letter of your answer on the line provided before the number of the item.

_____ 1. ALLEGORY : STORY ::
  (A) electrician : wire
  (B) electricity : energy
  (C) ballad : song
  (D) light : lamp
  (E) chapter : book

_____ 2. COMPREHENSIVE : LIMITED ::
  (A) covered : lidded
  (B) included : contained
  (C) panoramic : broad
  (D) narrow : wide
  (E) exclusive : snobbish

_____ 3. FELICITOUS : APPROPRIATE ::
  (A) ordinary : unusual
  (B) remarkable : common
  (C) affluent : wealthy
  (D) dynamic : repressed
  (E) luxurious : expensive

_____ 4. FEROCIOUS : LION ::
  (A) timid : mouse
  (B) thrown : mitt
  (C) rodentlike : cat
  (D) angry : shadow
  (E) reptilian : tears

_____ 5. INCONGRUOUS : HARMONIOUS ::
  (A) congressional : judicious
  (B) melodious : musical
  (C) acceptable : suitable
  (D) exciting : thrilling
  (E) reluctant : enthusiastic

_____ 6. INTRICACY : COMPLEXITY ::
  (A) sophistication : diplomacy
  (B) stateliness : democracy
  (C) commendation : praise
  (D) honesty : deceit
  (E) satisfaction : exultation

_____ 7. INTROSPECTIVE : SELF-ANALYSIS ::
  (A) vegetative : animal
  (B) functional : artist
  (C) reflective : mirror
  (D) aged : child
  (E) delicious : analyst

_____ 8. PROLOGUE : PLAY ::
  (A) solo : violin
  (B) audience : opera
  (C) preamble : constitution
  (D) delivery : speech
  (E) book : chapter

_____ 9. PROTAGONIST : CHARACTER ::
  (A) dancer : musical
  (B) conductor : symphony
  (C) scientist : test tube
  (D) choir : gang
  (E) beagle : dog

_____ 10. PROVOCATIVE : STIMULATING ::
  (A) final : initial
  (B) honest : timid
  (C) turbulent : stormy
  (D) trivial : crucial
  (E) nippy : giddy

CONNECTING NEW WORDS AND PATTERNS

Lesson 2 | ANALOGIES

Directions. For each of the following items, choose the lettered pair of words that expresses a relationship that is most similar to the relationship between the pair of capitalized words. Write the letter of your answer on the line provided before the number of the item.

_____ 1. BREVITY : SHORTNESS ::
(A) vastness : emptiness
(B) breadth : narrowness
(C) thrift : stinginess
(D) length : extent
(E) quality : control

_____ 2. CONNOTATION : SUGGEST ::
(A) implication : indicate
(B) integration : disintegrate
(C) pool : swim
(D) inflation : recede
(E) belief : worship

_____ 3. EMBELLISH : SIMPLIFY ::
(A) ring : encircle
(B) entangle : complicate
(C) thin : reduce
(D) subdue : tame
(E) agree : differ

_____ 4. EPITHET : DESCRIBE ::
(A) satire : praise
(B) brush : comb
(C) solvent : dissolve
(D) pencil : type
(E) investigation : disregard

_____ 5. EVOKE : SUMMON ::
(A) defy : resist
(B) laugh : enjoy
(C) inherit : die
(D) swim : submerge
(E) mix : separate

_____ 6. FORESHADOW : ANTICIPATION ::
(A) spend : travel
(B) exercise : strength
(C) own : loss
(D) fade : reappearance
(E) precede : disappearance

_____ 7. IMBIBE : BEVERAGE ::
(A) sharpen : book
(B) cut : independence
(C) impersonate : pumpkin
(D) ingest : fork
(E) devour : pastry

_____ 8. LAUDABLE : VIRTUE ::
(A) flammable : ignition
(B) wealthy : recluse
(C) benign : instruction
(D) unintelligible : gibberish
(E) early : tardiness

_____ 9. NOSTALGIC : DAYDREAMER ::
(A) wishful : star
(B) brave : hero
(C) insignificant : comics
(D) relaxed : parade
(E) despised : masterpiece

_____ 10. REITERATE : REPEAT ::
(A) dispense : distribute
(B) dismember : join
(C) deny : reconsider
(D) satisfy : upset
(E) mediate : hypnotize

CONNECTING NEW WORDS AND PATTERNS

Lesson 3 | ANALOGIES

Directions. For each of the following items, choose the lettered pair of words that expresses a relationship that is most similar to the relationship between the pair of capitalized words. Write the letter of your answer on the line provided before the number of the item.

_____ 1. ANECDOTE : ENTERTAINING ::
(A) tale : confusing
(B) joke : amusing
(C) yarn : educational
(D) myth : mysterious
(E) fable : boring

_____ 2. ASSERTION : CLAIM ::
(A) increase : loss
(B) secret : bulletin
(C) custom : celebration
(D) beat : rhythm
(E) rubble : plastic

_____ 3. CLIMACTIC : FINALE ::
(A) boring : length
(B) unique : similarity
(C) relaxing : vacation
(D) tight : looseness
(E) square : beauty

_____ 4. COHERENT : MUDDLED ::
(A) photographic : strange
(B) absorbing : new
(C) fantastic : ordinary
(D) clear : transparent
(E) idle : touchy

_____ 5. FORTE : WEAKNESS ::
(A) job : employee
(B) sturdiness : fragility
(C) trip : visitor
(D) habit : custom
(E) pitch : salesperson

_____ 6. FULMINATE : DISAGREE ::
(A) enrage : annoy
(B) refuse : agree
(C) agree : confer
(D) calm : arouse
(E) despair : hope

_____ 7. GOAD : RESTRAIN ::
(A) sleep : dream
(B) aggravate : fish
(C) press : pry
(D) spin : whirl
(E) reward : punish

_____ 8. INEXPLICABLE : MYSTERY ::
(A) plucky : chicken
(B) famous : history
(C) generous : donor
(D) clean : dump
(E) vertical : horizon

_____ 9. STIGMA : SHAME ::
(A) flag : suffering
(B) medal : pride
(C) license : pity
(D) ring : hatred
(E) scar : citizenship

_____ 10. SURMISE : GUESS ::
(A) disregard : ignore
(B) surprise : shock
(C) study : glance
(D) reckon : recognize
(E) startle : struggle

CONNECTING NEW WORDS AND PATTERNS

Lesson 4   ANALOGIES

Directions. For each of the following items, choose the lettered pair of words that expresses a relationship that is most similar to the relationship between the pair of capitalized words. Write the letter of your answer on the line provided before the number of the item.

_____ **1.** CONSONANT : ALPHABET ::
(A) noun : word
(B) poem : volcano
(C) capital : lowercase
(D) preposition : imperative
(E) word : sentence

_____ **2.** DECADENCE : BAD INFLUENCE ::
(A) celebration : award
(B) war : apathy
(C) prosperity : poverty
(D) disease : feast
(E) industrialization : failure

_____ **3.** ERRONEOUS : CORRECT ::
(A) sane : rational
(B) deformed : twisted
(C) skinny : tall
(D) beautiful : ugly
(E) peaceful : tranquil

_____ **4.** FLAUNT : PEACOCK ::
(A) climb : kangaroo
(B) hoard : squirrel
(C) build : cow
(D) sleep : rabbit
(E) migrate : beaver

_____ **5.** GIBE : JEER ::
(A) hurl : jest
(B) cure : scar
(C) destroy : build
(D) burn : raid
(E) braid : interweave

_____ **6.** HYPERCRITICAL : CRITICAL ::
(A) hypnotic : certain
(B) loud : audible
(C) hypersensitive : sensuous
(D) hysterical : theatrical
(E) round : square

_____ **7.** IRASCIBLE : IRRITABLE ::
(A) peaceful : harmonious
(B) steadfast : irrational
(C) sweet : tangy
(D) royal : haughty
(E) passionate : tepid

_____ **8.** MISCREANT : VILLAIN ::
(A) escort : tramp
(B) idler : voyager
(C) employee : employer
(D) meddler : busybody
(E) rebel : plaintiff

_____ **9.** OSTENTATIOUS : NOTICEABLE ::
(A) meager : excessive
(B) opposite : similar
(C) conceited : selfish
(D) concerned : envious
(E) wrathful : annoyed

_____ **10.** PRETENTIOUS : HUMBLE ::
(A) excessive : fantastic
(B) childish : youthful
(C) generous : miserly
(D) biased : prejudiced
(E) unreal : imaginary

CONNECTING NEW WORDS AND PATTERNS

Lesson 5 ANALOGIES

Directions. For each of the following items, choose the lettered pair of words that expresses a relationship that is most similar to the relationship between the pair of capitalized words. Write the letter of your answer on the line provided before the number of the item.

_____ 1. ABRIDGE : TEXT ::
    (A) lengthen : minute
    (B) shrink : fabric
    (C) extend : timer
    (D) enlarge : jar
    (E) expand : ballad

_____ 2. EXPLETIVE : PROFANE ::
    (A) anger : amusing
    (B) tribute : complimentary
    (C) pet : untamed
    (D) compliment : unkind
    (E) explanation : vague

_____ 3. IDIOMATIC : LANGUAGE ::
    (A) prosperous : nation
    (B) childless : family
    (C) traditional : customs
    (D) democratic : country
    (E) individual : group

_____ 4. IMPROMPTU : SPONTANEOUS ::
    (A) fragrant : smelly
    (B) encouraging : brave
    (C) contaminated : polluted
    (D) premeditated : thoughtless
    (E) crude : clever

_____ 5. INTANGIBLE : EMOTION ::
    (A) imaginary : life
    (B) visible : ghost
    (C) touchable : leprechaun
    (D) tangible : attitude
    (E) luminous : light

_____ 6. LUCRATIVE : UNPROFITABLE ::
    (A) artistic : poor
    (B) skillful : awkward
    (C) creative : cultured
    (D) incorrect : improper
    (E) futile : vain

_____ 7. SHREW : BAD-TEMPERED ::
    (A) dog : presidential
    (B) whim : necessary
    (C) buffoon : regal
    (D) charity : destructive
    (E) miser : stingy

_____ 8. SUPERCILIOUS : HAUGHTY ::
    (A) superb : adequate
    (B) superficial : aged
    (C) superstitious : ghastly
    (D) superfluous : excessive
    (E) supersonic : fatherly

_____ 9. TAWDRY : TASTEFUL ::
    (A) brave : plucky
    (B) fatal : magical
    (C) yawning : open
    (D) passive : peaceful
    (E) customary : unusual

_____ 10. VERBOSE : WORDY ::
    (A) vivid : strong
    (B) worthless : friendly
    (C) oral : spoken
    (D) bigoted : intimate
    (E) truthful : honorary

CONNECTING NEW WORDS AND PATTERNS

Lesson 6 | ANALOGIES

Directions. For each of the following items, choose the lettered pair of words that expresses a relationship that is most similar to the relationship between the pair of capitalized words. Write the letter of your answer on the line provided before the number of the item.

_____ 1. AMBIVALENT : CERTAIN ::
   (A) emotional : irrational
   (B) fickle : fishy
   (C) confused : dazed
   (D) absolute : conditional
   (E) opposite : contrary

_____ 2. ARCHIVES : DOCUMENTS ::
   (A) offices : buildings
   (B) pages : albums
   (C) courthouse : stepladder
   (D) library : hours
   (E) museum : artwork

_____ 3. AUTOCRAT : RULER ::
   (A) governor : system
   (B) costume : party
   (C) flock : shepherd
   (D) scorpion : spider
   (E) democracy : government

_____ 4. BENEFICENT : CHARITY ::
   (A) rude : politeness
   (B) impudent : obedience
   (C) wise : sage
   (D) angry : tranquility
   (E) bossy : submission

_____ 5. BETROTHED : MARRIED ::
   (A) weary : tired
   (B) planted : seeded
   (C) made : created
   (D) born : conceived
   (E) groggy : asleep

_____ 6. CONGENITAL : INBORN ::
   (A) contagious : virile
   (B) symptomatic : diagnosed
   (C) concerned : indifferent
   (D) cured : treatable
   (E) temporary : impermanent

_____ 7. PROCRASTINATE : POSTPONE ::
   (A) promote : hire
   (B) migrate : fly
   (C) schedule : plan
   (D) proceed : delay
   (E) falsify : verify

_____ 8. REPUGNANT : ATTRACTIVE ::
   (A) complimentary : polite
   (B) metallic : magnetic
   (C) repulsive : impulsive
   (D) gorgeous : beautiful
   (E) reduced : enlarged

_____ 9. SALLOW : SICK ::
   (A) bright-eyed : healthy
   (B) dressed : feverish
   (C) flushed : pale
   (D) wounded : injured
   (E) clean : ill

_____ 10. SORTIE : SUDDEN ::
   (A) music : symphonic
   (B) attack : vigorous
   (C) trip : automated
   (D) caravan : vehement
   (E) solo : voided

CONNECTING NEW WORDS AND PATTERNS

Lesson 7   ANALOGIES

Directions. For each of the following items, choose the lettered pair of words that expresses a relationship that is most similar to the relationship between the pair of capitalized words. Write the letter of your answer on the line provided before the number of the item.

_____ **1.** BLITHE : HAPPY ::
  (A) buoyant : heavy
  (B) brisk : brilliant
  (C) stringent : lenient
  (D) balmy : steamy
  (E) thoughtful : considerate

_____ **2.** CEDE : CLAIM ::
  (A) initiate : begin
  (B) list : count
  (C) beg : plead
  (D) agree : dispute
  (E) plant : farm

_____ **3.** EXONERATE : JURY ::
  (A) compete : athlete
  (B) infiltrate : damsel
  (C) forgive : sinner
  (D) negotiate : host
  (E) condemn : building

_____ **4.** FILIAL : OFFSPRING ::
  (A) familial : friends
  (B) paternal : father
  (C) maternal : aunt
  (D) responsible : liability
  (E) sisterly : brother

_____ **5.** INTERPOSE : INTERJECT ::
  (A) expose : expound
  (B) compose : impose
  (C) interpret : read
  (D) suppose : doubt
  (E) repose : recline

_____ **6.** PRECIPITATE : SUDDEN ::
  (A) profound : deep
  (B) cosmic : astronomical
  (C) premeditated : spontaneous
  (D) particular : general
  (E) considerate : impulsive

_____ **7.** PROFICIENT : UNSKILLED ::
  (A) profitable : gainful
  (B) decorative : ornamental
  (C) childish : mature
  (D) jumpy : nervous
  (E) knowledgeable : intelligent

_____ **8.** QUERY : RESPONSE ::
  (A) question : need
  (B) desire : perpetrator
  (C) puncture : leak
  (D) progress : proceedings
  (E) approach : rejection

_____ **9.** REMISSION : RELIEF ::
  (A) festival : song
  (B) retreat : army
  (C) recess : afternoon
  (D) fire : warmth
  (E) break : coffee

_____ **10.** SECULAR : RELIGIOUS ::
  (A) chronic : habitual
  (B) stable : relative
  (C) passive : active
  (D) vacant : void
  (E) obstinate : persistent

CONNECTING NEW WORDS AND PATTERNS

Lesson 8   ANALOGIES

Directions. For each of the following items, choose the lettered pair of words that expresses a relationship that is most similar to the relationship between the pair of capitalized words. Write the letter of your answer on the line provided before the number of the item.

_____ 1. ALTERCATION : QUARREL ::
  (A) obligation : duty
  (B) exclamation : surprise
  (C) foe : friend
  (D) reward : punishment
  (E) temptation : lie

_____ 2. ASSAIL : CONFRONT ::
  (A) sail : tack
  (B) wreck : construct
  (C) sleep : dawdle
  (D) demolish : damage
  (E) pulverize : dust

_____ 3. BRUNT : ATTACK ::
  (A) course : oatmeal
  (B) point : argument
  (C) introduction : newspaper
  (D) plane : cabin
  (E) document : busybody

_____ 4. BULWARK : FORTRESS ::
  (A) seawall : harbor
  (B) waves : ocean
  (C) uniform : trousers
  (D) balcony : view
  (E) keyboard : keys

_____ 5. HEINOUS : BAD ::
  (A) virtuous : cruel
  (B) sweltering : warm
  (C) healthy : ill
  (D) stable : sturdy
  (E) twisted : straight

_____ 6. INSIDIOUS : STRAIGHTFORWARD ::
  (A) genetic : familial
  (B) discreet : subtle
  (C) enjoyable : pleasant
  (D) attractive : repulsive
  (E) descriptive : agricultural

_____ 7. INVIDIOUS : OFFENSIVE ::
  (A) excessive : insufficient
  (B) haughty : proud
  (C) simple : brilliant
  (D) fickle : steadfast
  (E) relaxed : fitful

_____ 8. MARTYR : SUFFER ::
  (A) stenographer : perpetrate
  (B) explorer : despair
  (C) poet : write
  (D) singer : compose
  (E) composer : silence

_____ 9. PHALANX : SOLDIER ::
  (A) gun : weapon
  (B) line : cafeteria
  (C) captain : crew
  (D) herd : cow
  (E) car : road

_____ 10. REPRESSION : FREEDOM ::
  (A) drought : moisture
  (B) parties : manufacturing
  (C) garbage : dump
  (D) hunger : dinner
  (E) rubble : earthquake

CONNECTING NEW WORDS AND PATTERNS

Lesson 9 | ANALOGIES

Directions. For each of the following items, choose the lettered pair of words that expresses a relationship that is most similar to the relationship between the pair of capitalized words. Write the letter of your answer on the line provided before the number of the item.

_____ **1.** AFFINITY : REPULSION ::
  (A) infinity : endlessness
  (B) virtue : vice
  (C) control : reserve
  (D) potent : powerful
  (E) courage : bravery

_____ **2.** ARRAY : FINERY ::
  (A) helmet : armor
  (B) act : deed
  (C) trip : ticket
  (D) hull : ship
  (E) tape : splice

_____ **3.** AUDACIOUS : PIRATE ::
  (A) simple : thief
  (B) punctual : poacher
  (C) honest : crook
  (D) dishonest : rustler
  (E) kind : marauder

_____ **4.** BANDY : WORDS ::
  (A) lecture : police
  (B) advocate : literature
  (C) toss : balls
  (D) hit : bat
  (E) shed : snake

_____ **5.** DEIGN : QUEEN ::
  (A) volunteer : peasant
  (B) misbehave : judge
  (C) pardon : governor
  (D) rejoice : mourner
  (E) hurry : dawdler

_____ **6.** DEROGATORY : INSULT ::
  (A) apologetic : belief
  (B) flattering : offense
  (C) complimentary : praise
  (D) sarcastic : pleasantry
  (E) sincere : lie

_____ **7.** EFFICACIOUS : EFFECTIVE ::
  (A) beneficial : good
  (B) pious : quiet
  (C) candid : sweet
  (D) portly : greedy
  (E) eager : hesitant

_____ **8.** EPICURE : FOOD ::
  (A) oboe : pianist
  (B) trainer : hair
  (C) trial lawyer : court
  (D) fashion designer : clothing
  (E) soldier : bridge

_____ **9.** IMPERIOUS : MEEK ::
  (A) wild : tame
  (B) imperial : impertinent
  (C) exalted : tasty
  (D) calm : placid
  (E) dismal : tiny

_____ **10.** INGRATIATE : OFFEND ::
  (A) acquit : burglarize
  (B) dishonor : shame
  (C) betray : sulk
  (D) behave : party
  (E) resist : submit

CONNECTING NEW WORDS AND PATTERNS

Lesson 10 | ANALOGIES

Directions. For each of the following items, choose the lettered pair of words that expresses a relationship that is most similar to the relationship between the pair of capitalized words. Write the letter of your answer on the line provided before the number of the item.

_____ 1. AUSPICIOUS : FAVORABLE ::
    (A) adult : adolescent
    (B) suspicious : guilty
    (C) vicious : agonized
    (D) spacious : crowded
    (E) conspicuous : obvious

_____ 2. BUREAUCRACY : DEPARTMENTS ::
    (A) strings : apron
    (B) mall : stores
    (C) plane : bird
    (D) computers : system
    (E) vessel : ships

_____ 3. DEMEANOR : BEHAVIOR ::
    (A) fodder : stable
    (B) lawsuit : robe
    (C) run : trot
    (D) faith : belief
    (E) attitude : gesture

_____ 4. GUISE : IMPOSTOR ::
    (A) camouflage : troops
    (B) visibility : ghost
    (C) silence : discussion
    (D) trick : action
    (E) mood : feeling

_____ 5. INANE : MEANINGFUL ::
    (A) crazy : insane
    (B) remote : nearby
    (C) shunned : stunned
    (D) woolly : sheepish
    (E) foolish : whimsical

_____ 6. TRANSIENT : TEMPORARY ::
    (A) mannish : woman
    (B) editorial : newspaper
    (C) sarcastic : emotion
    (D) barren : land
    (E) courageous : brave

_____ 7. POLITIC : SHREWD ::
    (A) opposed : negated
    (B) transparent : clear
    (C) ugly : clumsy
    (D) verbal : active
    (E) moderate : excessive

_____ 8. PREMEDITATED : SPONTANEOUS ::
    (A) simple : sophisticated
    (B) puzzling : confusing
    (C) exuberant : enthusiastic
    (D) valiant : brave
    (E) navigable : deep

_____ 9. PURPORT : CLAIM ::
    (A) abstain : beg
    (B) retell : restore
    (C) suppose : assume
    (D) advise : dismay
    (E) amuse : cure

_____ 10. SCAPEGOAT : SUFFER ::
    (A) assassin : comfort
    (B) informer : trust
    (C) bodyguard : protect
    (D) pigeon : bray
    (E) victim : hunt

CONNECTING NEW WORDS AND PATTERNS

Lesson 11 ANALOGIES

Directions. For each of the following items, choose the lettered pair of words that expresses a relationship that is most similar to the relationship between the pair of capitalized words. Write the letter of your answer on the line provided before the number of the item.

_____ 1. AUGMENT : PLAN ::
(A) pass : law
(B) corrupt : honest
(C) crude : rude
(D) intelligent : educated
(E) earnest : sincere

_____ 2. DISSIPATE : SCATTER ::
(A) serve : reveal
(B) spread : wash
(C) distribute : cover
(D) evaporate : heat
(E) change : alter

_____ 3. DIVERGE : MERGE ::
(A) join : adjoin
(B) fork : split
(C) branch : broach
(D) divorce : marry
(E) emerge : grow

_____ 4. ENTOMOLOGY : SCIENCE ::
(A) philosophy : biography
(B) archaeology : fossil
(C) geography : galaxy
(D) geology : humankind
(E) poetry : literature

_____ 5. FACTION : GROUP ::
(A) elephants : India
(B) fraction : decimal
(C) subcommittee : committee
(D) gathering : congregation
(E) politicians : politics

_____ 6. FIORD : INLET ::
(A) apple : fruit
(B) star : moon
(C) plain : forest
(D) swamp : desert
(E) stream : ocean

_____ 7. OMNIVOROUS : BEARS ::
(A) sensitive : beetles
(B) striped : zebras
(C) carnivorous : bees
(D) old : monkeys
(E) smelly : grass

_____ 8. SUBSIDE : INCREASE ::
(A) submerge : immerse
(B) enlarge : expand
(C) shrink : swell
(D) spurt : gush
(E) scribble : skirt

_____ 9. TEPID : HOT ::
(A) short : sweet
(B) bored : thrilled
(C) cool : cold
(D) witty : clever
(E) strong : athletic

_____ 10. VOGUE : FASHION ::
(A) stain : soap
(B) boat : gondola
(C) hazard : danger
(D) erosion : corruption
(E) stampede : herd

CONNECTING NEW WORDS AND PATTERNS

Lesson 12 ANALOGIES

Directions. For each of the following items, choose the lettered pair of words that expresses a relationship that is most similar to the relationship between the pair of capitalized words. Write the letter of your answer on the line provided before the number of the item.

_____ 1. ACCOST : BULLY ::
   (A) trip : ballerina
   (B) fly : chauffeur
   (C) patrol : security guard
   (D) spend : shelter
   (E) befriend : enemy

_____ 2. APPRAISAL : VALUATION ::
   (A) philospher : writer
   (B) mortgage : deed
   (C) compliment : comment
   (D) decision : discussion
   (E) union : merger

_____ 3. CORRELATE : RELATE ::
   (A) incorporate : manufacture
   (B) correct : rectify
   (C) counterfeit : verify
   (D) antagonize : cooperate
   (E) bore : excite

_____ 4. EXHAUSTIVE : SUPERFICIAL ::
   (A) charming : friendly
   (B) excellent : superb
   (C) tiring : laborious
   (D) full : partial
   (E) plentiful : abundant

_____ 5. FURTIVE : THIEF ::
   (A) straightforward : spy
   (B) funny : clown
   (C) democratic : anarchy
   (D) weak : athlete
   (E) ancient : youth

_____ 6. PERMEATE : PENETRATE ::
   (A) treat : ignore
   (B) ooze : seep
   (C) meet : introduce
   (D) fill : deplete
   (E) breathe : smother

_____ 7. RAPACIOUS : SELFISH ::
   (A) clever : deceptive
   (B) violent : aggressive
   (C) meager : clean
   (D) civil : rude
   (E) impish : short

_____ 8. RECALCITRANT : RELUCTANT ::
   (A) confident : secretive
   (B) tolerant : bearable
   (C) careful : reckless
   (D) delighted : satisfied
   (E) obvious : headstrong

_____ 9. RECRIMINATION : ACCUSATION ::
   (A) injury : accident
   (B) reprimand : scolding
   (C) denial : burglary
   (D) criminal : victim
   (E) recess : trial

_____ 10. UNDERMINE : EROSION ::
   (A) astute : gullible
   (B) severe : grave
   (C) aggravated : intensified
   (D) contemporary : brief
   (E) modest : humble

CONNECTING NEW WORDS AND PATTERNS

Lesson 13 ANALOGIES

Directions. For each of the following items, choose the lettered pair of words that expresses a relationship that is most similar to the relationship between the pair of capitalized words. Write the letter of your answer on the line provided before the number of the item.

_____ 1. ACQUISITION : COLLECTION ::
   (A) support : column
   (B) frame : portrait
   (C) item : type
   (D) coupe : car
   (E) member : sorority

_____ 2. DEBACLE : SUCCESS ::
   (A) guest : visitor
   (B) fight : interchange
   (C) reason : motive
   (D) trot : movement
   (E) contraction : expansion

_____ 3. ENTHRALL : SPELLBIND ::
   (A) console : mourn
   (B) embrace : choose
   (C) sway : influence
   (D) elude : indulge
   (E) insist : intend

_____ 4. MICROCOSM : REPRESENTATIVE ::
   (A) cosmos : miniature
   (B) microscope : useless
   (C) sentence : confusing
   (D) microphone : indicative
   (E) flag : symbolic

_____ 5. PLATITUDE : TRITE ::
   (A) comment : kind
   (B) blasphemy : pious
   (C) threat : considerate
   (D) remark : witty
   (E) pet name : affectionate

_____ 6. RIGOROUS : STRICT ::
   (A) deft : clumsy
   (B) mobile : stationary
   (C) crucial : important
   (D) uncertain : positive
   (E) flimsy : substantial

_____ 7. SYNCHRONIZE : COORDINATE ::
   (A) hope : intend
   (B) resolve : differ
   (C) align : alienate
   (D) match : correspond
   (E) observe : compete

_____ 8. THWART : ASSIST ::
   (A) heckle : harass
   (B) clasp : release
   (C) litter : scatter
   (D) prune : trim
   (E) lose : defeat

_____ 9. ULTERIOR : UNDISCLOSED ::
   (A) interior : internal
   (B) ultimate : intimate
   (C) superior : larger
   (D) considered : dismissed
   (E) opened : closed

_____ 10. WILY : TRICKSTER ::
   (A) crafty : dentist
   (B) evil : hero
   (C) friendly : villain
   (D) round : ball
   (E) fast : sculptor

CONNECTING NEW WORDS AND PATTERNS

Lesson 14 ANALOGIES

Directions. For each of the following items, choose the lettered pair of words that expresses a relationship that is most similar to the relationship between the pair of capitalized words. Write the letter of your answer on the line provided before the number of the item.

_____ **1.** ABATE : LESSEN ::
   (A) swell : increase
   (B) ebb : flow
   (C) retire : hire
   (D) speed : progress
   (E) sing : rejoice

_____ **2.** CONTRITION : REMORSE ::
   (A) expectation : disappointment
   (B) sensation : feeling
   (C) intention : action
   (D) probation : guilt
   (E) expansion : luxury

_____ **3.** DEFILE : PURIFY ::
   (A) leak : ooze
   (B) alter : change
   (C) drench : soak
   (D) pollute : cleanse
   (E) file : grind

_____ **4.** ENCROACH : INTRUDER ::
   (A) steal : thief
   (B) befriend : warrior
   (C) betray : knight
   (D) voyage : anchor
   (E) bore : spokesperson

_____ **5.** FALLIBLE : PERFECT ::
   (A) famous : unknown
   (B) hungry : eaten
   (C) strict : stricken
   (D) lucky : cheated
   (E) vulnerable : hurt

_____ **6.** INNOCUOUS : LETHAL ::
   (A) understood : firm
   (B) vain : brave
   (C) innocent : naive
   (D) tardy : early
   (E) contented : satisfied

_____ **7.** PANACEA : CURE-ALL ::
   (A) pancreas : brain
   (B) pancake : waffle
   (C) medicine : poison
   (D) antidote : remedy
   (E) chemical : solution

_____ **8.** PROTRACT : LENGTHEN ::
   (A) protect : warn
   (B) shorten : abbreviate
   (C) extend : invite
   (D) withdraw : suggest
   (E) control : create

_____ **9.** VILIFY : SLANDERER ::
   (A) victimize : criminal
   (B) neigh : cow
   (C) harm : victim
   (D) praise : opponent
   (E) damage : musician

_____ **10.** WREST : PURSE SNATCHER ::
   (A) stare : glance
   (B) rip : tear
   (C) blend : meal
   (D) swing : batter
   (E) smash : crash

CONNECTING NEW WORDS AND PATTERNS

Lesson 15 | ANALOGIES

Directions. For each of the following items, choose the lettered pair of words that expresses a relationship that is most similar to the relationship between the pair of capitalized words. Write the letter of your answer on the line provided before the number of the item.

_____ **1.** ABUT : ADJOIN ::
    (A) ascend : descend
    (B) meet : exceed
    (C) analyze : suspect
    (D) involve : exclude
    (E) liberate : release

_____ **2.** ARABLE : GARDEN ::
    (A) treacherous : quicksand
    (B) poisonous : panda
    (C) agreeable : grouch
    (D) invisible : view
    (E) boiling : drink

_____ **3.** GRADATION : GRADUAL ::
    (A) aggravation : annoying
    (B) amazement : peculiar
    (C) graduation : disappointing
    (D) conjecture : certain
    (E) excitement : dull

_____ **4.** INCISE : CARVE ::
    (A) mourn : rejoice
    (B) dwindle : dupe
    (C) snare : catch
    (D) die : bury
    (E) dump : collect

_____ **5.** INDIGENOUS : EXOTIC ::
    (A) bizarre : strange
    (B) aloof : indifferent
    (C) broken : glued
    (D) foreign : familiar
    (E) delicate : tattered

_____ **6.** NURTURE : PARENT ::
    (A) dominate : dominion
    (B) cuddle : cow
    (C) nourish : weather
    (D) investigate : investor
    (E) command : general

_____ **7.** ORIENT : MAP ::
    (A) listen : radio
    (B) dance : boy
    (C) eat : cake
    (D) pant : dog
    (E) bake : oven

_____ **8.** SOLSTICE : SUMMER ::
    (A) season : spring
    (B) New Year's Day : holiday
    (C) century : decade
    (D) Tuesday : week
    (E) year : month

_____ **9.** STOIC : UNEXCITABLE ::
    (A) giant : short
    (B) miser : selfless
    (C) lamp : cruel
    (D) void : full
    (E) eccentric : unusual

_____ **10.** VANQUISH : CONQUERORS ::
    (A) oversee : foreigners
    (B) initiate : instigators
    (C) rule : lawyers
    (D) muddle : administrators
    (E) create : retailers

Why We Read Strategically

Reading is active. As you read, you step into the writer's world. When you come across a new idea, you usually look for a clue to help you determine the writer's meaning. You move ahead to see if the idea is explained, or you retrace your steps to look for any signs you missed.

You can use these same strategies to build your vocabulary. If you don't know the meaning of a word, you should look in the passage surrounding the word for hints. These hints are called context clues. The more you practice hunting for context clues, the better you can teach yourself new words, and the greater your vocabulary will grow. Strengthening your vocabulary skills also will help you to score higher on standardized vocabulary tests.

The following example shows the kinds of context clues you will find in Reading New Words in Context lessons.

Strategic Reading: An Example

The state of Oklahoma is a state of nations. Although many people are aware that large numbers of American Indians such as the Choctaw and the Chickasaw live in Oklahoma, they are not aware that the Indian nations of Oklahoma are **sovereign** peoples with their own constitutional governments. *In other words, like any other nation, they have the right to manage their own affairs.* However, because the tribes are nations within a nation, the United States government does have some **jurisdiction** over them. *For example, the federal government has the authority to govern its own activities when they take place on American Indian land.* Even in these cases, though, the federal government's authority is limited.

In this case, the writer uses *restatement* to provide a clue to the meaning of the word **sovereign**.

Here, an *example* is used to provide a clue to the meaning of **jurisdiction**.

The ancestors of large numbers of American Indians living in Oklahoma today came to Oklahoma on the **infamous** Trail of Tears. *In the 1830s, the United States government began to remove tribes of the Southeastern United States from their homelands. The government pushed these tribes on a forced march to the west that resulted in the death of up to one half of the members of some nations.* At the time, many Americans did not seem to recognize the inhumanity of this action. Today, *however*, almost everyone **acknowledges** the tragedy of the Indian Removal. It remains a *barbaric*, **hideous**, *and shameful* blot on the pages of United States history.

A *summary* of the events concerning the Trail of Tears provides a clue to the meaning of **infamous**.

Here, the writer makes the meaning of **acknowledges** clear through *contrast*. The use of *items in a series* clarifies the meaning of **hideous**.

Many people who live in states without large American Indian populations mistakenly believe that the tribes in Oklahoma live on large federal reservations. *This* **fallacy** may result from the assumption that American Indians have been unable *either* to accommodate modern society *or* to **reconcile** ancient tribal ways with the modern world. The fact is that American Indians in Oklahoma own their own tribal lands and are not tenants on government-owned property.

A pronoun reference is used here to provide a clue to the meaning of **fallacy**.

Note that a coordinating conjunction helps clarify the meaning of **reconcile**.

Today, the Choctaw, the Chickasaw, the Creek, the Seminole, and the Cherokee—as well as the other tribes in Oklahoma—are involved in modern occupations. American Indians are employed in the fields of education, civil service, law, medicine, computer technology, and so on. But maintaining the traditional cultures remains a **priority**, *the number-one concern*, of many tribal elders.

An appositive provides a clue to the meaning of **priority**.

In many cases, the younger tribal members in Oklahoma are most **reluctant** to abandon the values of their traditional culture *because they find those values important in their own lives*. Younger American Indians are also learning the old arts and crafts. A young Choctaw might learn to create the jewelry, headpieces, shawls, or leggings that *are* the traditional **garb** of the tribe. Others concentrate on preserving the stories and the language. Some research and write about the history of their people so that the events of the past will not be **irretrievably** lost.

The writer indicates the meaning of **reluctant** *through a cause-and-effect relationship*.

Note that a form of the verb to be (are) provides a clue to the meaning of **garb**.

As a poet who writes a verse in the sand watches the tide erase it forever, American Indians have watched the dreams and traditions of their grandparents fade into distant memories. Today, however, the Indian nations of Oklahoma struggle to regain their traditions and to make them meaningful in the present.

Figurative language is the key to understanding the meaning of **irretrievably**.

A Final Note

How can you learn strategic reading? Practice is a great way to improve your ability. The following lessons will help you recognize the different context clues a writer uses. As you complete each lesson, you will become a more effective reader.

READING NEW WORDS IN CONTEXT

Lesson 1 CONTEXT: The Literature

The passage gives you an opportunity to expand your vocabulary. Below are twenty Vocabulary Words that are used in the passage and in the exercises that follow it.

accentuate	despicable	intricacy	provocative
allegory	dissolute	introspective	rhetorical
ambiguous	felicitous	misanthrope	terse
comprehensive	ferocity	prologue	usurp
conjecture	incongruous	protagonist	vernacular

Heroes with a Mission: Bumppo and Batman

Batman and Natty Bumppo—a dynamic pairing that was never meant to be? The paths of these two fictional characters never met and their worlds were far apart. However, there may be as many connections as there are **incongruities** (1) between the two characters. Both Batman, the main character in Bob Kane's classic comic-book series, and Natty Bumppo, the **protagonist** (2) of James Fenimore Cooper's *The Leather-Stocking Tales*, are distinctive American heroes with important missions. Both characters embody values evident in the country at the time of their creations, Natty Bumppo in 1823 and Batman in 1939.

Hero of the Old Northwest

Natty Bumppo—also known as Leatherstocking, Hawkeye, Deerslayer, and Pathfinder—represents the Natural Man in a series of novels written by Cooper in the 1800s. Through Natty Bumppo, Cooper was able to **accentuate** (3) the moral problems that accompanied the westward movement of settlers. Cooper felt these problems needed to be highlighted because the American wilderness and the cultures it contained were under siege as civilization moved across the continent.

In an **allegory** (4), characters, settings, and actions symbolize ideas or moral qualities. In some ways, the Natty Bumppo novels can be viewed as **allegories** for America's westward expansion. During his lifetime, the character Bumppo witnesses the taming and settling of the western New York State wilderness. Because it spans an important period in American history, Natty Bumppo's life gives the reader a **comprehensive** (5) look at that era.

Cooper's stand on the environment, as reflected in his novels, is not **ambiguous** (6). Readers are shown exactly what he believes. Natty Bumppo, a skilled hunter and an early environmentalist, thinks that people should take from nature only what they need and not destroy it foolishly or wastefully. The **intricate** (7) narration of *The Leather-Stocking Tales*, which contains many detailed descriptions, provides numerous examples of abuses to the natural environment. Cooper and Natty Bumppo believe that "wholesome restraints" on society are necessary to protect the wilderness.

The wilderness of Natty Bumppo's youth gave way to cities and metropolises in the twentieth century. The times and the cities demanded new kinds of fictional heroes, even superheroes.

Brooding Bat Battles Urban Blight

Batman began battling the forces of evil in urban society—helping enforce "wholesome restraints" on society—in the May 1939 issue of *Detective Comics*. It soon became apparent that Batman was a **felicitous** (8) character; in the competitive world of comic-book heroes, he struck the right note at the suitable time. Batman's special territory is Gotham City, a fictional U.S. city after the Great Depression. At the time, twenty-five percent of the national labor force was unemployed. The city had become a place of unrest, crime, and danger.

Like Natty Bumppo, Batman is an admirable character concerned not only with written law but also with the higher, moral laws of human life. Batman is a vigilante obsessed with stopping crime, on a personal crusade against the **dissolute** (9), those people who lack moral restraint. One may see in Batman something of the typical Ernest Hemingway hero—a character of action with a strong code of honor and courage. Also, like Hemingway's heroes of few words, Batman speaks in **terse** (10) phrases, avoiding artificial wordiness and **rhetorical** (11) flourishes.

Batman, of course, is really millionaire Bruce Wayne, who carries out his war on crime dressed as a bat. What event preceded Wayne's decision to become a bat? The **prologue** (12) to his decision was a desire to avenge the death of his parents, who were murdered by criminals. Perhaps due to his traumatic childhood, Wayne is an **introspective** (13) character. He continually examines his thoughts and spends hours brooding over criminal activity in Gotham City. Batman's first exploits show him bursting with **ferocity** (14), but he is not quite so fierce in many later stories. Still, he is more than a match for such contemptible, vile criminals as the Penguin and the Riddler in their attempts to **usurp** (15), or seize, power; Batman eventually overcomes all these **despicable** (16) villains. Perhaps Batman's most famous opponent is the Joker, a real **misanthrope** (17). His evil actions confirm that he dislikes people just as much as Batman wants to protect them. But Batman himself is ultimately a loner, wary of the world at large. After a hard night of crime fighting, he returns to his Batcave, which not even the most cunning criminal can enter.

Heroes with Staying Power

Both Batman and Natty Bumppo are characters whose concerns remain relevant today. In other words, as we would say in the **vernacular** (18), or our everyday language, they are still "in." Natty Bumppo's sympathy with the wilderness and its life are evident in modern environmental movements and laws. Batman and other comic-book superheroes who swiftly conquer crime have remained popular fictional heroes. One guess as to why heroes like Batman and Natty Bumppo have been so popular is that society longs for a simple answer to its complex problems. Following that line of **conjecture** (19) explains why Batman has thrived in our comic books, television series, cartoons, books, and movies. The Batman movies starring Michael Keaton show that Batman is still a **provocative** (20) character, exciting and stimulating people of all ages.

EXERCISE 1 *Finding Synonyms* 👈

Directions. Reread the preceding passage. Then write on the line provided a synonym for each of the words in boldface. If you cannot think of an exact synonym, you may write a brief definition of the word.

1. incongruities _____

2. protagonist _____

3. accentuate _____

4. allegory _____

5. comprehensive _____

6. ambiguous _____

7. intricate _____

8. felicitous _____

9. dissolute _____

10. terse _____

11. rhetorical _____

12. prologue _____

13. introspective _____

14. ferocity _____

15. usurp _____

16. despicable _____

17. misanthrope _____

18. vernacular _____

19. conjecture _____

20. provocative _____

EXERCISE 2 *Reading Strategically* ☞

Directions. Now that you have read the passage and thought about the words in boldface, circle the letter of the correct answer to each of the following items. The numbers of the items are the same as the numbers of the boldface Vocabulary Words in the passage.

1. The writer provides a clue to the meaning of **incongruities** by
  (A) contrasting **incongruities** with the word *connections*
  (B) connecting **incongruities** with a number of unusual occurrences
  (C) using the image of a dynamic duo
  (D) telling us both characters are fictional
  (E) saying that the characters frequently appeared in the same stories

2. The writer provides a clue to the meaning of **protagonist** by
  (A) suggesting an essential conflict between the main characters Batman and Natty Bumppo
  (B) indicating that Natty Bumppo would be a suitable sidekick for Batman
  (C) suggesting that Natty Bumppo has a role similar to that of the main character Batman
  (D) linking **protagonist** to **incongruity**
  (E) linking **protagonist** to temporary fads

3. We can infer from the passage that when Cooper **accentuated** the moral problems of westward movement, he
  (A) belittled them
  (B) highlighted them
  (C) made them worse
  (D) ignored them
  (E) focused exclusively on them

4. In the passage, an **allegory** is
  (A) a moral quality
  (B) a movement
  (C) characters, settings, and actions
  (D) something that is known
  (E) a symbolic story

5. The writer tells us that Natty Bumppo's life provides a **comprehensive** look at an important period because it
  (A) covers only a brief part of that period
  (B) spans that period
  (C) was written centuries after the fact
  (D) is an autobiographical document
  (E) is so complicated that it is nearly unreadable

6. According to the passage, Cooper's stand on the environment is not **ambiguous** because he
  (A) keeps his beliefs a secret
  (B) ignores people's moral responses
  (C) misuses nature
  (D) tells readers exactly what he believes
  (E) is unsure of his own stand on the issues

7. When we read in the passage about the **intricate** narration of *The Leather-Stocking Tales,* we should realize that it is
    (A) highly detailed
    (B) simple
    (C) difficult to understand
    (D) written in a foreign language
    (E) delicate

8. In the passage, **felicitous** means
    (A) heroic
    (B) evil
    (C) suitable
    (D) fictional
    (E) territorial

9. According to the passage, **dissolute** people
    (A) are obsessed with cleanliness
    (B) are admirable
    (C) are moral
    (D) crusade against evil
    (E) lack moral restraint

10. Because his speech is **terse**, Batman is compared with Hemingway's heroes. They, like Batman,
    (A) speak in riddles
    (B) say few words
    (C) never say anything
    (D) speak loudly
    (E) talk endlessly

11. According to the passage, Batman does not speak in a **rhetorical** style because he
    (A) is a man of few words
    (B) is a hero
    (C) is an action character
    (D) has a strong code of honor and courage
    (E) avoids showy language

12. In the passage, the **prologue** to Batman's decision was
    (A) what happened later in his life
    (B) his plan to avenge his parents' deaths
    (C) a preceding event
    (D) wearing a cape and mask
    (E) being a millionaire

13. In the passage, to be **introspective** means
    (A) to think about criminal behavior
    (B) to have suffered a traumatic childhood
    (C) to be a selfish person
    (D) tending to examining one's own thoughts and feelings
    (E) to act without any consideration of the possible consequences

14. When the author tells us of Batman's **ferocity** in the early stories and says that in later stories the hero is not quite so fierce, we should realize that
    (A) **ferocity** does not ever last long
    (B) the same person did not write all of the stories
    (C) **ferocity** means bravery
    (D) **ferocity** relates to fierceness
    (E) being fierce has no relation to **ferocity**

15. We can infer from the passage that **usurp** is the same as
    (A) destroy
    (B) protect
    (C) take wrongly
    (D) treat
    (E) need drastically

16. How does the writer let us know that **despicable** may be defined as deserving of scorn?
    (A) The writer links **despicable** villains with contemptible criminals.
    (B) The writer uses the word *scornful*.
    (C) The writer compares the Penguin with the Riddler.
    (D) The writer links **despicable** with admirable.
    (E) The writer says **despicable** characters are no match for Batman.

17. In the passage, a **misanthrope** is shown to be a person who _____ people.
    (A) loves
    (B) dislikes
    (C) distrusts
    (D) tricks
    (E) is kind to

18. In the passage, how does the writer provide a clue to the meaning of **vernacular**?
    (A) The writer contrasts **vernacular** with everyday speech.
    (B) The writer links **vernacular** to Natty Bumppo.
    (C) The writer explains that **vernacular** has to do with environmental concerns.
    (D) The writer indicates that **vernacular** has to do with scholarly language.
    (E) The writer links **vernacular** to everyday language.

19. How does the writer provide a clue to the meaning of **conjecture**?
    (A) The writer associates **conjecture** with proven facts.
    (B) The writer calls **conjecture** an answer.
    (C) The writer says **conjecture** is the only reason.
    (D) The writer ties **conjecture** to the word *guess*.
    (E) The writer says answers are always complex.

20. What strategy does the writer use to tell you that **provocative** means stimulating?
    (A) The writer tells us Michael Keaton stars in the Batman movies.
    (B) The writer uses a simile.
    (C) The writer links comic books to television series and movies.
    (D) The writer implies that everyone is tired of Batman.
    (E) The writer tells us that Batman still has the power to excite us.

READING NEW WORDS IN CONTEXT

Lesson 2 — CONTEXT: The Literature

The passage gives you an opportunity to expand your vocabulary. Below are twenty Vocabulary Words that are used in the passage and in the exercises that follow it.

affluent	epithet	infer	perpetuate
banter	evasive	laudable	reiterate
brevity	evoke	lucid	scrutinize
connotation	foreshadow	nostalgic	stipend
embellish	imbibe	novice	symposium

Hart Crane and the Brooklyn Bridge

The Brooklyn Bridge, the first and most famous of New York City's suspension bridges, is an American legend. It's no wonder, then, that poet Hart Crane (1899–1932) chose the bridge as the central image uniting the history and hopes of the nation in his monumental poem *The Bridge*. A **symposium** (1) on the Brooklyn Bridge without some reference to Crane would be incomplete; a panel discussion or a collection of writings on the topic must include mention of Crane.

The History Behind the Bridge

Established as a National Historic Landmark in 1964, the bridge has been a national treasure since its opening in 1883 across New York City's East River. Mayor Seth Low (1830–1916) of Brooklyn was on hand to examine closely the opening of the bridge. As he **scrutinized** (2) the bridge, he was not at all **evasive** (3) in his comments. He said plainly and clearly, "No one shall see it and not feel proud." The bridge seems to inspire such **lucid** (4) thoughts, although it has also inspired quite a few crazy antics.

The Brooklyn Bridge was begun in 1869 by German American engineer John A. Roebling (1806–1869). After Roebling's death that year, his son Washington Roebling (1837–1926)

took over construction of the bridge. Engineering such a huge structure must have been demanding and time-consuming work. A **novice** (5) engineer certainly could not have planned the project. That would have been like an inexperienced child trying to build a house. Upon its completion, the bridge was the longest suspension bridge in the world. The majestic twin stone towers of the 1,595-foot-long bridge quickly became beloved symbols of New York City's and America's expansion and progress.

A Symbol for the Twentieth Century

Hart Crane was a poet who wanted to capture the essence of twentieth-century America, as well as the country's past, in a single poem. Recognizing the importance of the Brooklyn Bridge as a symbol, in the mid-1920s, Crane began writing a poem centered on the bridge. Crane even moved into Washington Roebling's old house at 110 Columbia Heights in order to feel closer to his subject. What can we **infer** (6) from this action? One conclusion we can draw is that Crane was extraordinarily dedicated to the project.

Hampered by personal problems and difficult relationships, Crane worked for several years on the poem, published as *The Bridge* in

1930. Because as a poet Crane was no one's employee, he did not receive a **stipend** (7). He did, however, receive a salary of sorts when an **affluent** (8), or wealthy, patron of the arts gave him a grant for his work on *The Bridge*.

Many critics regard *The Bridge* as Crane's greatest work, although they acknowledge its difficulties. *The Bridge* is not noted for its **brevity** (9). In fact, it contains more than twelve hundred lines and has fifteen sections. The imagery in the poem is at times vivid, at times obscure and complicated. For example, the poet uses the word *bedlamite* when referring to a person who crazily jumps from the bridge. (Bedlam was a well-known hospital for the mentally ill; to call a crazed person a bedlamite, or to use a word or phrase to characterize a person, is to use an **epithet** (10).) Crane also uses an abrupt and confusing arrangement of people, places, and moods. As you can imagine, the poem might appeal more to the artistic-minded than to those who prefer a **bantering** (11), joking, style.

The scope and the imagination of *The Bridge* are worthy of high praise. Especially **laudable** (12) is Crane's decision to **embellish** (13) his poem with many people, real and imaginary, from America's past. The poem is adorned throughout with such historical figures as Christopher Columbus and Captain John Smith, legendary characters such as Rip Van Winkle, and poets such as Walt Whitman and Edgar Allan Poe. (Critics now say that the section, "The Tunnel," on the troubled Poe **foreshadows** (14) events in Crane's future, because it hints at Crane's own tragic death two years after the publication of *The Bridge*.) Crane seems to have a real longing for and a desire to **perpetuate** (15) things past. These yearnings are reflected in his use of historical figures and in his **nostalgic** (16) references.

Settings continually change in the poem. It's as if Crane wanted to **imbibe** (17), or drink in, as much of the nation's spirit as he could and then share it with his readers. Following a journey through America's past and soul, the last section is called "Atlantis." Of course, what the word Atlantis suggests to the reader, the word's **connotation** (18), is important to the overall meaning of the poem. The word can **evoke** (19) an image of rebirth. But it can also bring out an image of demise, since Atlantis is said to have sunk into the ocean. In spite of the frequent shifts in time setting, the central image of the Brooklyn Bridge gives the poem unity. To Crane, the bridge was a metaphor that spanned the past and the future. In repeating the image of the bridge, Crane is also able to **reiterate** (20) another important theme, that the material world and the spiritual must be united.

EXERCISE 1 *Finding Synonyms*

Directions. Reread the preceding passage. Then write on the line provided a synonym for each of the words in boldface. If you cannot think of an exact synonym, you may write a brief definition of the word.

1. symposium _____

2. scrutinized _____

3. evasive _____

4. lucid _____

5. novice _____

6. infer _____

7. stipend _____

8. affluent _____

9. brevity _____

10. epithet _____

11. bantering _____

12. laudable _____

13. embellish _____

14. foreshadows _____

15. perpetuate _____

16. nostalgic _____

17. imbibe _____

18. connotation _____

19. evoke _____

20. reiterate _____

EXERCISE 2   *Reading Strategically* ☞

Directions. Now that you have read the passage and thought about the words in boldface, circle the letter of the correct answer to each of the following questions. The numbers of the items are the same as the numbers of the boldface Vocabulary Words in the passage.

1. Which part of a sentence in the passage provides a clue to the meaning of **symposium**?
   (A) The Brooklyn Bridge, the first and most famous of New York City's suspension bridges
   (B) poet Hart Crane . . . chose the bridge as the central image
   (C) a panel discussion or collection of writings
   (D) an American legend
   (E) his monumental poem

2. In the passage, **scrutinized** means
   (A) to examine closely
   (B) to comment at length
   (C) to open
   (D) to cross over
   (E) to identify

3. According to the passage, if the mayor had been **evasive** he would not have spoken
  (A) proudly
  (B) plainly and clearly
  (C) inspiringly
  (D) loudly and rudely
  (E) secretly and shyly

4. In the passage, to be **lucid** is to be _____.
  (A) confusing and rambling
  (B) divinely inspired
  (C) crazy
  (D) obscure
  (E) clearly understood

5. Because the Brooklyn Bridge project was so difficult, a **novice** engineer could not have done the job. To reinforce this point, the writer draws an analogy between a **novice** engineer and
  (A) an inexperienced child
  (B) a toy house
  (C) an enormous bridge
  (D) the American engineer John A. Roebling
  (E) Washington Roebling

6. In the passage, **infer** means
  (A) to be dedicated
  (B) to create
  (C) to be symbolic
  (D) to draw a conclusion
  (E) to move into someone else's house

7. How does the writer let us know that **stipend** may be defined as a fixed or regular payment?
  (A) The writer links the word to work.
  (B) The writer links the word to employment and salary.
  (C) The writer relates the word to the phrase "several years."
  (D) The writer includes the word *wealthy*.
  (E) The writer connects the word with a portion.

8. In the passage, **affluent** means
  (A) watery
  (B) unsalaried
  (C) granted
  (D) poor
  (E) wealthy

9. In the passage, the author writes that Crane's poem is not noted for its **brevity** because
  (A) it is very brief
  (B) it is very long
  (C) it is difficult
  (D) it is Crane's greatest work
  (E) it is vivid

10. According to the passage, Crane used _____ as an **epithet** for a mentally ill person.

    (A) an example
    (B) complicated language
    (C) the word *bedlamite*
    (D) abrupt, confusing imagery
    (E) juxtaposition

11. In the passage, **bantering** means

    (A) scary
    (B) artistic
    (C) joking
    (D) moods
    (E) confusing

12. The writer provides a clue to the meaning of **laudable** by

    (A) using the phrase "worthy of high praise"
    (B) connecting it with the word *decision*
    (C) relating it to the adjective *especially*
    (D) referring to the words *scope* and *imagination*
    (E) relating it to the word *laughable*

13. To let us know that **embellish** may be defined as "to improve by adding details," the writer

    (A) links the words *real* and *imaginary*
    (B) links the words **embellish** and *imaginary*
    (C) says that Crane **embellished** his poem with people from America's past
    (D) refers to the country's past
    (E) names some historical figures

14. According to the passage, critics today say that the section on Poe in *The Bridge* **foreshadows** Crane's future because

    (A) Crane longed for the past
    (B) it hints at Crane's own death
    (C) Poe and Crane had similar literary styles
    (D) Crane died before Poe did
    (E) **foreshadow** means to long for the past

15. If Crane was trying to **perpetuate** the country's past, we may assume that he

    (A) was using it for his own glory
    (B) wants it to be remembered
    (C) thinks it was unimportant
    (D) wants the bridge to be important
    (E) was dedicated to the United States

16. Which sentence in the passage provides a clue to the meaning of **nostalgic**?

    (A) "Crane seems to have a real longing for things past."
    (B) "The word can **evoke** an image of rebirth."
    (C) "Settings continually change in the poem."
    (D) "To Crane, the bridge was a metaphor that spanned the past and the future."
    (E) "The scope and the imagination of *The Bridge* are worthy of high praise."

17. When we read in the passage "It's as if Crane wanted to **imbibe** as much of the nation's spirit as he could," we should realize that

    (A) Crane had little interest in the United States
    (B) Crane already knew all there was to know about the spirit of the United States
    (C) Crane tried to close his mind to new experiences
    (D) Crane wanted figuratively to drink in the spirit of the United States
    (E) Crane drank only products made in the United States

18. In the passage, the **connotation** of a word is

    (A) the exact meaning of the word
    (B) a synonym for the word
    (C) what the word suggests to the reader
    (D) where the word comes from
    (E) the importance of the word in the English language

19. The writer suggests the meaning of **evoke** by

    (A) contrasting **evoke** with the phrase "image of rebirth"
    (B) referring to the poem
    (C) linking **evoke** to the phrase "bring out"
    (D) saying that the poem **evokes** a central image
    (E) using a metaphor

20. In the passage, **reiterate** means

    (A) to repeat
    (B) to unite
    (C) to span
    (D) to inspire
    (E) to erase

READING NEW WORDS IN CONTEXT

Lesson 3 | CONTEXT: The Literature

The passage gives you an opportunity to expand your vocabulary. Below are twenty Vocabulary Words that are used in the passage and in the exercises that follow it.

anagram	epilogue	goad	prodigy
anecdote	extemporaneous	hypochondriac	quixotic
assertion	fidelity	inexplicable	staunch
climactic	forte	noncommittal	stigma
coherent	fulminate	proboscis	surmise

Ralph Ellison's Invisible Man

Last week I went to a party with three friends. Yesterday, one of them asked me if I had been at the party.

"Didn't you know I was with you?" I asked. "What, was I invisible or something?"

"Oh, yeah," she replied.

This **anecdote** (1) shows how easy it is to become invisible to others; I could give brief accounts of a few more incidents like that. Sometimes people get so wrapped up in themselves that they don't see others.

I've noticed this a lot since I read *Invisible Man* by Ralph Ellison (1914 –1994). I think Ellison's **assertion** (2) is that we all struggle to avoid being labeled and to find our own identity. He also claims that as we struggle, we become invisible to others.

Although I have other strong points, analyzing novels really isn't my **forte** (3). Teachers usually have to **goad** (4) me to turn in book reports, just as you would have to prod a cat to jump into water. However, Ellison's book stays on my mind. I've even read several articles about it. At first, my English teacher found my keen interest **inexplicable** (5). But when I told her how much this novel had changed my way of seeing things, she understood. In fact, she encouraged me to write this essay.

Recognizing Racism

I used to think that people who complained about racism were like **hypochondriacs** (6)— always complaining about aches and pains that only existed in their heads. *Invisible Man* went further than any other book I've read by an African American author to change my mind about racism. I feel like I now have a better understanding of both what it is and how damaging it can be.

To begin with, don't confuse Ellison's book with *The Invisible Man*, a novel by H. G. Wells (1866–1946). Because I don't want to take a position on Wells' book, I'll remain **noncommittal** (7), except to say that I am not a **staunch** (8) supporter of science fiction. In fact, I don't care too much for it. Wells' man becomes invisible through a scientific discovery. To me, that seems as far-fetched as Pinocchio's **proboscis** (9) growing magically longer when he tells a lie. Noses don't magically grow, and people don't become invisible. However, one of the **climactic** (10) events in Wells' story could just as easily be a turning point in Ellison's novel. That point is the character's recognition of what it means to be invisible and a "helpless absurdity" in society. Such a sentiment would be shared by Ellison's character.

Although it does have some surreal qualities, Ellison's novel, unlike Wells', is firmly rooted in reality. The plot is about a young African American man—an aspiring student at Southern College—who finds that he has no unique identity to the power brokers of the United States. Instead, he is defined by the color of his skin, and he is routinely used and abused because of it. The Invisible Man struggles throughout the novel to gain a sense of his own identity, but in his encounters with other people he is continually made to feel as if there is a **stigma** (11) in being black! This mark of shame, of course, should not exist. Although in the prologue he tells about exploding suddenly and violently when called names by a passerby, the Invisible Man generally finds it easier to retreat from people's indifference or insensitivity than to **fulminate** (12).

Invisible Man, which has been called one of the country's most important post-World War II novels, is a **coherently** (13) organized novel. Its logical structure can be seen in the way the story begins and ends. Both prologue and **epilogue** (14) take place in a "hole," an underground room in which the narrator is living and from which he is sorting through his experiences. Right from the prologue, I was fascinated by the story, and I remained so all the way through the book's twenty-five chapters and down to the **epilogue**.

Armstrong and All That Jazz

You might **surmise** (15) from the little I've said that the book is strictly a novel of high-flown ideas. This guess would be far from the truth, however. The novel is filled with images of Harlem, of black folk history, and of surreal scenes, such as the narrator's room flooded with 1,369 light bulbs, operated free and unknowingly by Monopolated Light & Power Company. References to music, particularly jazz, also give the novel a lively quality. The narrator, like Ellison himself, appreciates the jazz playing and singing of Louis Armstrong (1901?–1971). Indeed, the stylistic inventiveness of Ellison's novel has the **extemporaneous** (16) freshness of improvised jazz.

I love jazz, and not just because the letters of my name, Lizzi Jake, form the **anagram** (17) *I like jazz.* I, too, listen to Louis Armstrong. Armstrong played with **fidelity** (18) to the jazz tradition. That is ironic, you know, because being faithful to the jazz tradition means bending and playing with a lot of the rules of traditional, mainstream music.

I'm digressing somewhat, but the jazz theme in *Invisible Man* is part of the book's wide appeal. People can relate to music, as they relate to the more serious themes of the book. You don't have to be a **prodigy** (19)— believe me, I'm not highly gifted—to identify with the universal suffering of invisible people such as the narrator.

I hope someday that people will no longer be treated as though they are invisible. That may be a **quixotic** (20) hope, but sometimes even foolishly idealistic hopes come true.

EXERCISE 1 *Finding Synonyms* ☞

Directions. Reread the preceding passage. Then write on the line provided a synonym for each of the words in boldface. If you cannot think of an exact synonym, you may write a brief definition of the word.

1. anecdote _____

2. assertion _____

3. forte _____

4. goad _____

5. inexplicable _____

6. hypochondriacs _____

7. noncommittal _____

8. staunch _____

9. proboscis _____

10. climactic _____

11. stigma _____

12. fulminate _____

13. coherently _____

14. epilogue _____

15. surmise _____

16. extemporaneous _____

17. anagram _____

18. fidelity _____

19. prodigy _____

20. quixotic _____

EXERCISE 2   *Reading Strategically* ☞

Directions. Now that you have read the passage and thought about the words in boldface, circle the letter of the correct answer to each of the following items. The numbers of the items are the same as the numbers of the boldface Vocabulary Words in the passage.

1. Which sentence in the passage provides a clue to the meaning of **anecdote**?
   (A) "Last week I saw a movie with three friends."
   (B) "Sometimes people get so wrapped up in themselves that they don't see others."
   (C) "'Oh, yeah,' she replied."
   (D) "I could give brief accounts of a few more incidents like that."
   (E) "'What, was I invisible or something?'"

2. In the passage, **assertion** means
   (A) an account
   (B) a claim
   (C) an identity
   (D) an extent
   (E) a struggle

3. We can infer from the passage that a **forte** is a
   (A) strong point
   (B) analysis
   (C) siege
   (D) a series of novels
   (E) a failing

4. Because a teacher usually has to **goad** the writer to turn in book reports, the writer must be urged to do it. To reinforce this point, the writer draws a simile between herself and
   (A) a writer who hates to analyze books
   (B) someone who doesn't like to read
   (C) a demanding teacher
   (D) a person who would rather read than think
   (E) a cat being forced to jump into water

5. In the passage, the teacher found the writer's interest **inexplicable** because
   (A) it was not easily understood
   (B) it was perfectly understandable
   (C) it concerned a cat
   (D) it was lacking in interest
   (E) it was inexcusable

6. In the passage, **hypochondriacs** are
   (A) racists
   (B) African American writers
   (C) people who are seriously ill
   (D) people with imagined aches and pains
   (E) people who are ignorant about racism

7. When we read in the passage that the writer will remain **noncommittal**, we should realize that the writer
   (A) will express a strong opinion
   (B) will write a book report about the book
   (C) will not take a position on the book
   (D) has not really read the book
   (E) will focus on the merits of the book

8. How does the writer provide a clue to the meaning of **staunch**?
   (A) The writer ties it to the word *position*.
   (B) The writer contrasts it with the phrase "I don't care too much for it."
   (C) The writer refers to science fiction.
   (D) The writer tells us that Ellison's book is entitled *Invisible Man*.
   (E) The writer uses a metaphor.

9. What strategy does the writer use to tell you that **proboscis** means "nose"?
   (A) The writer gives a synonym.
   (B) The writer uses **proboscis** to refer to Pinocchio's nose.
   (C) The writer later explains that the word means "far-fetched."
   (D) The writer compares science fiction to magic.
   (E) The writer uses the word in many contexts.

10. The writer lets us know that **climactic** may be defined as "pertaining to an ending or a climax" by
    (A) using the word to describe an event
    (B) relating the word to invisibility
    (C) relating **climactic** to the word *sentiment*
    (D) linking **climactic** to the phrase "helpless absurdity"
    (E) linking the words **climactic** and *turning point*

11. In the passage, a **stigma** is
    (A) a mark of shame
    (B) a tragedy
    (C) an invisible force
    (D) a sign of society
    (E) a difference of opinion

12. To **fulminate** means to issue a thunderous verbal attack. According to the passage, the Invisible Man normally did what instead of **fulminating**?
    (A) He left town.
    (B) He spoke out in public.
    (C) He became indifferent and insensitive.
    (D) He retreated.
    (E) He become physically violent and angry.

13. The writer lets us know that **coherently** may be defined as "with a logical or orderly arrangement" by
    (A) linking the words **coherently** and *novel*
    (B) giving an example of the book's logical structure
    (C) saying that the book is the most important book published in 1952
    (D) connecting the word to labeling
    (E) admiring the novel

14. What strategy does the writer use to tell that an **epilogue** comes after the chapters in a book?
  (A) The writer implies the story contains an **epilogue**.
  (B) The writer explains that the function of an **epilogue** is to introduce the characters.
  (C) The writer gives the order of the book: prologue, chapters, **epilogue**.
  (D) The writer expects you to know what an **epilogue** is.
  (E) The writer notes that the book has twenty-five chapters.

15. In the passage, if you **surmise,** then you
  (A) tell others
  (B) reject an idea
  (C) reach a resolution
  (D) have no idea
  (E) guess

16. Because jazz is often **extemporaneous,** the writer compares it in a simile to the stylistic inventiveness of Ellison's writing. Both have the quality of being
  (A) out of date
  (B) narrated
  (C) spontaneous and improvised
  (D) music
  (E) formal and stylized

17. In the passage, "I like jazz" is an **anagram** of _____ because the same letters are used but arranged differently.
  (A) Lizzi Jake
  (B) I love jazz
  (C) my name
  (D) the letters
  (E) I, too

18. When we read in the passage that Louis Armstrong played with great **fidelity** to the jazz tradition, we should realize that he
  (A) did not care about jazz
  (B) played jazz well
  (C) played faithfully in the jazz tradition
  (D) preferred traditional, mainstream music
  (E) played the fiddle

19. How does the writer provide a clue to the meaning of the word **prodigy**?
  (A) The writer says **prodigy** means a believable person.
  (B) The writer calls **prodigy** the theme of the book.
  (C) The writer contrasts a **prodigy** with someone who is not highly gifted.
  (D) The writer identifies **prodigy** as universal suffering.
  (E) The writer implies a **prodigy** is someone who is not extraordinarily bright.

20. In the passage, why does the author say that the hope for better treatment of people may be **quixotic**?
  (A) Better treatment may have already happened.
  (B) Hope for better treatment may be foolishly idealistic.
  (C) Better treatment of people is an impossible task.
  (D) Hope for better treatment may be insincere.
  (E) Hope for better treatment may be questionable.

Lesson 4 | CONTEXT: The Literature

The passage gives you an opportunity to expand your vocabulary. Below are twenty Vocabulary Words that are used in the passage and in the exercises that follow it.

bumptious	erroneous	miscreant	sanction
cite	flaunt	ostentatious	satiate
comely	gibe	pretentious	stereotype
consonant	hypercritical	repartee	subservient
decadence	irascible	rudiment	vivacious

Zora Neale Hurston and Henry Adams: Different Roads

Many roads can lead to the same destination. Similarly, people with widely different backgrounds can become successes in the same fields. Just look at the lives of Henry Adams (1838–1918) and Zora Neale Hurston (1891–1960). Both of these Americans became successful writers, editors, and educators. But it would be **erroneous** (1) to say that they shared similar upbringings. In fact, such an assumption would be incorrect, as Adams and Hurston had entirely different starts and experienced different opportunities along the way.

The Poor Little Rich Boy
Adams was from a distinguished family of statesmen, including two presidents. He was born in Boston and was raised with every advantage. Some might call his grand Beacon Hill boyhood home showy to the point of being **ostentatious** (2). Adams could be described by the **stereotype** (3) of a "rich kid"—he certainly embodied all the general notions people have of a privileged youth. He was educated privately, attended Harvard University, studied law at the University of Berlin, and traveled the European continent.

To his credit, Adams was not **pretentious** (4) about his background. He never made any

false claims to distinction, and the renown he won in several fields was due to his own hard work. He served as secretary to his father, who was a congressman and a diplomat; he wrote for newspapers and magazines; taught history at Harvard University; and edited the *North American Review*. Because he apparently did not display himself conspicuously or show off, we can assume that he did not choose to **flaunt** (5) his privileged background.

Adams' first major work as a historian concerned the administrations of Thomas Jefferson and James Madison. Adams wrote other historical studies and two novels. In *Mont-Saint-Michel and Chartres* and *The Education of Henry Adams*, Adams presents a pessimistic view of the modern age. He maintained that his education had not adequately prepared him for life in the twentieth century. A fundamental principle of his philosophy is that history is an energetic force. This **rudiment** (6) offered him little comfort, though, and he found himself most at home in the hopelessly bygone thirteenth century. He deplored the moral decay, the **decadence** (7), of his own time. He fully expected technological advances to destroy the world, and he viewed scientists as potential villains. There's no doubt that Adams would have thought the inventor of the atom bomb in particular to be the worst **miscreant** (8) of modern society. If he were alive today, Adams certainly wouldn't approve of arms races but would instead **sanction** (9) nuclear arms controls.

Her Eyes Were Set on Success

Hurston also achieved academic and literary success, but without the advantages of background enjoyed by Adams. She was born in Eatonville, Florida, the nation's first all-black, incorporated, self-governing town, where her father was a minister and mayor. Her mother was an encouraging influence. Mother and daughter seemed to have had an agreeable, harmonious, **consonant** (10) relationship. When Hurston was nine, however, her mother died. Her father remarried, and Hurston eventually left home.

Unlike Adams, Hurston could never take education for granted. From the age of fourteen, Hurston supported herself, working her way through Morgan Academy in Baltimore and then Howard University in Washington, D.C. Being on their own from such an early age can turn youths into angry adults. But rather than making Hurston **irascible** (11), deprivation only made her more determined. While working, she didn't seem to mind being in **subservient** (12) positions, realizing that these inferior positions would help her toward her goal. In her autobiography, *Dust Tracks on a Road*, Hurston indicated that she didn't make her way in school through good looks, like some **comely** (13) schoolmates, but with talent and determination. Nor was she **bumptious** (14); pushiness was not her style. Readers get the idea that she was quite spirited, lively, and **vivacious** (15). She was a good conversa-

tionalist and always met a pointed remark with a witty comeback—with a **repartee** (16).

It didn't take long for Hurston's writings to attract notice at Howard. She moved to New York City and became involved in the Harlem Renaissance. She won awards for her stories and plays, and she studied anthropology on a scholarship at Barnard College.

The 1930s were active and productive years for Hurston. She taught college and pursued graduate studies, coached drama, worked as an editor, and traveled to the Caribbean. She also published *Mules and Men*, a collection of African American folklore, and several novels. By plunging herself into all of these projects, Hurston attempted to **satiate** (17) her lifelong goal to document, preserve, and celebrate African American culture, a desire she could never entirely satisfy.

Ahead of Their Times

The writings of both Adams and Hurston may be more appreciated today than during their lifetimes. While in his own day Adams may have seemed **hypercritical** (18) of the modern era, the devastating wars of this century show that his criticism of technology was not overly harsh after all. Scholars now consider him an authority on the historical times about which he wrote, and they often **cite** (19) his works, quoting him as a legitimate source of information. In the 1940s and 1950s, Hurston endured many a **gibe** (20) for her portrayals of African American life in the South, and her social essays received similar derision and taunts. Today, Hurston's efforts to record the culture of southern African American life and her vision of racial pride have won her many admirers, including writer Alice Walker.

EXERCISE 1 *Finding Synonyms* 👉

Directions. Reread the preceding passage. Then write on the line provided a synonym for each of the words in boldface. If you cannot think of an exact synonym, you may write a brief definition of the word.

1. erroneous _____

2. ostentatious _____

3. stereotype _____

4. pretentious _____

5. flaunt _____

6. rudiment _____

7. decadence _____

8. miscreant _____

9. sanction _____

10. consonant _____

11. irascible _____

12. subservient _____

13. comely _____

14. bumptious _____

15. vivacious _____

16. repartee _____

17. satiate _____

18. hypercritical _____

19. cite _____

20. gibe _____

EXERCISE 2 *Reading Strategically* ✍

Directions. Now that you have read the passage and thought about the words in boldface, circle the letter of the correct answer to each of the following items. The numbers of the items are the same as the numbers of the boldface Vocabulary Words in the passage.

1. In this passage, **erroneous** means
   (A) correct
   (B) otherwise
   (C) incorrect
   (D) thoughtful
   (E) different

2. In the passage, to be **ostentatious** is to be _____.
   (A) rich
   (B) too showy
   (C) poverty stricken
   (D) distinguished
   (E) well traveled

3. We can infer from the passage that Adams fits the **stereotype** of a "rich kid" because
   (A) he defied all expectations of what the rich should be
   (B) he attended college
   (C) he became a lawyer
   (D) he rose from poverty to become well known
   (E) he had all of the advantages and privileges of wealth

4. The writer lets us know that **pretentious** may be defined as "unjustly claiming or demanding a position of distinction" by
   (A) saying that Adams depended on family connections for his fame
   (B) saying that Adams had excellent credit
   (C) suggesting that Adams actually earned distinction on his own
   (D) pointing out that Adams became a teacher
   (E) using a synonym

5. When the author tells us that we can assume that Adams chose not to **flaunt** his upbringing, we should realize that he
   (A) did not show off
   (B) became successful
   (C) remained wealthy
   (D) lived a good life
   (E) always had to be the center of attention

6. What strategy does the writer use to tell you that **rudiment** is defined as a fundamental principle?
   (A) The writer shows that **rudiment** obviously refers to his philosophy.
   (B) The writer explains that a **rudiment** is shown to be little comfort.
   (C) The writer uses a metaphor for **rudiment**.
   (D) The writer ties **rudiment** to the phrase "fundamental principle."
   (E) The writer says that because history is an energetic force it is a **rudiment**.

7. In the passage, **decadence** is

(A) ten years
(B) moral decay
(C) scientific discoveries
(D) an energetic force
(E) a virtue

8. We can infer from the passage that **miscreant** means

(A) project
(B) inventor
(C) modern society
(D) explosion
(E) villain

9. If Adams would **sanction** arms controls, as the writer suggests, we may expect that Adams

(A) would be in favor of them
(B) would strongly oppose them
(C) would study them
(D) would question them
(E) would ignore them

10. The writer provides a clue to the meaning of **consonant** by

(A) defining the word in another sentence
(B) telling us that **consonant** means "disagreeable"
(C) placing **consonant** in a series with *agreeable* and *harmonious*
(D) referring back to a previous paragraph
(E) putting **consonant** in a series with the phrase "encouraging influence"

11. In the passage, what does **irascible** mean?

(A) self-supporting
(B) angry
(C) determined
(D) educated
(E) overworked

12. When we read in the passage that Hurston didn't seem to mind **subservient** positions, we should realize that

(A) she never planned to get a better job
(B) **subservient** positions are wonderful jobs
(C) she preferred the jobs she had
(D) she was willing to work at inferior jobs
(E) she worked because she wanted to, not because she had to

13. We can infer from the passage that **comely** means

(A) unpleasant
(B) good-looking
(C) smart
(D) talented
(E) hard-working

14. In the passage, **bumptious** means
(A) bumbling
(B) quiet
(C) brave
(D) determined
(E) pushy

15. The writer provides a clue to the meaning of **vivacious** by
(A) placing it in a series with spirited and lively
(B) contrasting it with lively
(C) explaining that Hurston was talented and determined
(D) using it to describe readers
(E) giving antonyms for it

16. We can infer from the passage that a **repartee** is a
(A) burst of tears
(B) challenging riddle
(C) smart comeback
(D) stammering response
(E) fit of anger

17. How does the writer provide a clue to the meaning of **satiate**?
(A) The writer relates **satiate** to celebration.
(B) The writer explains that **satiate** is connected to Hurston's hunger for personal recognition.
(C) The writer provides examples of how Hurston attempts to undermine or destroy her desires.
(D) The writer links Hurston's attempt to **satiate** a desire with a goal that she could never satisfy.
(E) The writer defines **satiate** as "to convince."

18. The author of the passage mentions that Adams was **hypercritical** of the modern era. We should realize that this means he
(A) was very excited about the modern era
(B) wished that he had been born a hundred years earlier
(C) made overly harsh comments about the modern era
(D) was very sensitive to criticism of the modern era
(E) was an authority on the modern era

19. We can infer from the passage that **cite** means to _____ a source of information.
(A) ignore
(B) copy
(C) criticize
(D) quote
(E) authorize

20. How does the writer provide a clue to the meaning of the word **gibe**?
(A) The writer refers to endurance.
(B) The writer associates **gibe** with derisive remarks and taunts.
(C) The writer says it was because of her portrayals of southern African Americans.
(D) The writer also calls it a compliment.
(E) The writer says it means complaining.

READING NEW WORDS IN CONTEXT

Lesson 5 CONTEXT: The Literature

The passage gives you an opportunity to expand your vocabulary. Below are twenty Vocabulary Words that are used in the passage and in the exercises that follow it.

abridge	finality	intangible	subterfuge
affable	furor	invoke	supercilious
bolster	garrulous	lucrative	tawdry
emendation	idiomatic	reciprocate	verbose
expletive	impromptu	shrew	wistful

Anne Bradstreet: The Nation's First Poet

The first accomplished American poet wasn't Edgar Allan Poe or Henry Wadsworth Longfellow. In fact, the first American poet wasn't a man. And the distinction does not go to Emily Dickinson. To find America's first distinguished poet, you must go all the way back to the 1600s.

That's when Anne Bradstreet (c. 1612–1672) lived and—when she wasn't managing a house and raising eight children—wrote her poems. Bradstreet's *The Tenth Muse Lately Sprung Up in America,* published in England in 1650, is the first volume of original verse written in America. The volume's publication was achieved by **subterfuge** (1). The poet's brother-in-law secretly took the volume to England where he had it published without her knowledge. Bradstreet was sure that the Puritan community would be in an uproar over a woman publishing a volume of poetry, but no **furor** (2) occurred.

The Tenth Muse was successful in London. It sold well, so we may presume it produced a profit and so was a **lucrative** (3) venture. The book's favorable reception didn't make the deeply religious Bradstreet haughty, conceited, or **supercilious** (4). Instead, the poet drew strength from her success; in fact, it **bolstered** (5) her resolve to write more.

The Puritan Poet and Her Muse

Bradstreet was born Anne Dudley around 1612 in Northampton, England. At the age of sixteen, she married Simon Bradstreet. Two years later, in 1630, the Dudleys and the Bradstreets sailed to New England to avoid religious persecution, and they became Massachusetts colonists. (Both her father and husband eventually became Massachusetts governors.)

Clinging to their Puritan faith, the Bradstreets and the other colonists fought the land, weather, famine, and disease. As a devout Puritan, Bradstreet believed that a woman should play a supporting role in her home and in the community. Based on her writings, Bradstreet also had some notions of women's equality: "I am obnoxious to each carping tongue / Who says my hand a needle better fits." These lines are not meant to indicate that Bradstreet was a **shrew** (6) who couldn't control her bad temper. Instead, they reflect the views of a hard-working housewife and poet who used her writing to express early feminist views.

The poems in *The Tenth Muse,* mostly composed before Bradstreet was thirty, are lengthy poems written in a very formal, learned style. When anthology editors use poems from *The Tenth Muse* today, they often **abridge** (7) them. However, you can still find copies of the uncondensed poems. If you compare poems from the first and second editions of *The Tenth Muse,* you will probably notice more than one **emendation** (8), as Bradstreet made numerous corrections to the original volume.

Bradstreet's later poetry, more widely known today, is generally short and concerned with domestic and family themes. Of course, you wouldn't expect gaudy, showy, or **tawdry** (9) subjects in Puritan poetry, but Bradstreet's subjects are particularly natural and simple. Her subjects include birth, death, her children, her husband, and her illnesses. Some poems deal with **intangible** (10) themes such as love. Bradstreet's poems about her family show that she was a loving person and, presumably, **affable** (11), pleasant, and kind as well. And poems such as "To My Dear and Loving Husband," in which she writes "Thy love is such I can no way repay," indicates that she felt her husband **reciprocated** (12) her love several times over. Although a strong Puritan spirituality dominated Bradstreet's life, her poems are rooted in practical concerns rather than **wistful** (13) or yearning sentiments. Instead, she shows the divine in the everyday life of a wife and mother. In some of these poems, you can feel her **impromptu** (14), spontaneous inspirations. In typical Puritan fashion, she often **invokes** (15) God, finding comfort and guidance in calling upon a higher power. You certainly won't find an **expletive** (16) in Bradstreet's poems. Even in "Upon the Burning of Our House July 10, 1666," in which the speaker watches her home and her possessions go up in flames, she utters no curses but instead blesses God's name. By the end of the poem, Bradstreet has no unsettled feelings about the disaster; she concludes with comforting **finality** (17) that earthly possessions do not matter for "My hope and treasure lies above."

A Poet's Use of Language

The poems reflect the style of the times, and Bradstreet's words are characteristic of the English language of the 1600s. Examples of such **idiomatic** (18) words include *ought,* meaning "anything whatever" and *pelf,* meaning "worldly goods." Unlike her early poems, Bradstreet's later poems are not wordy or **verbose** (19). Bradstreet seems to have found her poetic voice in these later, more brief poems. It's probably safe to assume that Bradstreet was not a **garrulous** (20) figure who talked too much about trivialities.

Anne Bradstreet was a remarkable woman who, in her own way, defied colonial society's and the Puritan religion's conventional ideas about the place of a woman. In so doing, she helped define and establish a literary tradition for a new country.

EXERCISE 1 *Finding Synonyms*

Directions. Reread the preceding passage. Then write on the line provided a synonym for each of the words in boldface. If you cannot think of an exact synonym, you may write a brief definition of the word.

1. subterfuge _____

2. furor _____

3. lucrative _____

4. supercilious _____

5. bolstered _____

6. shrew _____

7. abridge _____

8. emendation _____

9. tawdry _____

10. intangible _____

11. affable _____

12. reciprocated _____

13. wistful _____

14. impromptu _____

15. invokes _____

16. expletive _____

17. finality _____

18. idiomatic _____

19. verbose _____

20. garrulous _____

EXERCISE 2 *Reading Strategically* 👈

Directions. Now that you have read the passage and thought about the words in boldface, circle the letter of the correct answer to each of the following items. The numbers of the items are the same as the numbers of the boldface Vocabulary Words in the passage.

1. In the passage, Bradstreet's brother-in-law carried out a **subterfuge**, or a sort of _____, to publish the poems.
   (A) consensus
   (B) contract
   (C) campaign
   (D) subscription
   (E) deception

2. In the passage, **furor** means
   (A) secret discussion
   (B) calm acceptance
   (C) public uproar
   (D) battle
   (E) anger

3. If the publication of Bradstreet's first volume of poetry was a **lucrative** venture, as the author suggests, then we may expect that the volume
   (A) produced a profit
   (B) was a disaster
   (C) was a business partnership
   (D) was a literary project
   (E) made little money

4. How does the writer let us know that **supercilious** may be defined as "overly proud"?
   (A) The writer relates the word to success.
   (B) The writer associates **supercilious** with the words *haughty* and *conceited*.
   (C) The writer contrasts **supercilious** with an antonym.
   (D) The writer has established pride as characteristic of Bradstreet's personality.
   (E) The writer is critical of Bradstreet's success.

5. In the passage, Bradstreet was **bolstered** by the success of *The Tenth Muse* because
   (A) the success discouraged her
   (B) the success was dependent on future writing
   (C) the success had no effect on her
   (D) the success gave her strength
   (E) the success was unknown to her

6. **Shrew** usually means a small mammal. However, in the passage the word is used in a different way. In the passage, **shrew** means a
   (A) muse
   (B) bad-tempered woman
   (C) colonial housewife
   (D) skilled English-language poet
   (E) feminist

7. We can infer from the passage that **abridge** means to
   (A) condense
   (B) lengthen
   (C) rewrite
   (D) critique
   (E) remove

8. In the passage, an **emendation** is a(n)
   (A) illustration
   (B) correction
   (C) reprint
   (D) dedication
   (E) disclaimer

9. In the passage, a **tawdry** subject is one that is
   (A) silly
   (B) late
   (C) family related
   (D) pure and simple
   (E) gaudy or showy

10. How does the writer provide a clue to the meaning of **intangible**?

    (A) The writer uses love as an example of an **intangible** theme.

    (B) The writer uses a synonym for **intangible.**

    (C) The writer uses **intangible** in a series of similar words.

    (D) The writer restates the meaning in different words.

    (E) The writer contrasts **intangible** with the word *concrete*.

11. In the passage, _____ is another word for **affable**.

    (A) capable

    (B) efficient

    (C) pleasant

    (D) wife

    (E) affluent

12. In the passage, _____ is another word for **reciprocated**.

    (A) scorned

    (B) analyzed

    (C) returned

    (D) begrudged

    (E) absorbed

13. The writer tells you that **wistful** is defined as "full of melancholy yearning" by

    (A) defining the word

    (B) joining **wistful** with the word *yearning*

    (C) using a synonym for **wistful**

    (D) describing Bradstreet's poetry as **wistful**

    (E) comparing the words **wistful** and *poetry*

14. The writer provides a clue to the meaning of **impromptu** by

    (A) relating it to everyday life

    (B) calling poetry "inspired"

    (C) merging the domestic and the spiritual

    (D) linking it to the word *spontaneous*

    (E) relating it to the Divine

15. In the passage, one who **invokes** God

    (A) is hateful

    (B) is typical

    (C) is a Puritan

    (D) calls upon God

    (E) rejects comfort and guidance

16. In the passage, **expletive** means

    (A) a curse

    (B) a certainty

    (C) poetic

    (D) difficult to find

    (E) typically Puritan

17. When we read in the passage that Bradstreet concludes with comforting **finality,** we should realize that **finality** means

    (A) beginning

    (B) a prayer that calls on God for guidance

    (C) the quality of being settled

    (D) a comforting thought

    (E) the quality of being unsure

18. How does the writer provide a clue to the meaning of **idiomatic**?

    (A) The writer quotes lines of Bradstreet's poetry.

    (B) The writer uses **idiomatic** to describe words belonging to a given language and era.

    (C) The writer relates **idiomatic** to poetry only.

    (D) The writer explains that **idiomatic** means to talk only of trivial matters.

    (E) The writer includes **idiomatic** in a series of words similar in meaning.

19. In the passage, **verbose** means

    (A) imaginative

    (B) silent

    (C) concise

    (D) poetic

    (E) wordy

20. In the passage, a **garrulous** person

    (A) is impossible

    (B) is untruthful

    (C) talks too much, especially about trivialities

    (D) is scholarly

    (E) talks too little and is hard to get along with

READING NEW WORDS IN CONTEXT

Lesson 6 | CONTEXT: The People

The passage gives you an opportunity to expand your vocabulary. Below are twenty Vocabulary Words that are used in the passage and in the exercises that follow it.

adamant	beneficent	frustrate	repugnant
ambivalent	betrothed	interminable	resilient
antagonize	congenital	intrepid	sallow
archives	consensus	peremptory	sortie
autocrat	factious	procrastinate	supplication

The Pilgrims: Surviving "The Starving Time"

North America was a rude awakening for the Puritan Pilgrims. After sailing from England aboard the *Mayflower* in 1620, they encountered a harsh and dangerous land. Their first year was especially discouraging, filled with hardships, disease, and death. These setbacks would have been enough to **frustrate** (1) even the most determined colonists. William Bradford (1590–1657), in his history, *Of Plymouth Plantation*, refers to the experience as "the starving time." Yet these devout Puritans believed in the generosity and goodness of their god. They relied completely on God's **beneficence** (2). Through their prayers of **supplication** (3), they received the guidance and strength that they asked for.

The Puritan Faith

The Puritans were a Protestant sect that tried to reform the traditional and ritualized Church of England. The Puritans believed that grace from God was not **congenital** (4). People were not born with grace but achieved it through a lifetime of good work. They believed in a more personal relationship with their god, one between the individual worshiper and his or her god. They felt that the Church of England was too **peremptory** (5), arrogant, and dictatorial. The Puritans tried to create a more democratic community, where decisions were made by **consensus** (6) rather than by one person. In the Puritan church, all the worshipers had some input in the religious service. The Church of England, on the other hand, was run in a much more **autocratic** (7) way: only church officials made decisions. The criticism the Puritans experienced was often fierce, but they remained **adamant** (8), yielding not an inch in their faith. As a result of persecution, the Pilgrims eventually sought religious freedom in the New World. Calling themselves Pilgrims, a group of more than one hundred set off in the *Mayflower* for the colony of Virginia. They landed instead on the coast of what is now Massachusetts on November 11, 1620.

The coast's stark sand dunes must have been a disappointment to the travelers. With winter approaching, the Pilgrims decided there could be no **procrastination** (9) in settling there—housing and shelter were built immediately. Even the most **intrepid** (10), or courageous, of the colonists probably had mixed, changing, or **ambivalent** (11) feelings about their new home. All the Pilgrims remained committed and united, however; there were no **factious** (12) members who quarreled or refused to do their share of the work.

Colonial Life

From William Bradford's writings, one gets a vivid impression of the colony's early months. Bradford records that half the colonists died within three months. The winter was harsh, made more difficult by the lack of proper supplies and shelter. The cold weather lasted so long that it seemed **interminable** (13). Scurvy and other diseases proved fatal to many colonists and the lack of food left others looking sickly, pale, and **sallow** (14). The few healthy colonists willingly took care of the sick and tended to even the most **repugnant** (15) of chores that those with queasy stomachs would find disgusting. The Pilgrims were **resilient** (16), however, and were able to bounce back after the long winter. They were fortunate, too, in being befriended by Squanto (1585?–1622), one of a few surviving members of the Patuxet tribe. He helped the colonists make peace with the local Wampanoag tribe, whom the Pilgrims had **antagonized** (17) during the winter by taking and eating some of their grain. Squanto mediated between the angry Wampanoag and the starving Pilgrims, and he later taught the Pilgrims how to plant and harvest crops of their own. The result of this harvest was, of course, the famous first Thanksgiving in the autumn of 1621.

Documents of Early Colonial Life and Legend

Many scholars agree that William Bradford's firsthand look at Pilgrim life is one of the most important documents in early American history. Bradford began writing his history of Plymouth Colony in 1630. Until 1647, he wrote annual accounts of the settlement. The Plymouth church's records contained the first nine chapters of Bradford's history. The church doubled as **archives** (18), serving as a place for the storage and preservation of such important historical material. The original manuscript was lost during the Revolutionary War, perhaps during a military **sortie** (19), or defensive attack. In any event, historians believe the manuscript was picked up as a souvenir by a British soldier and carried back to England where it was discovered in 1855 and published the following year.

William Bradford was dedicated not only to recording the history of the New World but also to making history. He was elected thirty times to lead the Pilgrim community. His assistant governor was John Alden (1599–1687). The story of how Alden became **betrothed** (20) and later married to Priscilla Mullens (1602?–1685?) is famous, thanks to the Henry Wadsworth Longfellow poem "The Courtship of Miles Standish." Clearly, Bradford's records were crucial to the documentation of early American history and were the basis for some famous American legends.

EXERCISE 1 *Finding Synonyms*

Directions. Reread the preceding passage. Then write on the line provided a synonym for each of the words in boldface. If you cannot think of an exact synonym, you may write a brief definition of the word.

1. frustrate _____

2. beneficence _____

3. supplication _____

4. congenital _____

Name _____ Date _____ Class _____

5. peremptory _____

6. consensus _____

7. autocratic _____

8. adamant _____

9. procrastination _____

10. intrepid _____

11. ambivalent _____

12. factious _____

13. interminable _____

14. sallow _____

15. repugnant _____

16. resilient _____

17. antagonized _____

18. archives _____

19. sortie _____

20. betrothed _____

EXERCISE 2 *Reading Strategically* ☞

Directions. Now that you have read the passage and thought about the words in boldface, circle the letter of the correct answer to each of the following items. The numbers of the items are the same as the numbers of the boldface Vocabulary Words in the passage.

1. How does the writer let us know that **frustrate** may be defined as "to cause feelings of discouragement and bafflement"?
   (A) The writer says that the New World was a rude awakening for the Pilgrims.
   (B) The writer tells how harsh and dangerous the land was.
   (C) The writer links **frustrate** to the words *setback* and *discouraging*.
   (D) The writer relates **frustrate** to determination.
   (E) The writer relates **frustrate** to disease and death.

2. We can infer from the passage that **beneficence** means
   (A) anger and ill will
   (B) indifference
   (C) goodness and generosity
   (D) attention
   (E) efficiency and practicality

3. In this passage, **supplication** means
   (A) an application
   (B) a request
   (C) a demand
   (D) a conquest
   (E) curses

4. According to the passage, the Puritans believed that grace is not **congenital,** or present at birth, because
   (A) there is no such thing as grace
   (B) only members of the Church of England may have grace
   (C) grace is only achieved through a lifetime of good work
   (D) grace is granted only at death
   (E) the members of their community are not devout enough

5. The writer provides clues to the meaning of **peremptory** by
   (A) associating **peremptory** with the words *arrogant* and *dictatorial*
   (B) linking **peremptory** to democratic
   (C) explaining that the Puritans received criticism
   (D) providing the synonym *individual*
   (E) describing the nature of the relationship of the Pilgrims with their god

6. In the passage, **consensus** means
   (A) religious devotion
   (B) opposition to authority
   (C) common sense
   (D) general agreement
   (E) authority

7. When we read in the passage that the Puritans considered the Church of England **autocratic,** we should realize that they thought it
   (A) worked automatically
   (B) responded to the will of its members
   (C) was an efficient organization
   (D) operated with too few rules and regulations
   (E) did not include worshipers in decision making

8. According to the passage, if you are **adamant,** you are
   (A) unyielding
   (B) faithless
   (C) arrogant
   (D) religious
   (E) persecuted

9. We can infer from the passage that **procrastination** is defined as "to postpone or delay" because
   (A) the writer notes that shelter and housing were built immediately
   (B) the writer explains that the Pilgrims were reluctant to stay in the New World
   (C) the writer suggests that the Pilgrims had mixed feelings about their new homes
   (D) the writer notes the lack of commitment shown by the Pilgrims
   (E) the Pilgrims refused to work in the New World

10. In the passage, **intrepid** means
  (A) mixed
  (B) disappointed
  (C) courageous
  (D) united
  (E) scurvy

11. When the writer describes the Pilgrims' feelings as **ambivalent,** we should realize that their feelings were
  (A) definite
  (B) determined
  (C) personal
  (D) mixed
  (E) angry and bitter

12. According to the passage, _____ characterizes a **factious** group.
  (A) poor leadership
  (B) quarreling among the members
  (C) hunger
  (D) **procrastination**
  (E) total unity and profound commitment

13. We can infer from the passage that if the winter lasted so long that it seemed **interminable,** then it must have seemed
  (A) endless
  (B) short
  (C) difficult
  (D) frustrating
  (E) queasy

14. How does the writer provide a clue to the meaning of the word **sallow**?
  (A) The writer says it means "fatal."
  (B) The writer places **sallow** in a series with *sickly* and *pale.*
  (C) The writer relates **sallow** to the words *disgusting* and *queasy.*
  (D) The writer says it is commonplace.
  (E) The writer says it is a kind of bird.

15. In the passage, most people find **repugnant** chores _____.
  (A) enjoyable
  (B) disgusting
  (C) abundant
  (D) hazardous
  (E) painful

16. The writer provides a clue to the meaning of **resilient** by explaining that the Pilgrims
  (A) were able to bounce back
  (B) starved and many died
  (C) were fortunate to meet Squanto
  (D) were able to make peace with the Wampanoag
  (E) barely survived the long winter

17. In the passage, **antagonized** means

    (A) pleased

    (B) fed

    (C) angered

    (D) taught

    (E) harvested

18. In the passage, what does it mean that the church doubled as the **archives** for Bradford's writings?

    (A) The church was in a cave.

    (B) The church was used for the storage of financial documents only.

    (C) The church was interested in the documents.

    (D) The church was used to store and preserve important documents.

    (E) The church is a place of history.

19. In the passage, a **sortie** is

    (A) an exit

    (B) a military officer

    (C) a sordid act

    (D) a defensive attack

    (E) an indecisive act

20. In the passage, to be **betrothed** means to be _____.

    (A) separated

    (B) friends

    (C) engaged

    (D) betrayed

    (E) married

READING NEW WORDS IN CONTEXT

Lesson 7 │ CONTEXT: The People

This letter gives you an opportunity to expand your vocabulary. Below are twenty Vocabulary Words that are used in the letter and in the exercises that follow it.

blithe	expedite	interpose	provocation
cede	filial	intrinsic	query
chagrin	forgo	plebeian	remission
debonair	incoherent	precipitate	secular
exonerate	incredulous	proficient	shibboleth

A Letter from Lenox Avenue

Dear Terrell,
Hello from Lenox Avenue, the main street in Harlem! It's strange to be here in New York City. Harlem buzzes with an **intrinsic** (1) vitality that is its essential characteristic. It's crowded, noisy, busy. There's poverty, even unrest. You'd be **incredulous** (2) if I said Harlem is a treasure—or at least you should be skeptical—but it's true.

But my main interest isn't Lenox Avenue today. You've been in my American Literature class. I'm excited, and you probably know why. To me, just being where the Harlem Renaissance of the 1920s took place is **provocation** (3) for excitement.

During the Harlem Renaissance, Harlem was the world's largest African American community. What happened to **precipitate** (4) this growth? A big factor was people coming north to take industrial jobs during and after World War I. Harlem also was the African American cultural and intellectual capital of the nation. This is where artists—writers, musicians, and actors—gathered.

As I walk down Lenox Avenue, I think about the poets of the Harlem Renaissance who once strolled these streets. If only James Weldon Johnson (1871–1938), Claude McKay (1890–1948), Countee Cullen (1903–1946), and (my favorite) Langston Hughes (1902–1967) could walk by me now! I'd love to **query** (5) them about what Harlem was like back then; their answers to my questions would be most interesting, I'm sure!

The energy in your poetry reminds me of theirs. I'll **forgo** (6) making direct comparisons, though. I'll refrain because I don't want to embarrass you. But I know you'd appreciate Lenox Avenue, too. I'll tell you a little bit about these great poets.

Pride was the main theme of Johnson's poetry. He also produced *The Book of American Negro Poetry*, an important early anthology of poems by African Americans. He was not only a **proficient** (7) poet and editor, but had many other skills as well. He was also an expert teacher, lawyer, diplomat, and political leader.

Injustices to African Americans was an important theme of McKay's poems. McKay, a native of Jamaica, won a prize for his poetry that allowed him to come to the United States to study. As somewhat of an outsider, McKay could comment on African American life. In his poem "America," he writes with disappointment, embarrassment, and **chagrin** (8) of one African American man's feelings for this country.

Cullen thought of himself mainly as an old-fashioned lyric poet, like the English Romantics. He was a native of New York City, had a Master's degree from Harvard, and was an editor and a prolific poet. I imagine that Cullen was the type of person who was charming and smooth, who always conducted himself gracefully. In short, I imagine him to be **debonair** (9). Yet his poetry addressed important racial issues. His poem "Tableau," for instance, describes two boys, one African American and one white, walking arm in arm. Cullen makes it clear that society would like to **interpose** (10) its prejudices between the two friends, but no such interference comes.

The most famous of the Harlem Renaissance poets was Langston Hughes. He was born in Joplin, Missouri, and first came to Harlem in 1921. His special interest was capturing the everyday feelings and lives of poor African Americans, especially those in Harlem. Like other African American poets of the time, Hughes used dialect as a **shibboleth** (11) to distinguish his poetry from mainstream poetry. In other words, he used dialect to make his poetry a distinct statement about racial and class issues. He also had a talent for turning **plebeian** (12), common, or crude images into art. Hughes was a dedicated poet

whose career suffered no **remission** (13). He experienced no setbacks such as writer's block as he went on to produce fifteen volumes of verse over the course of fifty years. From his writings, which also included plays, opera, fiction, and essays, one can tell that Hughes was a complex man, capable of being both serious and **blithe** (14). His poetry is filled with both **secular** (15) and spiritual images.

Interestingly, Hughes originally came to Harlem to study engineering according to his father's wishes. Hughes could not fulfill his **filial** (16) duty to his father, however, and turned to literature. I think his success as a poet is enough to **exonerate** (17) him of any charges of failure.

I hope you've decided to take the independent study class next year. Mr. Anderson had to **cede** (18) the class to me; he had to give it up because of ill health. I'd like for us to study—you guessed it—the Harlem Renaissance poets. How can you resist now? You need to decide quickly. Maybe this letter will help **expedite** (19) your decision.

I hope you've been able to understand my ramblings. If I've been **incoherent** (20), give me a poor grade. See you soon at school!

Sincerely,
Mrs. Helms

EXERCISE 1 *Finding Synonyms* ☞

Directions. Reread the preceding passage. Then write on the line provided a synonym for each of the words in boldface. If you cannot think of an exact synonym, you may write a brief definition of the word.

1. intrinsic _____

2. incredulous _____

3. provocation _____

4. precipitate _____

5. query _____

6. forgo _____

7. proficient _____

180 LESSON 7

8. chagrin _____

9. debonair _____

10. interpose _____

11. shibboleth _____

12. plebeian _____

13. remission _____

14. blithe _____

15. secular _____

16. filial _____

17. exonerate _____

18. cede _____

19. expedite _____

20. incoherent _____

EXERCISE 2 *Reading Strategically* ☞

Directions. Now that you have read the passage and thought about the words in boldface, circle the letter of the correct answer to each of the following items. The numbers of the items are the same as the numbers of the boldface Vocabulary Words in the passage.

1. In the passage, **intrinsic** means
(A) vitality
(B) essential
(C) inherited
(D) strange
(E) considerate

2. In the passage, an **incredulous** person is
(A) believing
(B) skeptical
(C) poor
(D) informed
(E) excited

3. According to the passage, being in Harlem is **provocation** for excitement because the writer

(A) is very interested in seeing where the Harlem Renaissance took place

(B) is bored with Harlem and is anxious to return home

(C) has never been to New York before and finds it exhilarating

(D) is a teacher

(E) is easily provoked

4. We can infer from the passage that to **precipitate** growth is to _____ growth.

(A) slow down

(B) interfere with

(C) stunt

(D) rain on

(E) bring on

5. What strategy does the writer use to tell you that **query** means "to question"?

(A) The writer includes a definition of the word.

(B) The writer wishes the poets were alive to answer her questions.

(C) The writer relates the word to embarrassment.

(D) The writer explains that the poets used to walk on Lenox Avenue.

(E) The writer gives an example of a query by asking Terrell how he is.

6. In the passage, **forgo** means to

(A) go

(B) think about

(C) stop

(D) refrain from

(E) refuse to

7. When we read in the passage that James Weldon Johnson was a **proficient** writer, we should realize that he was a(n)

(A) professional writer

(B) efficient writer

(C) skillful writer

(D) appropriate writer

(E) important writer

8. When the writer of the passage mentions that McKay wrote his poem "America" with **chagrin,** we should realize that McKay

(A) wrote with embarrassment and disappointment

(B) wrote of one African American man's experience

(C) wrote of injustices to African Americans

(D) was eager to come to the United States to study

(E) was an outsider to American culture

9. In the passage, someone who is **debonair** is

(A) well educated

(B) short tempered

(C) prolific

(D) extremely rude and unpleasant

(E) charming and graceful

10. How does the writer let us know that **interpose** may be defined as "to interfere or intervene"?

    (A) The writer later uses the word *prejudices*.
    (B) The writer later uses the word *interference*.
    (C) The writer says Cullen makes the situation clear.
    (D) The writer links the word to society.
    (E) The writer expects people to be unprejudiced.

11. What strategy does the writer use to tell you that **shibboleth** means "language or words that distinguish one class from another"?

    (A) The writer restates **shibboleth** in other words.
    (B) The writer gives a specific example of a **shibboleth**.
    (C) The writer says Hughes turned crude images into art.
    (D) The writer associates the word with mainstream poetry.
    (E) The writer captures everyday feelings with the word.

12. How does the writer provide a clue to the meaning of **plebeian**?

    (A) The writer relates **plebeian** to talent.
    (B) The writer connects **plebeian** with art.
    (C) The writer calls Hughes **plebeian**.
    (D) The writer links **plebeian** to the word *common*.
    (E) The writer says **plebeian** means "elegant and graceful."

13. When we read that Hughes's career suffered no **remission,** we should realize that it

    (A) had no purpose
    (B) experienced no crippling setbacks
    (C) made him rich and famous
    (D) never encountered any obstacles
    (E) made him feel guilty

14. In the passage, **blithe** is used as an antonym for, or contrast to, the word *serious*. Therefore it may be defined as _____.

    (A) sad
    (B) passionate
    (C) cheerful
    (D) thoughtful
    (E) depressing

15. The author tells us that Hughes's poetry is filled with both **secular** and spiritual images. Therefore

    (A) **secular** means worldly
    (B) **secular** and *spiritual* are synonyms
    (C) **secular** means sacred
    (D) **secular** means poetic
    (E) **secular** reflects the imagination

16. When we read in the passage that Hughes failed in his **filial** duty, we should realize that

    (A) **filial** means sincere and well-meaning
    (B) **filial** is associated with a son or daughter
    (C) **filial** means to be required
    (D) Hughes failed in his chosen career of engineering
    (E) Hughes lost respect for his father

17. According to the passage, why is it possible to **exonerate** Hughes of any charges of failure?

(A) Hughes's father forgave him for failing engineering.
(B) Engineering is a more difficult subject than literature.
(C) Hughes's literary success clears him of any such charges.
(D) The writer is sympathetic to Hughes.
(E) The writer condemns Hughes.

18. We can infer from the passage that to **cede** means to

(A) be independent
(B) become ill
(C) teach
(D) transplant something
(E) give up something

19. If the letter helps **expedite** Terrell's decision, as the passage suggests, we may expect that it will help him to

(A) decide quickly
(B) delay deciding
(C) abandon the idea of taking the class
(D) be excited
(E) stop deciding

20. When we read in the passage that the writer is worried about being **incoherent**, we should realize that she fears that

(A) her letter is messy
(B) her letter is not well-organized
(C) her writing is too lengthy
(D) her letter was sent to the wrong address
(E) her writing is too forceful

READING NEW WORDS IN CONTEXT

Lesson 8 **CONTEXT: The People**

The passage gives you an opportunity to expand your vocabulary. Below are twenty Vocabulary Words that are used in the passage and in the exercises that follow it.

acquiesce	bulwark	insidious	phalanx
altercation	coalition	invidious	predecessor
assail	deprecate	martyr	redress
beleaguer	exodus	palliate	repression
brunt	heinous	peripheral	waive

The Cherokee Removal

There are those who weep when thinking of the Trail of Tears. That's the route the Cherokees followed during the forced **exodus** (1) from their homeland. Some people today **assail** (2) this mass departure by attacking it in books and articles as one of the most **heinous** (3), vile, or wicked acts in American history. You can decide for yourself after considering the facts of the case.

Jackson's Role in the Removal

Who ordered the journey? The most serious accusations concerning the cause of the Cherokee Indian removal usually are directed at President Andrew Jackson (1767–1845), who served in office from 1829 to 1837. As a result, Jackson bears the **brunt** (4) of the blame in many people's opinions. Jackson sided with southern states that refused to recognize tribal governments. The states wanted the Cherokees' land for farming and for mining gold. Southern Cherokees refused to **waive** (5) the right to have their own governments. This right had been guaranteed in treaties and was at the center of the Cherokees' argument. However, the Jackson administration treated the Indians' rights as **peripheral** (6) to their claim. Consequently,

Jackson ignored the Cherokees' rights to their property and their government. In a case involving the Cherokee Nation in Georgia, the Supreme Court sided with the tribes. Still Jackson defied the Supreme Court, not with **insidious** (7) plots but by openly trying to persuade the tribes to move to what is now Oklahoma.

In 1830, Congress supported Jackson by approving money to relocate the southern tribes. Many people, neither understanding nor caring about the lives of the American Indians, went along with the president's policy; others found the policy **invidious** (8), sure to arouse anger and hatred. Some members of Congress openly **deprecated** (9) Jackson's policy, but their strong disapproval didn't change anything.

At the time, there were about seventy thousand American Indians in Georgia, Alabama, Mississippi, and Florida. The Cherokee Nation flourished in Georgia, Alabama, Tennessee, and North Carolina. The Cherokees were a well-organized community that had their own constitution, written language, and newspaper. Like the European settlers with whom they coexisted, they wanted to farm the land and live by the fruit of their labor.

The removal of the Cherokees and the destruction of the Cherokee Nation are tragic results of Jackson's policy. In 1838, federal troops acted on the orders of President Martin Van Buren (1782–1862), who followed the removal policy of his **predecessor** (10), Andrew Jackson, and started rounding up the Cherokees. Soldiers **beleaguered** (11) the Cherokees, surrounding their homes in order to force them out. In some instances, the soldiers destroyed the Cherokee's homes and property and the victims lost everything. One soldier called his role in the Cherokee removal "the cruelest work I ever knew." The Cherokees could not resist the **phalanx** (12) of soldiers that massed and invaded their communities like brutally efficient army ants. They had no choice but to **acquiesce** (13) and give in like defeated prisoners in an unnamed war. After all, who possibly could **redress** (14) their treatment? Would the president offer remedy? There was no one to be a **bulwark** (15), a strong support or protection. The Cherokees were placed in detention camps to await their removal to the West.

Some Cherokees escaped the soldiers. Others died at the hands of the government. Such was the fate of Tsali Wasituna. A soldier mistreated Tsali's wife. An angry argument presumably occurred, and Tsali ended up killing the soldier during the **altercation** (16). Tsali escaped, but later surrendered to save others of his people. Because he was put to death for the sake of a cause—his people—he is regarded as a **martyr** (17).

The Long, Hard Journey West

In October 1838, the largest group of Cherokees (about fifteen thousand) started the journey west. Their route took them from Georgia, through Tennessee, Kentucky, Illinois, Missouri, and Arkansas, to Oklahoma, then called Indian Territory. Most of them walked (sometimes through days and days of blowing snow), but the sick, the old, and the children rode in wagons. The trip was extremely difficult because the winter was so severe: Food and shelter were scarce, clothing was inadequate, and no help was available. There was no way to **palliate** (18) the suffering, no way to relieve the distress. Some four thousand Cherokees died along the way. Their deaths weren't the result of outright killing but, rather, of the slow, sure slaughter of a forced, suppressing march. The route became known as the Trail of Tears and has become symbolic of **repression** (19). One Cherokee later described the journey: "Children cry and many men cry, and all look sad like when friends die, but they say nothing and just put heads down and keep on towards West. Many days pass and people die very much."

Once settled in Oklahoma, survivors of the Trail of Tears joined with the Chickasaw, Choctaw, Creek, and Seminole nations in the Indian Territory to form an alliance. This **coalition** (20) was named the Five Civilized Tribes.

EXERCISE 1   *Finding Synonyms* ✍

Directions. Reread the preceding passage. Then write on the line provided a synonym for each of the words in boldface. If you cannot think of an exact synonym, you may write a brief definition of the word.

1. exodus _____

2. assail _____

3. heinous _____

4. brunt _____

5. waive _____

6. peripheral _____

7. insidious _____

8. invidious _____

9. deprecated _____

10. predecessor _____

11. beleaguered _____

12. phalanx _____

13. acquiesce _____

14. redress _____

15. bulwark _____

16. altercation _____

17. martyr _____

18. palliate _____

19. repression _____

20. coalition _____

EXERCISE 2 *Reading Strategically* ✍

Directions. Now that you have read the passage and thought about the words in boldface, circle the letter of the correct answer to each of the following items. The numbers of the items are the same as the numbers of the boldface Vocabulary Words in the passage.

1. How does the writer let us know that an **exodus** may be defined as a "departure, usually of a large group of people"?
(A) The writer relates the word to American history.
(B) The writer puts **exodus** in a series with the words *books* and *articles*.
(C) The writer restates the word as the mass departure of the Cherokees.
(D) The writer describes the route the Cherokees followed.
(E) The writer is critical of the removal of the Cherokees.

2. The writer provides a clue to the meaning of **assail** by
   (A) relating it to the word *forced*
   (B) linking it to the word *attacking*
   (C) implying that it means "approve of"
   (D) later using the word *praise*
   (E) earlier saying it means "ignore"

3. In the passage, **heinous** means
   (A) history
   (B) attack
   (C) consideration
   (D) departure or exit
   (E) vile or wicked

4. In the passage, to bear the **brunt** of the blame means
   (A) to not be blamed at all
   (B) to refuse to accept any blame
   (C) to be responsible for only a small part of the blame
   (D) to express regret or apologize
   (E) to bear the largest part of the blame

5. According to the passage, why did the American Indians in the South refuse to **waive** or relinquish their rights?
   (A) The rights were guaranteed in treaties.
   (B) The rights were misunderstood.
   (C) The rights were based on traditions of the tribes.
   (D) The rights were based on oral agreements.
   (E) The rights had nothing to do with government.

6. We can infer from the passage that another word for **peripheral** is
   (A) relinquish
   (B) rights
   (C) incidental
   (D) guaranteed
   (E) inconsiderate

7. We can infer from the passage that **insidious** means
   (A) open and honest
   (B) public
   (C) hidden and sinister
   (D) internal
   (E) warlike and confrontational

8. When we read in the passage that some people found Jackson's policy **invidious,** we should realize that
   (A) they agreed with it wholeheartedly
   (B) they found the policy attractive
   (C) they didn't understand its complicated language
   (D) they feared it would cause anger and hatred
   (E) they weren't invited to take part in it

9. What strategy does the writer use to suggest the meaning of **deprecated**?
  (A) The writer relates **deprecated** to strong disapproval.
  (B) The writer relates **deprecated** to the word *policy*.
  (C) The writer says it means "to go along."
  (D) The writer implies that the word means "offensive."
  (E) The writer relates **deprecated** to the word *approval*.

10. According to the passage, President Van Buren's **predecessor** was
  (A) the Cherokees
  (B) his vice president
  (C) President Andrew Jackson
  (D) President William Henry Harrison
  (E) the army

11. In the passage, **beleaguered** means
  (A) burned to the ground
  (B) surrounded in order to defeat
  (C) rebuilt from the ground up
  (D) invited into
  (E) watched carefully

12. How does the writer provide a clue to the meaning of the word **phalanx**?
  (A) The writer links **phalanx** to Civil War veterans.
  (B) The writer links it to the image of an organized mass of army ants.
  (C) The writer links **phalanx** to cruel work.
  (D) The writer links it to the image of a group of straggling, ineffective soldiers.
  (E) The writer indicates that a **phalanx** is irresistible.

13. Because the Cherokees were forced to **acquiesce,** they are compared by simile to
  (A) a formation of massed soldiers
  (B) those who resist and win a nameless war
  (C) those who give up hope
  (D) beaten prisoners
  (E) those without choice

14. We can infer from the passage that another word for **redress** is
  (A) remedy
  (B) attire
  (C) retire
  (D) address
  (E) embellish

15. In the passage, **bulwark** means
  (A) a detention camp
  (B) a removal
  (C) a strong support
  (D) a defeat
  (E) a waiting period

16. In the passage, **altercation** means
- (A) mistreatment
- (B) murder
- (C) an escape
- (D) an angry argument
- (E) a peaceful settlement

17. If Tsali Wasituna was a **martyr** as the author of the passage suggests, we may expect that
- (A) he was a spy for President Van Buren
- (B) he tried to escape
- (C) he was put to death for the sake of a cause
- (D) he did not try to defend his wife but instead protected himself
- (E) he struck a soldier

18. How does the writer provide a clue to the meaning of **palliate**?
- (A) The writer equates **palliate** with suffering.
- (B) The writer implies that **palliate** means "death".
- (C) The writer links **palliate** with the word *relieve*.
- (D) The writer explains the word in the next paragraph.
- (E) The writer says that **palliate** means "representation."

19. According to the passage, the Trail of Tears is associated with **repression** because
- (A) most of the Cherokees had to walk to Indian Territory
- (B) some four thousand Cherokees died along the way
- (C) the Cherokees were forced to move to Indian Territory
- (D) it was snowing for many days
- (E) the trip was extremely difficult

20. In the passage, a **coalition** is
- (A) an alliance
- (B) a civilization
- (C) a survivor
- (D) an agreement
- (E) a representative

READING NEW WORDS IN CONTEXT

Lesson 9 | CONTEXT: The People

The passage gives you an opportunity to expand your vocabulary. Below are twenty Vocabulary Words that are used in the passage and in the exercises that follow it.

affinity	degenerate	equestrian	ingratiate
array	deign	fastidious	malevolent
audacious	derogatory	felony	oscillate
bandy	efficacious	flay	rationalize
convivial	epicure	imperious	relent

P. T. Barnum: The Prince of Humbugs

By exhibiting the enormous (Jumbo, the elephant), the tiny (Tom Thumb, a midget), the amazing if not actually true (the Fejee Mermaid), and the beautiful (Jenny Lind, the Swedish singer), an extraordinary showman mesmerized audiences during the 1800s. That showman was the **audacious** (1), the bold, and the insolent P. T. (Phineas Taylor) Barnum (1810–1891). He was the self-proclaimed "Prince of Humbugs" and the founder of "The Greatest Show on Earth." Barnum was a legend in his own time and remains a legend even today.

P. T. Barnum: Entertainer or Huckster?

Barnum entered the world of entertainment in 1835 with a national touring exhibit of a woman he claimed was 161 years old. Actually, Joice Heth, who claimed to have been George Washington's nurse, was not yet 80. From the beginning of his career, Barnum had an **affinity** (2) for the unusual. He also had a natural attraction to tall tales, and he freely stretched the truth to help business. He was noted for his **efficacious** (3) promotions and advertisements; they usually produced their desired effect—to manipulate the public and enrich himself. To **rationalize** (4) his sometimes dishonest methods, Barnum is

reported to have explained, "There's a sucker born every minute."

In 1841, Barnum purchased the American Museum in New York City, where the main exhibit soon became Tom Thumb, a perfectly proportioned midget from Connecticut whose real name was Charles Sherwood Stratton. At the time Barnum discovered him, Tom was five years old, was only twenty-five inches tall, and weighed under sixty pounds. Barnum proclaimed him "General Tom Thumb," a dwarf eleven years of age from England. Tom starred in his own shows at the museum. Barnum would **array** (5) him in elaborate costumes. Dressed up, Tom would **bandy** (6) with other performers by exchanging jokes, or he would do one of his popular impersonations, such as of Emperor Napoleon. In 1844, Barnum took Tom to England, where Tom managed to **ingratiate** (7) himself with the English audiences, including Queen Victoria. Similarly, he won the favor of audiences in France and Belgium.

The Greatest Show on Earth: A Jumbo Affair

Barnum's traveling circus, begun in 1871, is probably his most famous enterprise. This "Greatest Show on Earth," which included animals and a museum, later became the Ringling Brothers and Barnum & Bailey Circus. Certainly the biggest star of the circus was Jumbo, a huge, six-ton African elephant. For years, Jumbo had been a leading attraction at a London zoo, and his sale by the London Zoological Society to Barnum's circus for $10,000 enraged the British. The British people regarded Barnum as overbearing and domineering. They thought the sale to the **imperious** (8) Barnum was a serious crime, practically a **felony** (9). They began to **flay** (10) Barnum in the press and by word of mouth. This severe criticism didn't bother P. T., though. He loved even unfavorable publicity; he knew that **derogatory** (11) comments simply made him and Jumbo more famous. Barnum refused to give in to popular sentiments, and so he would not **relent** (12). Jumbo was leaving England. Ten horses pulled the wagon containing Jumbo to the London docks to begin his journey to America. The elephant and the **equestrian** (13) accompaniment must have been a sight to see! By the time Jumbo came to the United States in 1882, Jumbomania had seized the country. Unfortunately, Jumbo was fatally injured in a train accident three years later. But the elephant had been such a popular attraction that the word jumbo found a permanent place in the English language as a synonym for large.

The Other Faces of P. T. Barnum

Although best known today for his amusement and circus activities, Barnum was involved in many other interests and causes. He was a state legislator in Connecticut and a mayor of Bridgeport, Connecticut. He was an abolitionist, an opponent of slavery, and he also worked in the temperance movement against the sale and consumption of alcohol. He personally took a dim view of drinking alcohol, and he would not **deign** (14) to have any liquor himself. In lectures throughout the country, Barnum spoke of his refusal to condescend to drinking. He likely had refined tastes in food, but could not be considered an **epicure** (15) because he did not take his meals with wine.

Like other popular speakers of the time, Barnum attempted to push people toward success. Barnum probably helped reform many **malevolent** (16) evildoers and **degenerate** (17) persons with low moral standards. Barnum was an optimistic person and was usually in good health. And because he was by nature **convivial** (18), he enjoyed social situations. In his professional and political careers, Barnum had definite ways of doing things. As a result, he sometimes was viewed as **fastidious** (19). In many of his activities, Barnum was controversial, and public opinion would **oscillate** (20) between admiring and condemning him. But by all accounts, to borrow Barnum's words, he was one of the greatest promoters on earth.

EXERCISE 1 *Finding Synonyms* ☞

Directions. Reread the preceding passage. Then write on the line provided a synonym for each of the words in boldface. If you cannot think of an exact synonym, you may write a brief definition of the word.

1. audacious _____

2. affinity _____

3. efficacious _____

4. rationalize _____

5. array _____

6. bandy _____

7. ingratiate _____

8. imperious _____

9. felony _____

10. flay _____

11. derogatory _____

12. relent _____

13. equestrian _____

14. deign _____

15. epicure _____

16. malevolent _____

17. degenerate _____

18. convivial _____

19. fastidious _____

20. oscillate _____

EXERCISE 2 Reading Strategically

Directions. Now that you have read the passage and thought about the words in boldface, circle the letter of the correct answer to each of the following items. The numbers of the items are the same as the numbers of the boldface Vocabulary Words in the passage.

1. The writer provides a clue to the meaning of **audacious** by
  (A) linking it to the words *bold* and *insolent*
  (B) linking it to the word *legend*
  (C) implying that it means "dishonest"
  (D) saying it means "exhibiting"
  (E) relating it to the words *mesmerized audiences*

2. According to the passage, what does it mean that Barnum had an **affinity** for the unusual?

(A) He could not stand being around unusual people or things.
(B) He tried to avoid the unusual.
(C) He had a natural attraction to the unusual.
(D) He was unusual.
(E) He was completely indifferent to the unusual.

3. In the passage, something that is **efficacious**

(A) is not effective enough
(B) offends people
(C) promotes a worthy cause
(D) has the intended effect
(E) manipulates people

4. When we read in the passage that Barnum could **rationalize** his sometimes dishonest methods, we should realize that he

(A) did not try to explain what he did
(B) did not care about the general public's response to his methods
(C) changed the way he behaved
(D) devised self-satisfying but questionable reasons for his actions
(E) felt that he was always a reasonable man even under extreme pressure

5. We can infer from the passage that to **array** means to

(A) star
(B) feed
(C) question
(D) praise
(E) dress

6. In the passage, **bandy** means

(A) to argue
(B) to exchange light talk
(C) to compete
(D) to impersonate Napoleon
(E) to perform

7. What strategy does the writer use to tell you that **ingratiate** means to get the approval of another?

(A) The writer links **ingratiate** with the phrase "won the favor of."
(B) The writer defines the word.
(C) The writer implies that the word means "to offend or insult."
(D) The writer states that the word applies only to members of a royal family.
(E) The writer uses an antonym for the word.

8. In the passage, **imperious** means

(A) highly regarded
(B) domineering and overbearing
(C) royal
(D) offensive and unmannered
(E) soft spoken and withdrawn

9. We can infer from the passage that a **felony** is a
   (A) sale
   (B) severe criticism
   (C) serious crime
   (D) domination
   (E) serious disagreement

10. How does the writer let us know that **flay** can mean "to attack with stinging criticism"?
    (A) The writer relates **flay** to the word *serious*.
    (B) The writer links **flay** and the word *British*.
    (C) The writer gives an example of **flaying** language.
    (D) The writer links **flay** to publicity.
    (E) The writer relates **flay** to the words *severe criticism*.

11. When we read in the passage that the comments were **derogatory,** we should realize that
    (A) they were favorable
    (B) they were full of praise
    (C) they were not flattering
    (D) they were not understandable
    (E) they were famous the world over

12. According to the passage, Barnum would not **relent** in his determination to purchase Jumbo because he _____ to give in to popular demand.
    (A) refused
    (B) could not decide whether
    (C) agreed
    (D) promised
    (E) felt guilty enough

13. The writer provides a clue to the meaning of **equestrian** by
    (A) explaining Barnum's quest to obtain Jumbo
    (B) linking it to the word *accompaniment*
    (C) describing the circumstances surrounding Jumbo's accidental death
    (D) mentioning that ten horses pulled Jumbo's wagon
    (E) giving several examples of **equestrian** activities

14. If P. T. Barnum would not **deign** to drink any liquor himself, as the author of the passage suggests, we may expect that he
    (A) drank heavily
    (B) felt that drinking alcohol was beneath him
    (C) only drank liquor with friends
    (D) had given up drinking several years before
    (E) would not speak to anyone who drank alcohol

15. According to the passage, P. T. Barnum was not an **epicure** because he
    (A) would eat anything that was set in front of him
    (B) drank a lot and could not sleep
    (C) did not indulge in both good food and wine
    (D) never ate gourmet food without drinking equally fine wine
    (E) seldom ate

16. According to the passage, what does it mean to be **malevolent**?

    (A) to be evil
    (B) to cause cancer
    (C) to be kind
    (D) to reform
    (E) to be a man

17. According to the passage, **degenerate** means

    (A) driven by blind ambition
    (B) having low moral standards
    (C) reform-minded
    (D) having inherited the gene for a small build
    (E) popular with the general public

18. How does the writer provide a clue to the meaning of **convivial**?

    (A) The writer gives an antonym for the word.
    (B) The writer implies that **convivial** means "hardiness or good health."
    (C) The writer links the word to optimism.
    (D) The writer relates **convivial** to enjoying social situations.
    (E) The writer says that **convivial** means "natural and down to earth."

19. How does the writer let us know that **fastidious** may be defined as displaying careful attention to detail?

    (A) The writer relates it to being careless and irresponsible.
    (B) The writer considers it only one view.
    (C) The writer relates it to being a professional showperson.
    (D) The writer compares it to being controversial.
    (E) The writer says Barnum had definite ways of doing things.

20. According to the passage, what does it mean that opinion would **oscillate** between admiration and condemnation?

    (A) Opinion was always admiring.
    (B) Opinion was always condemning.
    (C) Opinion moved back and forth.
    (D) Opinion caused many arguments between Barnum and Tom Thumb.
    (E) Opinion made everyone including his own employees turn against Barnum.

READING NEW WORDS IN CONTEXT

Lesson 10   CONTEXT: The People

The passage gives you an opportunity to expand your vocabulary. Below are twenty Vocabulary Words that are used in the passage and in the exercises that follow it.

abash	bureaucracy	immemorial	proxy
allure	contraband	inane	purport
arbitrary	deference	integral	scapegoat
auspicious	demeanor	politic	syndicate
browbeat	guise	premeditated	transient

Interstellar Diary

Diary entry #107, Pandora Space Station, 2414 A.D.

My usual calm **demeanor** (1) was shattered this morning, just as we were nearing the fourth moon of Neptune. How can one's bearing remain unmoved when he is ordered to become a **scapegoat** (2)? At 0900 hours, Capt. Ragg told me that I must bear the blame for a crime I did not commit. The crime was the carrying of **contraband** (3), smuggled goods, aboard the space station.

"The actual smuggler must not, cannot, be known," Capt. Ragg said. "That is all I can say aboard this station."

Yet, I protested. "Sir, it's a senseless, stupid, **inane** (4) charge," I responded, knowing that it would do no good to protest. His own stern manner and harsh words would quickly **browbeat** (5) me into silence.

"You will change clothes and put on the **guise** (6) of an interplanetary tailor. Your disguise is in your cabin. Then report to the main deck to appear before representatives of the **syndicate** (7)."

"Sir, what is this **syndicate**?"

"A **syndicate** is a group of people or companies that have banded together to carry on some business. You should know that. This particular **syndicate** is responsible for the Pandora Space Station."

Smorgsson the Interplanetary Tailor

"Once you go undercover, you will **purport** (8) to be Smorgsson the tailor. Also, you will state that the jewel-covered garments—the **contraband** in question—are of your making, and that they are designed for the mystical rituals of the Trivslings. These supernatural rituals will be familiar to the **syndicate**."

"Their questions will **abash** (9) me," I said.

"Don't let yourself be thus embarrassed," Capt. Ragg responded.

"But, sir, what will become of me? Why am I, a ten-year guard, being so ordered?"

"Because you plotted to carry unauthorized garments to the Trivslings, you will be charged with **premeditated** (10) insubordination. You will be sentenced to die."

"But I didn't do it! I'm a **scapegoat,** remember? Can't I choose a **proxy** (11) to stand in for me—perhaps a guard without so much experience?"

"No, you have been chosen by random computer selection. It doesn't matter. Life is **transient** (12), like a fleeting bird. Do you remember birds?"

"What?" I yelped, ignoring the bird discussion. "Do you mean my selection was **arbitrary** (13), that it was based on some whim and is not even part of an **integral** (14) design? Is there no chance for a reconsideration?"

"None," Capt. Ragg said, pausing in thought. "I can see you like to look out for your own interests. In a word, you are **politic** (15). I admire that."

"There is one chance. Not many people know about it," Capt. Ragg continued. "Before the **syndicate** sentences you, ask for the Right of Test. By ancient law in this galaxy, they cannot refuse. But it will be most difficult to pass."

"I'll try anything," I said. "But what is the test? What is it about?"

"That you won't know until they tell you. But whatever the subject is, you must give a correct response to every single question, or you are doomed."

With the word *doomed* pounding in my head, I returned to my cabin, where I changed clothes. The guard then took me before the justices of the **syndicate**, where I listened to the charges.

Before the Syndicate

Before sentencing, I said, "In **deference** (16) to the **syndicate**, and with the same courteous regard to the laws of this galaxy, may I please request the Right of Test?"

The **syndicate** seemed surprised but agreed. Its members discussed the topic for a few minutes, and then announced that I would be tested on the American space program.

I tried to look glum, but secretly I rejoiced because I am an American and have always been fascinated by the space program. Because of the space program's **allure** (17), I have studied a great deal about it.

"The American space venture had an **auspicious** (18) start," the chief judge said. "Name, in order, the first three programs in the United States space race that contributed to this favorable beginning. Give dates for each program."

"They are," I replied, "the Mercury program, 1958 to 1963, the Gemini program, 1962 to 1966, and the Apollo moon program, 1961 to 1972."

Silence greeted my answer. Then came the next question.

"As you probably know, the American government had, and has, a complicated **bureaucracy** (19), with many departments running the government. What was the date on which the civilian space agency, the National Aeronautics and Space Administration, was formed?"

"October 1, 1958," I said unhesitatingly. The **syndicate** members looked surprised. The test continued in this fashion for about an hour. Finally, the questions stopped, and the **syndicate** president spoke.

"Since time **immemorial** (20)—before even the oldest among us can remember—the Right of Test must have existed and come down to us. We are bound to honor its verdict. For a tailor, you know much about the U.S. space program. You are free. Resume your duties as tailor."

I had nearly forgotten my supposed identity as a tailor, and in my surprise and confusion, I nearly blew my cover. But I managed to back out of the deck without incident. What a day! And thank goodness for the American space program!

EXERCISE 1 *Finding Synonyms* ✍

Directions. Reread the preceding passage. Then write on the line provided a synonym for each of the words in boldface. If you cannot think of an exact synonym, you may write a brief definition of the word.

1. demeanor _____

2. scapegoat _____

3. contraband _____

4. inane _____

5. browbeat _____

6. guise _____

7. syndicate _____

8. purport _____

9. abash _____

10. premeditated _____

11. proxy _____

12. transient _____

13. arbitrary _____

14. integral _____

15. politic _____

16. deference _____

17. allure _____

18. auspicious _____

19. bureaucracy _____

20. immemorial _____

EXERCISE 2 *Reading Strategically* 👈

Directions. Now that you have read the passage and thought about the words in boldface, circle the letter of the correct answer to each of the following items. The numbers of the items are the same as the numbers of the boldface Vocabulary Words in the passage.

1. The writer provides a clue to the meaning of **demeanor** by
(A) linking it to the word *calm*
(B) relating it to the word *usual*
(C) implying that it means "shattering"
(D) restating **demeanor** as "bearing"
(E) contrasting it to an antonym

2. In the passage, a **scapegoat**
(A) is ordered to do something
(B) takes the blame for another's crimes
(C) is a martyr
(D) smuggles goods aboard space stations
(E) blames others for mistakes or crimes

3. In the passage, **contraband** means
(A) actuality
(B) high-priced merchandise
(C) smuggled goods
(D) cargo
(E) a jewel smuggler

4. How does the writer provide a clue to the meaning of **inane**?
(A) The writer links it in a series to the words *senseless* and *stupid*.
(B) The writer describes it as "smuggling."
(C) The writer relates it by contrast to the words *harsh* and *stern*.
(D) The writer implies that it means "protest."
(E) The writer relates it to the word *charge* with a pronoun reference.

5. If the captain **browbeats** the narrator with his stern manner and harsh words, we may expect that the narrator would
(A) be happy
(B) be bullied
(C) be embarrassed
(D) need first aid
(E) frown

6. We can infer from the passage that to put on the **guise** of someone else means to
(A) trade places
(B) wear festive clothing
(C) wear the uniform of a jeweller
(D) assume the same outward appearance
(E) impersonate a military officer or other official

7. In the passage, a **syndicate** is
   (A) a group of people or companies that deal exclusively in smuggled goods
   (B) a fraternal order for American astronauts
   (C) a group of people or companies banded together to carry on some business
   (D) a united protest made by a group of unrelated people
   (E) several companies that compete with each other to carry out business deals

8. What strategy does the writer use to tell us that **purport** means "to present the (often false) appearance of being someone or something"?
   (A) The writer relates the word to knowledge about tailoring and making jewel-covered garments.
   (B) The writer links **purport** to knowing how to sew.
   (C) The writer relates the word to the spiritual rituals of the Trivslings.
   (D) The writer speaks of a costume party where the narrator is to wear jewel-covered garments.
   (E) The writer gives the example of going undercover as a tailor.

9. Which sentence in the passage provides a clue to the meaning of **abash**?
   (A) "Their questions will **abash** me."
   (B) "But, sir, what will become of me?"
   (C) "These supernatural rituals will be familiar to the syndicate."
   (D) "Don't let yourself be thus embarrassed."
   (E) "Why am I, a ten-year guard, being so ordered?"

10. When we read in the passage that the writer will be charged with **premeditated** insubordination, we should realize that he's being
    (A) blamed for acting without planning ahead
    (B) charged with reacting to outside pressure
    (C) blamed for plotting his actions in advance
    (D) blamed for living in the past
    (E) charged with being insolent

11. In the passage, **proxy** means
    (A) a guard
    (B) someone who stands in for someone else
    (C) someone who is experienced in undercover work
    (D) someone who is blamed for someone else's crimes
    (E) someone who is unable to remember his or her true identity

12. According to the passage, because life is **transient,** undeserved death doesn't matter. To reinforce this point, Captain Ragg draws a simile between life and a
    (A) fleeting bird
    (B) random computer selection
    (C) quick fox
    (D) caged bird
    (E) distant memory

13. If the author's selection for blame is **arbitrary,** we may expect that it is
    (A) premeditated
    (B) scientific
    (C) a result of careful planning
    (D) arguable
    (E) based on some whim

14. What strategy does the writer use to tell us that **integral** means complete?
  (A) The writer links **integral** to the word *selection*.
  (B) The writer includes a complete definition of the word.
  (C) The writer gives us a clue to the meaning of **integral** by using it in a series with related synonyms.
  (D) The writer asks a direct question about the word and gives an exact answer.
  (E) The writer links **integral** to the words *part* and *design*.

15. According to the passage, those who are **politic**
  (A) are most concerned about others
  (B) protect their own interests
  (C) run for office
  (D) believe in public-opinion polls
  (E) are greedy

16. In the passage, **deference** means
  (A) a humble request
  (B) a harsh sentence
  (C) a sacred rite of passage
  (D) courteous regard
  (E) a discourtesy

17. In the passage, **allure** means
  (A) American
  (B) programs
  (C) interest
  (D) fascination
  (E) rejoicing

18. How does the writer provide a clue to the meaning of **auspicious**?
  (A) The writer gives an antonym for the word.
  (B) The writer implies with reference to the first three programs that it means "unfavorable."
  (C) The writer restates it with the words *space race*.
  (D) The writer links it to the word *favorable*.
  (E) The writer says that **auspicious** means "venture."

19. We can infer from the passage that **bureaucracy** is related to
  (A) the duties of a tailor
  (B) unfounded civilian concerns about a space agency
  (C) having many departments that run an operation
  (D) being outdated by the current civilian space agency
  (E) hesitation

20. According to the passage, time **immemorial** is time that
  (A) is before anyone can remember
  (B) is yet to come
  (C) everyone remembers with great pride
  (D) never existed except in someone's mind
  (E) is counted in years

| Lesson 11 | **CONTEXT:** The Land |

The passage gives you an opportunity to expand your vocabulary. Below are twenty Vocabulary Words that are used in the passage and in the exercises that follow it.

abstain	dissipate	fiord	subside
assay	diverge	idyll	taint
augment	entity	inherent	tepid
catharsis	entomology	omnivorous	unremitting
credence	faction	prototype	vogue

These Plantations of God: Emerson's Nature

Ralph Waldo Emerson (1803–1882) defined himself as a poet—not in the sense of one who writes verse, but as "a perceiver and dear lover of the harmonies that are in the soul and in matter. . . ." These harmonies between humans and nature were, in his opinion, the key to spiritual understanding. In his 1836 book, *Nature,* Emerson discussed his idea of nature as a tool for spiritual enlightenment rather than for progress. This idea was not in **vogue** (1) in the mechanical world of the nineteenth century, but it gained popularity quickly and soon was adopted by people across America.

The Founding Thinker of Transcendentalism

Emerson's theory that people could find the truth of God and themselves through individual communion with nature became a **prototype** (2), or model, for the Transcendentalist movement in literature. His influence in this field probably was greater than in any other, and what began as a single **faction** (3) of writers eventually influenced many writers outside their small group.

Another central part of Emerson's idea of nature was his belief in the Over-Soul, which

Emerson defined as "one soul which animates all" human beings. Emerson's Over-Soul represents the concept of a unifying **entity** (4), a being that exists both in humans and in nature. Emerson argued that during a heightened religious experience, the human soul came into contact with this universal being. He also tried to explain why at moments of spiritual intensity we feel that we **diverge** (5) from the life around us, yet become connected with it as well.

Emerson's ideas connected people with nature, but Emerson was not a natural scientist. Although he had some education in the natural sciences, his writings do not approach the natural world scientifically. He would not look at the insect world, for example, with an **entomologist's** (6) eye—studying insects' biological and behavioral traits—but with a spiritual eye. Similarly, he did not write about such geographical features as **fiords** (7), for although these long, narrow, steep-sided inlets of the sea are important natural formations, the nuts and bolts of the natural world did not concern Emerson. Instead, he focused his writing on the **catharsis** (8), the purification, the ridding of negative emotions, that nature could provide. This spiritual view of nature has been criticized by recent environmentalists. They claim that seeing nature as a spiritual tool ignores its physical reality and does nothing but further **augment** (9) already increasing problems.

However, if some environmentalists argue that Emerson's ideas are invalid, the example set by some of his followers gives his thought **credence** (10). For instance, Emerson's most famous follower Henry David Thoreau (1817–1862) chose to **abstain** (11) from eating fish. Similarly, he refrained from eating all red meat. Perhaps Thoreau believed, as some environmentalists believe, that a meatless diet **taints** (12), or pollutes, the environment less than an **omnivorous** (13) diet, in which both plants and animals are eaten.

A Timeless Appeal

Fortunately, arguments about the effect of Emerson's philosophy on environmental attitudes have not caused interest in the philosophy itself to **subside** (14). In fact, interest has increased in some academic circles. In a technological world where many people feel powerless, the idea of returning to nature is especially appealing.

As time continues to **assay** (15), or test, Emerson's philosophies, a number of points remain in their favor. First, Emerson wrote on a variety of subjects and spoke in different ways to different members of the population. Second, people recognize the **inherent** (16) beauty of his writing. This essential beauty is clear in many of his sayings, such as "In the woods, too, man casts off his years, as the snake his slough, and at what period so ever of life, is always a child." At times, Emerson's *Nature* reads like an **idyll** (17) with its descriptions of simple, natural scenes. Phrases such as "these plantations of God" evoke images of the harmony and simplicity of country life. Finally, Emerson was an individual thinker who never tired of supporting his ideas. His **unremitting** (18) dedication to his ideas proved to be worthwhile, for the effects of his pioneering philosophies have been far-reaching.

Although public interest in many writers over time has scattered like thinning clouds, interest in Emerson has shown no inclination toward **dissipating** (19). From the initial **tepid** (20) response that he received from a cautious church-going community in New England, Emerson went on to begin a new area of thought—one which has influenced American philosophy and enriched the relationship between human beings and nature.

EXERCISE 1 *Finding Synonyms* ☞

Directions. Reread the preceding passage. Then write on the line provided a synonym for each of the words in boldface. If you cannot think of an exact synonym, you may write a brief definition of the word.

1. vogue _____

2. prototype _____

3. faction _____

4. entity _____

5. diverge _____

6. entomologist _____

7. fiords _____

8. catharsis _____

9. augment _____

10. credence _____

11. abstain _____

12. taints _____

13. omnivorous _____

14. subside _____

15. assay _____

16. inherent _____

17. idyll _____

18. unremitting _____

19. dissipating _____

20. tepid _____

EXERCISE 2 *Reading Strategically* ✍

Directions. Now that you have read the passage and thought about the words in boldface, circle the letter of the correct answer to each of the following items. The numbers of the items are the same as the numbers of the boldface Vocabulary Words in the passage.

1. What strategy does the writer use to tell you that **vogue** is defined as "prevailing style" or "popular acceptance"?
   (A) The writer links **vogue** with the fact that Emerson was very concerned with being well dressed.
   (B) The writer explains that something that was not in **vogue** later became popular.
   (C) The writer refers to the ever-popular idea of spiritual enlightenment.
   (D) The writer defines the word.
   (E) The writer adds a parenthetical phrase that clearly defines **vogue**.

2. In the passage, a **prototype**
   (A) is a kind of printing
   (B) is communion with nature
   (C) is a model
   (D) is a theory
   (E) will be attainable only in the distant future

3. If Transcendentalism initially involved a single **faction** of writers, as the author of the passage suggests, we may expect

(A) all writers at the time were involved in Transcendentalism in one way or another
(B) there were militant uprisings in the literary community
(C) all writers presented a united front
(D) the Transcendentalists were a highly secretive group of writers who fought among themselves
(E) only one group of writers was initially involved in Transcendentalism

4. In the passage, **entity** means

(A) unifying
(B) being
(C) humanity
(D) experience
(E) Over-Soul

5. The writer lets us know that **diverge** may be defined as "to go in a different direction" or "to differ from" by

(A) defining **diverge** in an appositive
(B) contrasting **diverge** with the word *connected*
(C) relating the word to intensity
(D) implying that the word means "explanation or summary"
(E) using synonyms of **diverge**

6. We can infer from the passage that an **entomologist** studies

(A) the stars
(B) spiritual matters
(C) physical ways
(D) insects
(E) science

7. In the passage, a **fiord** is a

(A) collection of insects that are studied in a scientific way
(B) desert island
(C) long, narrow, steep-sided inlet of the sea
(D) type of geologic feature that greatly interested Emerson
(E) make of car

8. How does the writer provide a clue to the meaning of **catharsis**?

(A) The writer places it in a series with the words *purification* and *ridding*.
(B) The writer links **catharsis** to the raw materials found in nature.
(C) The writer relates the word to the environment.
(D) The writer calls it "a provision."
(E) The writer gives an example of a **catharsis** that Emerson experienced during his lifetime.

9. When we read in the passage that environmentalists feel Emerson's view does nothing but **augment** problems, we should realize that they feel that

(A) it reduces problems
(B) it gets rid of problems
(C) the problems can't get any worse
(D) it adds to the problems
(E) it makes the problems more manageable

10. According to the passage, an idea without **credence** is
    (A) believable
    (B) valid
    (C) invalid
    (D) acted upon
    (E) environmentally sound

11. According to the passage, to **abstain** from something means to
    (A) refrain
    (B) continue
    (C) enjoy
    (D) not refrain
    (E) not enjoy

12. In the passage, **taints** means
    (A) helps
    (B) no red meat
    (C) the environment
    (D) meatless diet
    (E) pollutes

13. In the passage, to be **omnivorous** means to eat
    (A) only meat
    (B) only vegetables and grains
    (C) only grass
    (D) only vegetables
    (E) vegetables, grains, and meat

14. When we read in the passage that interest in Emerson's philosophy did not **subside,** we should realize that
    (A) interest did not increase
    (B) interest did not self-destruct
    (C) interest did not decrease
    (D) his ideas did not gain acceptance
    (E) his ideas did not create arguments

15. In the passage, to **assay** is to
    (A) write
    (B) test
    (C) mine gold
    (D) philosophize
    (E) keep time

16. We can infer from the passage that something that is **inherent** is
    (A) lacking a key part or characteristic
    (B) not recognizable to the naked eye
    (C) an essential characteristic
    (D) unpopular
    (E) naturally beautiful

17. When we read that Emerson's *Nature* reads like an **idyll,** we should realize that it

(A) reads like clockwork
(B) should be read only in one's spare time
(C) is too difficult for the average reader to comprehend fully
(D) is boring
(E) describes simple, harmonious nature scenes

18. In the passage, **unremitting** describes Emerson's dedication because he never _____ supporting his ideas.

(A) liked
(B) agreed with
(C) had hope of
(D) tired of
(E) found anyone

19. Interest in Emerson has shown no inclination of **dissipating**. To illustrate this, the writer uses a simile of

(A) clouds scattering
(B) interest in many writers
(C) time passing
(D) the public being fickle
(E) the transient nature of criticism

20. The writer provides a clue to the meaning of **tepid** by

(A) calling the response "passionate and heated"
(B) implying that it has something to do with church
(C) using it to describe New England
(D) indicating that it is the response of cautious people
(E) implying that it means "enthusiastic"

Lesson 12 | CONTEXT: The Land

The passage gives you an opportunity to expand your vocabulary. Below are twenty Vocabulary Words that are used in the passage and in the exercises that follow it.

accost	camaraderie	furtive	proletarian
appraisal	correlate	mercenary	rapacious
apprise	elation	permeate	recalcitrant
austere	enormity	pernicious	recrimination
bestow	exhaustive	populace	undermine

Rachel Carson's Other Road

When did the modern, worldwide environmental protection movement begin? The start is generally considered to be the publication in 1962 of *Silent Spring*. This book by American marine biologist Rachel Carson (1907–1964) detailed for the first time the dangers of chemical pesticides to humans and all of nature. The **exhaustive** (1) job of doing thorough research, gathering complete information, and writing *Silent Spring* took Carson five years. Her diligent work paid off, however, for the book greatly appealed to the general public. The **populace** (2) was very interested in Carson's research, and *Silent Spring* became a controversial best-seller with far-reaching effects.

Carson's Findings: The Danger of Pesticides

The use of highly toxic pesticides to combat pests and weeds began during the 1940s and steadily increased to **permeate** (3), or spread throughout, farms, cities, and homes. In 1960, approximately 638 million pounds of pesticides were put into the environment. Manufacturing pesticides at that time amounted to a $250 million business. But Carson believed the use of pesticides **undermined** (4) and threatened the fragile interrelationships of life in nature.

The overuse of chemical pesticides, Carson said, was killing wildlife, causing cancer and other disorders in people, contaminating food, killing natural predators that controlled pests, and creating disturbing changes among pests themselves. By spreading the information she gathered, Carson worked successfully to **apprise** (5) people of the dangers of widespread pesticide use. She also succeeded in her goal to **correlate** (6) or show the documented relationship between pesticide pollution and a startling increase in human illness and environmental problems.

Two Roads: Making Choices About the Environment

In *Silent Spring*, Carson warned that the human race had two choices—to continue down the road to self-destruction by continuing to use poisonous chemicals, or to take an alternate route by developing biologically safe methods of pest control. Carson made plain that following the first road would be a great wickedness that would be **pernicious** (7) to the environment. In other words, continuing this **enormity** (8) would be highly destructive to the natural world.

The **recrimination** (9) from the pesticide industry was intense, but Carson was not intimidated by its countercharge. If anyone from the industry tried to **accost** (10) her, she calmly rebutted their aggressive speech, as she was confident in her scientific evidence. One chemical company spokesman, who said pesticides did not harm humans or the environment, was especially **recalcitrant** (11); he was defiant and very difficult to deal with. Some of Carson's supporters believed the pesticide industry was **mercenary** (12), interested only in big profits.

State and federal government agencies took Carson's warnings seriously and started reviewing their policies concerning the use of pesticides. The President's Science Advisory Committee endorsed Carson's **appraisal** (13) in its 1963 report on pesticide use. Similarly, her assessment of the pesticide problem and resulting concern led to the virtual ban on the powerful pesticide DDT. Even more significantly, the book triggered public demands that modern technology and industry be responsible for maintaining the environment. Many came to understand the dangers of allowing **rapacious** (14) people to heartlessly and greedily plunder the environment for their own use. One can only imagine the **elation** (15), or joy, Carson must have felt as a result of her triumphs.

The Making of a Naturalist
Just who was Rachel Carson, the science writer who became a household name through championing the environment? At the time *Silent Spring* was published, Carson was fifty-five years old and a full-time writer.

She was a shy, private person who led an **austere** (16), plain, simple life. Her three previous books, *Under the Sea-Wind, The Sea Around Us,* and *The Edge of the Sea,* already had established her reputation as an outstanding writer of literature and science.

She was born in Pennsylvania in 1907. Because her mother once worked as a school teacher and her father worked as an insurance salesman and farmer, Carson's family could be considered **proletarian** (17). A good student in high school and college, she earned a Master's degree in marine biology from Johns Hopkins University in 1932. Three years later she began a long association with the U.S. Fish and Wildlife Service as a writer and editor. She enjoyed the **camaraderie** (18) among workers at the service and had many friendly relationships.

Since childhood, Carson had been interested in both writing and the sea, and she decided to go into science so that she would have the qualifications and background to write about her favorite subject. She was not at all **furtive** (19) or secretive about her plans. Carson thought it natural to combine literature and science. She believed that the goal of both is to shed light on the truth.

Carson, who died in 1964, remains a hero in the environmental movement and respected as a nature writer. Admirers have chosen to **bestow** (20) numerous honors on Carson. In 1980, she was posthumously awarded the Presidential Medal of Freedom.

EXERCISE 1 *Finding Synonyms* ✍

Directions. Reread the preceding passage. Then write on the line provided a synonym for each of the words in boldface. If you cannot think of an exact synonym, you may write a brief definition of the word.

1. exhaustive _____
2. populace _____
3. permeate _____
4. undermined _____
5. apprise _____
6. correlate _____
7. pernicious _____
8. enormity _____
9. recrimination _____
10. accost _____
11. recalcitrant _____
12. mercenary _____
13. appraisal _____
14. rapacious _____
15. elation _____
16. austere _____
17. proletarian _____
18. camaraderie _____
19. furtive _____
20. bestow _____

EXERCISE 2 *Reading Strategically* ✍

Directions. Now that you have read the passage and thought about the words in boldface, circle the letter of the correct answer to each of the following items. The numbers of the items are the same as the numbers of the boldface Vocabulary Words in the passage.

1. How does the writer provide a clue to the meaning of **exhaustive**?

   (A) The writer tells us that Carson took five years to write *Silent Spring*.

   (B) The writer contrasts **exhaustive** with the words *diligent work*.

   (C) The writer refers to the dangers of chemical pesticides to the natural world.

   (D) The writer links **exhaustive** to the words *thorough* and *complete*.

   (E) The writer defines the word in the next sentence.

2. In the passage, the **populace** is

   (A) the general public

   (B) a large group of writers

   (C) a small group

   (D) a best-seller

   (E) churchgoers

3. The writer provides a clue to the meaning of the word **permeate** by

   (A) linking it to the steadily increasing use of chemical pesticides

   (B) contrasting it with the phrase "steadily increased it"

   (C) referring to the word *threatened*

   (D) implying that it means to "withdraw from use in farms, cities, or homes"

   (E) linking it to the phrase "spread throughout"

4. In the passage, to be **undermined** is to

   (A) use pesticides

   (B) destroy life

   (C) kill wildlife

   (D) be threatened

   (E) cause cancer

5. We can infer from the passage that to **apprise** is to

   (A) learn from

   (B) ask

   (C) inform

   (D) broadcast

   (E) excite

6. In the passage, to **correlate** is to

   (A) overuse pesticides to the point of causing disease in humans

   (B) show the relationships among various things

   (C) warn people

   (D) write about the effect of chemicals on the environment

   (E) influence people through popular writing

7. How does the writer let us know that **pernicious** may be defined as "causing great harm"?

(A) The writer explains that something that is **pernicious** is highly destructive.
(B) The writer implies that something that is **pernicious** is beneficial.
(C) The writer relates it to plain speaking.
(D) The writer lets us know that pesticides are never harmful to the natural world.
(E) The writer links the word to biologically safe methods of pest control.

8. In the passage, **enormity** means

(A) largeness
(B) abnormality
(C) a wicked action
(D) good idea
(E) way of traveling

9. The writer suggests the meaning of **recrimination** by

(A) including it in a series with the phrase "pesticide industry"
(B) linking **recrimination** to the word *intimidated*
(C) restating it as "countercharge"
(D) defining it as "intense"
(E) giving a specific example of a **recrimination**

10. According to the passage, in what way did people from the pesticide industry try to **accost** Rachel Carson?

(A) with violent physical attacks
(B) in newspaper ads
(C) with scientific evidence
(D) with positive reviews of her book
(E) with aggressive speech

11. In the passage, those who are **recalcitrant** are

(A) helpful and eager to cooperate
(B) defiant and difficult to deal with
(C) narrow-minded and prejudiced
(D) humorless and negative
(E) mean and cruel

12. In the passage, a **mercenary** is a person or company interested only in

(A) profits
(B) helping
(C) pesticides
(D) being difficult
(E) the environment

13. When we read in the passage that the President's Science Advisory Committee endorsed Carson's **appraisal,** we should realize that they agreed with her

(A) methods
(B) hopes
(C) assessment
(D) lack of concern
(E) political views

14. In the passage, people who are **rapacious** are
   (A) concerned about the environment
   (B) dangerous
   (C) extremely hungry
   (D) raving mad
   (E) heartless and greedy

15. When we read in the passage that one can only imagine Carson's **elation,** we should realize that she
   (A) was probably depressed
   (B) was curious about the future
   (C) distrusted industry
   (D) was probably happy and excited
   (E) was sorry she had bothered to write *Silent Spring*

16. The writer provides a clue to the meaning of **austere** by
   (A) linking it to the words *plain* and *simple*
   (B) relating it to the phrase "household name"
   (C) linking it to the words *shy* and *private*
   (D) following it with a description of Carson as a writer
   (E) using it as an metaphor for *life*

17. How does the writer let us know that **proletarian** may be defined as pertaining to those who earn a living by selling their labor?
   (A) The writer refers to Carson's education.
   (B) The writer tells about the occupations of Carson's parents.
   (C) The writer relates the word exclusively to farming.
   (D) The writer says that Carson's family was politically active.
   (E) The writer links **proletarian** to science.

18. According to the passage, **camaraderie** describes the good _____ Carson experienced at her job.
   (A) co-workers
   (B) expressions
   (C) fortune
   (D) opportunities
   (E) friendships

19. In the passage, to be **furtive** is to be
   (A) open
   (B) fortunate
   (C) critical
   (D) secretive
   (E) natural

20. We can infer from the passage that to **bestow** is to
   (A) recommend
   (B) confiscate
   (C) present
   (D) release
   (E) ignore

READING NEW WORDS IN CONTEXT

Lesson 13 | CONTEXT: The Land

The passage gives you an opportunity to expand your vocabulary. Below are twenty Vocabulary Words that are used in the passage and in the exercises that follow it.

acquisition	deluge	microcosm	synchronize
alleviate	enthrall	oracular	tenacity
arduous	grandiose	platitude	thwart
brusque	impetuous	rigorous	ulterior
debacle	insatiable	sluice	wily

Appropriately, Windmills

You could always believe Dad, the best farmer this part of the state ever knew. Craftiness was completely foreign to him. There wasn't a **wily** (1) bone in his six-foot, four-inch body. With him, what you saw was what he was—he never had an **ulterior** (2) motive in his life.

He was a hard worker. I know that is an overused saying, a **platitude** (3). It was true, though. He used to say the farm was a miniature world—he called it his **microcosm** (4)—and he said it was his job to keep the world turning. He was never happy doing easy jobs but thrived on **rigorous** (5) work.

Dad was smart, too, and he read just about every newspaper and book he could find. Every evening he made sure that his reading was **synchronized** (6) with my schoolwork. Dad said he liked to learn along with me so I wouldn't get too far ahead of him.

He wasn't really interested in world events or the **debacles** (7) of collapsing political systems. But nothing **enthralled** (8) him more than a true story about a new invention. He was especially captivated by articles about windmills.

"The windmill," he once told me, "is a symbol of the farm. A symbol of progress and perseverance, persistence, **tenacity** (9). It's a symbol of people harnessing nature. Don't you forget it."

I wasn't sure what he meant, but I have never forgotten it.

Dad had an **insatiable** (10) interest in windmills. He read everything he could find to satisfy his need to know everything about windmills. Most interesting to Dad were several newspaper and magazine articles about British economist E. F. Schumacher's windmills and his "appropriate technology" theory. One of the last conversations we had before he passed away was about Schumacher and those windmills.

The theory of appropriate or intermediate technology states that different kinds of technology are needed by different kinds of societies. For example, on our farm the **acquisition** (11) of an expensive, state-of-the-art milking machine would have been unnecessary. We only had two cows, so we could milk them by hand in half an hour. Although I found milking an **arduous** (12) task, it was much more efficient in our case to milk by hand than to invest in a costly machine.

Dad said Schumacher was an **oracle** (13) of the future, and he told me to mark Schumacher's wise and prophetic ideas.

"Schumacher applies technology to real life," he said. "It's about time technology started to **alleviate** (14), rather than cause, human suffering."

"Schumacher's plans aren't **grandiose** (15)," Dad said. "They're modest, and that's the kind of thinking I'd like to see more of."

In my mind I have a picture of Dad standing by an **impetuous** (16) windmill, a celestial propeller spinning at a furious rate. I see him proudly surveying the **deluge** (17) of water pouring into the tank and racing along the wooden channel called the **sluice** (18). He built this windmill himself. He suffered a series of minor setbacks, but he would not let them **thwart** (19), or defeat, his belief in "appropriate technology."

After Dad died, I read Schumacher's book *Small is Beautiful*. I wish Dad had been able to read it. When I finished, I could imagine him saying, not in a **brusque** (20) or abrupt way, but kindly, "You're getting ahead of me, boy."

EXERCISE 1   *Finding Synonyms* ✍

Directions. Reread the preceding passage. Then write on the line provided a synonym for each of the words in boldface. If you cannot think of an exact synonym, you may write a brief definition of the word.

1. wily _____

2. ulterior _____

3. platitude _____

4. microcosm _____

5. rigorous _____

6. synchronized _____

7. debacles _____

8. enthralled _____

9. tenacity _____

10. insatiable _____

11. acquisition _____

12. arduous _____

13. oracle _____

14. alleviate _____

15. grandiose _____

16. impetuous _____

17. deluge _____

18. sluice _____

19. thwart _____

20. brusque _____

EXERCISE 2 *Reading Strategically* ☞

Directions. Now that you have read the passage and thought about the words in boldface, circle the letter of the correct answer to each of the following items. The numbers of the items are the same as the numbers of the boldface Vocabulary Words in the passage.

1. The writer provides a clue to the meaning of **wily** by
  (A) telling us that **wily** means "open"
  (B) contrasting **wily** with the word *craftiness*
  (C) implying that **wily** means "believable"
  (D) linking **wily** to the word *craftiness*
  (E) relating **wily** to the word *foreign*

2. In the passage, the writer's father never had an **ulterior** motive because he
  (A) was crafty
  (B) was foreign
  (C) was open and honest about his intentions
  (D) liked to keep his intentions secret from his family and neighbors
  (E) talked a lot, but he never did any work

3. According to the passage, a **platitude** is
  (A) a duck-billed animal
  (B) an overused saying
  (C) a compliment
  (D) a feeling of thankfulness
  (E) a lie

4. In the passage, the word **microcosm** means
  (A) close examination
  (B) the world
  (C) a miniature world
  (D) anything that is tiny
  (E) the cosmos

5. How does the writer let us know that **rigorous** may be defined as "harsh" or "trying"?
  (A) The writer contrasts **rigorous** with easy.
  (B) The writer relates **rigorous** to thrived.
  (C) The writer describes the **rigorous** work.
  (D) The writer refers to his father's motives.
  (E) The writer mentions his father's farm.

6. We can infer from the passage that things that are **synchronized**

(A) are unrelated
(B) are from books
(C) occur at different times
(D) occur at the same time
(E) are related to homework

7. What strategy does the writer use to tell you that **debacle** may be defined as a "sudden disastrous downfall or defeat"?

(A) The writer gives a synonym for the word.
(B) The writer relates **debacles** to news stories about world events.
(C) The writer gives the example of collapsing political systems.
(D) The writer lets us know that **debacles** occur regularly around the world.
(E) The writer links the word to South America.

8. In the passage, someone who is **enthralled** is

(A) disgusted
(B) full of energy
(C) captivated
(D) bored
(E) reading

9. The writer provides a clue to the meaning of **tenacity** by

(A) calling it a "symbol of progress"
(B) stating that windmills are a symbol of the farm
(C) relating windmills to farms
(D) giving the example of windmills being used to harness nature
(E) linking it to the words *perseverance* and *persistence*

10. In the passage, having an **insatiable** interest means to

(A) have a strong interest
(B) have an unquenchable or unsatisfiable interest
(C) have an easily satisfied interest
(D) have a curiosity about newspapers and magazine articles
(E) be bored easily by a single subject

11. We can infer from the passage that **acquisition** means

(A) usefulness
(B) obtainment
(C) expense
(D) machine
(E) technology

12. In the passage, milking is an **arduous** task because

(A) it is hard, tedious work
(B) it is not laborious enough
(C) it is labor-saving
(D) it cannot be exported
(E) production is not dependent on technology

13. How does the writer provide a clue to the meaning of **oracle**?

    (A) The writer refers to oral, as opposed to written, communication.

    (B) The writer tells about the tone and pitch of Schumacher's voice.

    (C) The writer relates the word to knowledge about farming.

    (D) The writer says that Schumacher talked to the writer's father.

    (E) The writer implies that an **oracle** has "wise and prophetic ideas."

14. According to the passage, to **alleviate** human suffering is to _____ it.

    (A) aggravate

    (B) reduce

    (C) create

    (D) cause

    (E) compound

15. We can infer from the passage that those who make **grandiose** plans

    (A) never intend to do anything

    (B) carry through on them

    (C) make plans that are overly grand

    (D) change plans that don't work

    (E) wait for someone else to do the work

16. To illustrate the great speed that makes the imaginary windmill **impetuous,** the writer uses the metaphor of

    (A) an impulsive person running straight into danger

    (B) the normal actions of windmills

    (C) a speeding train hurtling down the tracks

    (D) a celestial propeller spinning at a furious rate

    (E) his father running

17. When we read in the passage that there is a **deluge** of water, we should realize that it is

    (A) a large amount

    (B) a drought

    (C) a trickle

    (D) only enough to fill a tank

    (E) only temporary

18. In the passage, a **sluice** is

    (A) a modern mining method

    (B) a fruit drink

    (C) a channel that conducts water

    (D) a huge water tank

    (E) a farm building used to house water lines

19. In the passage, **thwart** means to

    (A) believe

    (B) be appropriate

    (C) help

    (D) defeat

    (E) slow

20. In the passage, **brusque** means
    (A) teasing
    (B) kindly
    (C) briskly
    (D) abrupt
    (E) joking

READING NEW WORDS IN CONTEXT

Lesson 14   CONTEXT: The Land

The passage gives you an opportunity to expand your vocabulary. Below are twenty Vocabulary Words that are used in the passage and in the exercises that follow it.

abate	effete	insular	protract
abominable	encroach	inure	stint
concerted	fallible	panacea	vegetate
contrition	indolence	presumptuous	vilify
defile	innocuous	propagate	wrest

The Eye of the Wolf

Aldo Leopold (1886–1948) learned to think like a mountain, and he challenged others to do so. How? Through experience and education, a person can develop a respect for nature and can learn not to **encroach** (1) on nature's rights or intrude upon nature's ways.

In an essay entitled "Thinking Like a Mountain," from his classic book *A Sand County Almanac,* Leopold tells about shooting an old wolf. Leopold looked into the dead wolf's eyes and felt remorse, regret, and **contrition** (2) for his deed. As a young U.S. forest ranger in the Southwest, Leopold had thought there needed to be fewer wolves, in order to protect the deer population. In meeting the wolf's gaze, however, Leopold realized that the wolf and the mountain provided an unspoken truth. Leopold understood that he had made a mistake and thus was **fallible** (3). He had acted arrogantly toward nature, and only gradually did he learn why such **presumptuous** (4) behavior was wrong. He came to understand that predators play an important role in nature's balancing act.

The experience probably would have been an **innocuous** (5) one for anyone less interested in nature than Leopold, but it made a great impact on him. Since childhood, he had felt a special bond with the outdoors, and it was almost impossible to **wrest** (6), or pull, him from his activities in the natural world.

Destined to Be Outdoors

Leopold's parents can take some of the credit for their son's dedication to nature. Indeed, if his parents had made a **concerted** (7) effort, both of them insisting that he seek more academic interests, then the development of land conservation and animal and plant preservation in the United States might have been quite different. Leopold's influence on the nation's environmental policies was profound. Today, he is regarded as a pioneer and a hero of environmental concerns.

Leopold was born in 1886 in Burlington, Iowa. As a boy, he enjoyed bird-watching, camping, fishing, and hunting. His father taught him to set hunting limits so that species could continue to **propagate** (8) and thus avoid extinction by breeding and multiplying. Each summer the family vacationed on one of the islands in the Great Lakes. Leopold loved these **insular** (9) retreats and spent hours exploring by himself.

As he grew older, Leopold's interest in nature did not **abate** (10); it intensified. He wanted to lead an active life, not **vegetate** (11) in the office of a bank or in a stuffy law library. Just because he thought like a mountain didn't mean he was an inactive rock. He didn't want to be a businessman like his father. He wanted a career that would allow him to be outside and in nature. He wanted to mingle with horses, deer, javelinas, and other four-legged animals. To Leopold, a life spent solely in the company of bankers, business people, and other bipeds appeared bleak beyond words. As a result, he enrolled in Yale's graduate program in forest management. At twenty-two, Leopold graduated and was hired by the newly created U.S. Forest Service.

Leopold's first big assignment was to map the Apache National Forest in the Arizona Territory. During his **stint** (12) in the Forest Service, he tried to convince the agency to carry out his ideas for managing its land. To Leopold, nothing could be more **abominable** (13) than not having access to the wilderness, and his goal was to see to it that the public did not suffer from this horrid situation, either. He wanted the Forest Service to put aside substantial amounts of unspoiled land for the public's **protracted** (14) enjoyment. Thanks largely to Leopold, the public now has had long-term enjoyment of many lands virtually unmarked by civilization. The Forest Service followed his recommendations and began a program that has preserved millions of acres of wilderness. Leopold also initiated a wildlife management program in national forests.

A Sand County Almanac

Later in his career, Leopold turned to teaching and writing. At the University of Wisconsin, he became the country's first professor of game management. He later set up the Department of Wildlife Ecology there. Never **indolent** (15) or lazy concerning the environment, Leopold also became involved in many conservation groups. *A Sand County Almanac*, his own enormously popular collection of essays and reflections on nature, was published in 1949, a year after his death. The title refers to an old farm Leopold bought to restore. Because the farm's once-fertile, sandy soil had been abused by years of poor farming methods, it had become **effete** (16).

In his writings, Leopold advocates some simple remedies for problems between humans and nature. These remedies did not promise to be **panaceas** (17) that would miraculously cure all of our ecological problems. Leopold believed that the best way to solve problems was not to start them and that people should therefore make decisions about the land based on potential environmental impact. Leopold didn't want to see any land spoiled or **defiled** (18). By land, he meant not only soil but also water, plants, and animals. He realized that society had become **inured** (19) to the dangerous attitude that regards land merely as property, but he believed undesirable habits or customs could be reversed with education. People should live in harmony with nature and not try to conquer it, he said. Through the years, Leopold's ideas have been mostly praised with kind words rather than **vilified** (20). As a result of his many efforts and ideas, Leopold is included in the National Wildlife Federation's Conservation Hall of Fame.

EXERCISE 1 — *Finding Synonyms* ✍

Directions. Reread the preceding passage. Then write on the line provided a synonym for each of the words in boldface. If you cannot think of an exact synonym, you may write a brief definition of the word.

1. encroach _____

2. contrition _____

3. fallible _____

4. presumptuous _____

5. innocuous _____

6. wrest _____

7. concerted _____

8. propagate _____

9. insular _____

10. abate _____

11. vegetate _____

12. stint _____

13. abominable _____

14. protracted _____

15. indolent _____

16. effete _____

17. panacea _____

18. defiled _____

19. inured _____

20. vilified _____

EXERCISE 2 Reading Strategically ✍

Directions. Now that you have read the passage and thought about the words in boldface, circle the letter of the correct answer to each of the following items. The numbers of the items are the same as the numbers of the boldface Vocabulary Words in the passage.

1. In the passage, **encroach** means
   - (A) develop
   - (B) respect
   - (C) intrude
   - (D) experience
   - (E) ignore

2. According to the passage, to feel **contrition** means to
   - (A) be regretful
   - (B) be proud
   - (C) suppress true feelings
   - (D) gloat
   - (E) be sympathetic

3. According to the passage, because Leopold was **fallible,** he
   - (A) had poor balance
   - (B) was always wrong
   - (C) tried to be perfect
   - (D) made a mistake
   - (E) understood nature

4. The writer provides a clue to the meaning of **presumptuous** by
   - (A) relating **presumptuous** to behavior
   - (B) implying that **presumptuous** means "wrong"
   - (C) implying that **presumptuous** has to do with gradual understanding
   - (D) saying that **presumptuous** is related to hunting
   - (E) linking **presumptuous** behavior to the phrase "had acted arrogantly"

5. How does the writer let us know that **innocuous** may be defined as "harmless, lacking in impact"?
   - (A) The writer relates **innocuous** to the phrase "less interested in nature."
   - (B) The writer contrasts **innocuous** with the phrase "made a great impact."
   - (C) The writer implies that **innocuous** experiences happen in childhood.
   - (D) The writer refers to many other experiences.
   - (E) The writer mentions Leopold's sensitivity as an example of an **innocuous** experience.

6. When we read in the passage that it was almost impossible to **wrest** Leopold from his outdoor activities, we should realize that
   - (A) he would gladly do other things if he could get away from the country
   - (B) he liked nature a little bit
   - (C) he enjoyed having the company of his parents on his hikes
   - (D) his interest in nature was short-lived
   - (E) he could not be torn away from his pursuits

7. What strategy does the writer use to tell you that **concerted** may be defined as "done together"?

    (A) The writer contrasts the word with its antonym.

    (B) The writer says Leopold's parents both loved nature.

    (C) The writer gives an example of a possible **concerted** effort.

    (D) The writer indicates that a **concerted** effort is an effort made in vain.

    (E) The writer uses the metaphor of an orchestral performance.

8. We can infer from the passage that when species **propagate** they

    (A) produce offspring

    (B) are hunted

    (C) become extinct

    (D) continue to decline in numbers

    (E) avoid hunting limits

9. The writer provides a clue to the meaning of **insular** by

    (A) relating it to time

    (B) implying that **insular** times involve group activities

    (C) relating it to life on an island and solitary retreats

    (D) linking it to exploration

    (E) relating it to vacations

10. The writer provides a clue to the meaning of the word **abate** by

    (A) defining it in an appositive phrase

    (B) implying that it means "to increase"

    (C) contrasting it with the word *intensified*

    (D) relating it to age

    (E) using it as an adjective to describe increasing activity

11. To illustrate the meaning of the word **vegetate,** the writer uses the metaphor of

    (A) Leopold being an unthinking mountain

    (B) a career being a tall mountain

    (C) a four-legged animal being a vegetable

    (D) Leopold being an inactive rock

    (E) his father being a businessman

12. In this passage, **stint** means

    (A) in order to earn promotions

    (B) give generously

    (C) managing lands

    (D) doing it improperly

    (E) time spent performing a task

13. In the passage, an **abominable** situation is

    (A) beneficial

    (B) horrible

    (C) related to snowmen

    (D) unspoiled

    (E) frightening

14. In the passage, **protracted** enjoyment may be defined as pleasure that is _____ in time.

    (A) lengthy
    (B) brief
    (C) nonexistent
    (D) reversed
    (E) removed

15. In the passage, **indolent** means

    (A) concerned
    (B) lazy
    (C) active
    (D) interested
    (E) asleep

16. When we read in the passage that the soil had become **effete,** we should realize that it

    (A) was very fertile
    (B) had all been eroded by the wind
    (C) was jointly owned
    (D) was sterile
    (E) was more productive than before

17. How does the writer provide a clue to the meaning of **panacea**?

    (A) The writer refers to Leopold's writings.
    (B) The writer tells about the problems between man and nature.
    (C) The writer links **panacea** to miraculous cures.
    (D) The writer says that Leopold was an advocate.
    (E) The writer relates **panacea** to the phrase environmental impact.

18. We can infer from the passage that to **defile** is to

    (A) spoil
    (B) improve
    (C) use
    (D) water
    (E) sell

19. In the passage, to become **inured** means to become

    (A) curious
    (B) used to
    (C) annoyed by
    (D) furious
    (E) insured

20. In the passage, the word **vilified** means

    (A) wholeheartedly praised
    (B) suspiciously analyzed
    (C) carefully read
    (D) rudely disregarded
    (E) verbally abused

READING NEW WORDS IN CONTEXT

Lesson 15 | CONTEXT: The Land

The passage gives you an opportunity to expand your vocabulary. Below are twenty Vocabulary Words that are used in the passage and in the exercises that follow it.

abut	bilateral	haggard	orient
arable	entourage	impunity	solstice
askew	flail	incise	somnolent
attrition	gird	indigenous	stoic
baleful	gradation	nurture	vanquish

Imagining the Spirit of the Hopi Farmer

Enter the world of the Hopi of two hundred years ago. Adjust your mental compass, and **orient** (1) yourself to northeastern Arizona. The Hopi, members of the Pueblo Native American group in the Southwest and descendants of the Anasazi people, lived there then, as they do now, on three mesas.

Now focus your imagination on an old Hopi farmer. Is he coming into view? He's leaning against the small fence that's **askew** (2), like a lopsided snake slithering across the desert. The fence is near the farmer's house in the village, or pueblo.

From the slump of his thin body, he looks tired, exhausted, and **haggard** (3). He may even be **somnolent** (4) because he has been awake since well before dawn. The day has been long, too, since the first day of summer, or the summer **solstice** (5), recently took place.

However, the expression on his lined, tan face is **stoic** (6). As a result, he appears unaffected by either pain or pleasure. Why? The Hopi have been farming this difficult land for many years, and they accept the challenge. A people of lesser strength and with less faith in nature would have been **vanquished** (7) by the land; the Hopi, however, have overcome the many hardships.

A Day in the Life of a Hopi Farmer

The Hopi land is desert plateau, hot and dry. It does not rain much, although there is heavy snow in the winter. In the low areas, sagebrush and cactuses are among the native plants. Other **indigenous** (8) plants on the mesas include pine and juniper.

Our yesteryear farmer tends the family field, which actually is owned by his wife. His field **abuts** (9) two others; the common boundary is near a natural spring. Land suitable for cultivation is difficult to find, but his is **arable** (10). He cleared the field in March, and then surrounded it with stones and brush to help block the blowing sands. This **girding** (11) of the field took him several days.

Daily he **nurtures** (12) his crop by caring for the corn, squash, beans, pumpkins, and melons. The main Hopi food is corn, especially blue and white corn, so he has planted a lot of it, deep in the earth. In his duties, the farmer is carrying on an age-old tradition. The Hopi traditionally have been peaceful people tending their crops. Their name, in fact, means peaceful, wise, or good.

The farmer has been in the field all day. He goes home alone, unaccompanied by any others, or without an **entourage** (13). It seems to him that there are fewer farmers in the pueblo these days due to **attrition** (14). In this case, the gradual reduction is blamed on death.

But if the farmer is thinking about the death of his friends, why is a small smile appearing on his face? Perhaps he is remembering a humorous incident earlier today when two boys from the pueblo were **flailing** (15) at rats in the cornfield. They were unable to strike any of the pests with their sticks. However, one of the boys accidently hit the farmer with a stick and was terrified at the thought of hitting an elder. The farmer simply smiled and offered the boy **impunity** (16), freedom from punishment.

A Farmer's Faith in the Fourth World

Although he has spring water for the crops, the farmer at the end of this day and every day hopes for rain. There's never enough water in this land. On a rock by his field, he has **incised** (17) a line for each time it has rained this year; there are only six engravings. He knows that it's still a long time until late summer and the annual Snake Dance when Hopi dancers will appeal to the spirits for rain.

The farmer, still leaning on the fence but about to enter his house, thinks that storm clouds in the west look **baleful** (18). To him, however, the threat that the clouds carry is a joyous thing. Perhaps rain is coming, he thinks. Yes, there is a definite **gradation** (19) in the clouds. In other words, the clouds are gradually changing from light to a dark, stormy stage in the southwest skies.

Only the spirits know what will happen, though, he decides. The farmer gives silent thanks to the spirits for the Fourth World, the earth's surface. The Hopi have a sort of **bilateral** (20) or mutually binding relationship with the spirits. The farmer believes, like all Hopi, that the land is sacred, and he does what he can to take care of it. In return, the spirits take care of the Hopi people.

The farmer finally goes inside to his wife and the thin bread called *piki* that she has made from the blue corn.

Now readjust your mental compass and leave the farmer and the long-ago Hopi pueblo. Remember his way of life, though, and compare it with your own.

EXERCISE 1 *Finding Synonyms* ✍

Directions. Reread the preceding passage. Then write on the line provided a synonym for each of the words in boldface. If you cannot think of an exact synonym, you may write a brief definition of the word.

1. orient _____

2. askew _____

3. haggard _____

4. somnolent _____

5. solstice _____

6. stoic _____

7. vanquished _____

8. indigenous _____

9. abuts _____

10. arable   _____

11. girding   _____

12. nurtures _____

13. entourage _____

14. attrition _____

15. flailing _____

16. impunity _____

17. incised   _____

18. baleful   _____

19. gradation _____

20. bilateral _____

EXERCISE 2 *Reading Strategically* ✍

Directions. Now that you have read the passage and thought about the words in boldface, circle the letter of the correct answer to each of the following items. The numbers of the items are the same as the numbers of the boldface Vocabulary Words in the passage.

1. How does the writer let us know that **orient** means "to position with respect to the points of the compass"?
  (A) The writer relates it to two hundred years in the past.
  (B) The writer says, "Adjust your mental compass."
  (C) The writer mentions northeastern Arizona.
  (D) The writer relates **orient** to the phrase "the world."
  (E) The writer implies that **orient** refers to the east.

2. **Askew** means crooked or out of line. To illustrate this point, the writer draws a simile between a fence and
  (A) a stone wall
  (B) the village or pueblo
  (C) a serpentine wall
  (D) a lopsided snake
  (E) a rugged coastline

3. The writer provides a clue to the meaning of the word **haggard** by
  (A) relating it to too much sleep
  (B) relating it to the phrase "thin body"
  (C) defining the word in the next sentence
  (D) drawing a simile between a **haggard** man and a very long day
  (E) linking it to the words *tired* and *exhausted*

4. According to the passage, why may the farmer be **somnolent**?

   (A) He may be **somnolent** because he has worked hard all day and is ready to eat.

   (B) He may be **somnolent** because he woke up well before dawn.

   (C) He may be **somnolent** because he is hot and needs a bath.

   (D) He may be **somnolent** because the evening is getting cooler.

   (E) He may be **somnolent** because he just woke up from a nap and feels well rested.

5. In the passage, the summer **solstice** is

   (A) the last day of summer

   (B) the first day of winter

   (C) the first day of summer

   (D) the shortest day of the year

   (E) exactly three-quarters of the way through the calendar year

6. When we read in the passage that the farmer's expression is **stoic,** we should realize that

   (A) his face is very expressive

   (B) his face is not as it appears

   (C) his face does not feel pleasure or pain

   (D) his face shows neither pleasure nor pain

   (E) he looks unhappy whether or not he really is

7. What strategy does the writer use to tell us that **vanquished** may be defined as "defeated"?

   (A) The writer contrasts it with the word *strength*.

   (B) The writer says the land is difficult.

   (C) The writer relates **vanquished** to the phrase "they accept the challenge."

   (D) The writer contrasts **vanquished** with the phrase "overcome the many hardships."

   (E) The writer implies that the challenge has been too great for the Hopi to withstand.

8. The writer provides a clue to the meaning of **indigenous** by

   (A) defining the word as "imported"

   (B) relating the plants to the Hopi

   (C) using the word *other* to relate **indigenous** to the word *native*

   (D) implying that few plants grow because the mesas are hot and dry

   (E) implying that the plants were all transplanted from cooler, damper areas

9. Because the Hopi's field **abuts** two other fields, the fields have

   (A) a common boundary

   (B) corn growing in them

   (C) spring water

   (D) the same configuration

   (E) the same acreage

10. We can infer from the passage that land that is **arable** is

   (A) windy

   (B) covered with brush and stones

   (C) sandy

   (D) difficult to farm

   (E) suitable for farming

11. In the passage, the **girding** of a field means that the farmer has _____ it.
   (A) cleared
   (B) surrounded
   (C) over-cultivated
   (D) opened
   (E) neglected

12. In the passage, to **nurture** means to
   (A) plant vegetables
   (B) to work daily
   (C) to care for
   (D) to water
   (E) to rotate

13. We can infer from the passage that earlier, when there were many farmers, there was an **entourage** that
   (A) left the farmer unaccompanied
   (B) walked home alone
   (C) quit earlier in the day
   (D) never spoke
   (E) accompanied the farmer

14. In the passage, **attrition** means
   (A) gradual reduction
   (B) small numbers
   (C) death
   (D) casting blame
   (E) farming difficult land

15. According to the passage, the boys **flailing** at rats in the cornfield were trying to
   (A) frighten the farmer
   (B) be funny
   (C) make the others think there were lots of rats in the cornfield
   (D) rid the field of rats
   (E) herd the rats into the cornfield

16. In the passage, **impunity** is
   (A) hiding behind a smile
   (B) freedom from punishment
   (C) hitting someone accidentally
   (D) making an offer
   (E) punishment

17. How does the writer provide a clue to the meaning of **incise**?
   (A) The writer refers to the farmer's hopes.
   (B) The writer later tells about plow marks.
   (C) The writer links **incised** to the word *engravings*.
   (D) The writer says that the farmer carves pictures on a rock.
   (E) The writer relates **incised** to the annual Snake Dance.

18. In the passage, **baleful** is
- (A) threatening
- (B) western
- (C) cheerful and smiling
- (D) related to cloud formations
- (E) disappearing

19. How does the writer let us know that **gradation** may be defined as a "gradual change from one stage, tone, or shade to another"?
- (A) The writer relates **gradation** to the words *ominous*, **baleful**, and *sinister*.
- (B) The writer describes the sudden change in the climate of Arizona.
- (C) The writer tells of the clouds dispersing.
- (D) The writer links **gradation** to a change in the color of the clouds.
- (E) The writer means that it is raining.

20. In the passage, the word **bilateral** means
- (A) one-sided
- (B) two-faced
- (C) relating to latitude
- (D) mutually binding
- (E) believing in two gods

Vocabulary Words

abash
abate
abominable
abridge
abstain
abut
accentuate
accost
acquiesce
acquisition
adamant
affable
affinity
affluent
allegory
alleviate
allure
altercation
ambiguous
ambivalent
anagram
anecdote
antagonize
appraisal
apprise
arable
arbitrary
archives
arduous
array
askew
assail
assay
assertion
attrition
audacious
augment
auspicious
austere
autocrat

baleful
bandy
banter
beleaguer
beneficent

bestow
betrothed
bilateral
blithe
bolster
brevity
browbeat
brunt
brusque
bulwark
bumptious
bureaucracy

camaraderie
catharsis
cede
chagrin
cite
climactic
coalition
coherent
comely
comprehensive
concerted
congenital
conjecture
connotation
consensus
consonant
contraband
contrition
convivial
correlate
credence

debacle
debonair
decadence
deference
defile
degenerate
deign
deluge
demeanor
deprecate
derogatory

despicable
dissipate
dissolute
diverge

effete
efficacious
elation
embellish
emendation
encroach
enormity
enthrall
entity
entomology
entourage
epicure
epilogue
epithet
equestrian
erroneous
evasive
evoke
exhaustive
exodus
exonerate
expedite
expletive
extemporaneous

faction
factious
fallible
fastidious
felicitous
felony
ferocity
fidelity
filial
finality
fiord
flail
flaunt
flay
foreshadow
forgo

forte
frustrate
fulminate
furor
furtive

garrulous
gibe
gird
goad
gradation
grandiose
guise

haggard
heinous
hypercritical
hypochondriac

idiomatic
idyll
imbibe
immemorial
imperious
impetuous
impromptu
impunity
inane
incise
incoherent
incongruous
incredulous
indigenous
indolence
inexplicable
infer
ingratiate
inherent
innocuous
insatiable
insidious
insular
intangible
integral
interminable
interpose

Vocabulary Words (continued)

intrepid
intricacy
intrinsic
introspective
inure
invidious
invoke
irascible

laudable
lucid
lucrative

malevolent
martyr
mercenary
microcosm
misanthrope
miscreant

noncommittal
nostalgic
novice
nurture

omnivorous
oracular
orient
oscillate
ostentatious

palliate
panacea
peripheral
permeate

pernicious
perpetuate
phalanx
platitude
plebeian
politic
populace
precipitate
predecessor
preemptory
premeditated
presumptuous
pretentious
proboscis
procrastinate
prodigy
proficient
proletarian
prologue
propagate
protagonist
prototype
protract
provocation
provocative
proxy
purport

query
quixotic

rapacious
rationalize
recalcitrant
reciprocate

recrimination
redress
reiterate
relent
remission
repartee
repression
repugnant
resilient
rhetorical
rigorous
rudiment

sallow
sanction
satiate
scapegoat
scrutinize
secular
shibboleth
shrew
sluice
solstice
somnolent
sortie
staunch
stereotype
stigma
stint
stipend
stoic
subservient
subside
subterfuge
supercilious

supplication
surmise
symposium
synchronize
syndicate

taint
tawdry
tenacity
tepid
terse
thwart
transient

ulterior
undermine
unremitting
usurp

vanquish
vegetate
verbose
vernacular
vilify
vivacious
vogue

waive
wily
wistful
wrest